WHAT'S UP WITH ASTRONOMY?

WHAT'S UP WITH ASTRONOMY?

First Edition

Chris McCarthy

San Francisco State University

cognella®

SAN DIEGO

Bassim Hamadeh, CEO and Publisher
Kristina Stolte, Senior Field Acquisitions Editor
Susana Christie, Senior Developmental Editor
Amy Smith, Senior Project Editor
Abbey Hastings, Production Editor
Jess Estrella, Senior Graphic Designer
Kylie Bartolome, Licensing Associate
Natalie Piccotti, Director of Marketing
Kassie Graves, Vice President, Editorial
Jamie Giganti, Director of Academic Publishing

Cover image copyright © [date] Depositphotos/[contributor]
Interior image copyright © [date] Depositphotos/[contributor]

Printed in the United States of America.

3970 Sorrento Valley Blvd., Ste. 500, San Diego, CA 92121

To my parents, Donna and Brian McCarthy

Contents

Preface: Why Study Astronomy?

In my opinion, the most important reason to learn about astronomy is to understand how science works and how it impacts our lives and our society. Not everyone needs to be a writer, lawyer, or medical professional. But in order for any modern civilization to work well, people in general must be literate, be aware of some basic laws, and of healthy ways to live. This will also allow them to prosper and enjoy their own lives. Similarly, some level of **scientific literacy** is sorely needed in our modern society, where topics such as health care, technology, and global warming have an impact on millions of people. In this book, we will discuss how astronomy became a science and how modern scientific theories are questioned and checked.

Astronomy is not just a science—it is the *oldest* science. As long as humans have lived, they have looked to the skies with wonder, awe, curiosity, and sometimes fear. In fact, the *astr-* in astronomy means "star." But in ancient times, if you were under the influence of a "bad star," then it was called a "dis-aster!" By learning about astronomy, we connect ourselves with our distant ancestors, wherever on Earth they may have been. And the objects of their wonder—the Sun, the Moon, the planets, and stars—are still available for us to observe today.

Do you think out of the box? The study of astronomy requires us to stretch our minds and consider larger and larger things: other planets, galaxies, the whole universe. It also helps us understand our life here on Earth in a new way. We also need to consider **different points of view**, or perspectives, to get the whole picture. This ability, to think outside of the confines that may have limited our thought previously, helps in many ways.

These are my top reasons to study astronomy, but you may have your own reasons. Have you learned about some exciting discoveries from news reports? Are you curious about the possibilities of extraterrestrial life? Has your spiritual background or curiosity led you to wonder about the origin of the universe? Are you, or some of your friends, interested in *astrology* and curious about its origins?

Whatever your interest, I encourage you to pursue it as you learn about astronomy. Look for answers to your questions in this book, in other books and in reliable online resources, and in people: your colleagues and instructors. This pursuit of curiosity is how all understanding of the universe began.

Acknowledgments

I am grateful to my colleagues at San Francisco State University, with whom I have discussed astronomy and science education: Adrienne Cool, John Michael Brewer, Jeanne Digel, Matt Horrigan, Jessica Fielder, Jim Gibson, Kimberly Tanner, Kimberly Seashore, Kim Coble, Joe Barranco, Anthony Kelly, Russell McArthur, and especially Heather Murdock, who inspired me to write this book.

Thank you to my wife Rachel and my son Seeger for their support while writing the book. I began writing this book while on vacation in a cabin rented by Phil and Carol Cloues, to whom I am grateful.

To my many teachers and mentors at UC Berkeley, UC Los Angeles, San Francisco State, and in the San Diego County public schools, I offer my sincere thanks. Your efforts were critical to my success. I'd also like to thank my students, whose numerous curious questions inspired me to become a better teacher and to write this book.

Finally, I wish to thank my parents, Donna and Brian, for raising a curious kid.

Introduction

About this book: I wrote this book after teaching introductory astronomy at San Francisco State University for 14 years. There are a number of good astronomy textbooks for sale today, but most of them are very expensive. Student budgets have always been tight, but my students in particular face severe economic challenges. Students shouldn't have to choose between textbooks they need for classes and paying rent or buying food and necessities. Some books are expensive because they are too long; they include more material than can be effectively taught in a typical semester course at a university. This book is deliberately succinct and to the point. Some topics are discussed only briefly. However, a list of books, webpages, and other sources at the end of each chapter will provide you with a jumping-off point if you find something you've just read very interesting. You'll also notice there are a lot of footnotes. None of them contain essential information; it's okay to just ignore them and read on if you like. Some of them explain a point in more detail, and others present information I thought was interesting, inspiring, ironic, or even bizarre. Feel free to peruse the ones that sound interesting to you.

Most textbook authors use a writing style that is excessively formal and academic. This is not well suited to my audience—California students who aren't studying astronomy or even science—and it doesn't capture the excitement and enthusiasm that I feel for the subject. Astronomy is fun! And I hope my writing style reflects that.

Perhaps the most important reason for me to write a new textbook is what I'll call the human factor. While some textbooks contain brief biographical sketches of astronomers, most overlook the fact that astronomy, like all science, is done by human beings. This means that the people who helped us understand the universe experienced the joys and sorrows of life, just as we do. Many of their accomplishments were made in spite of great adversity, whether it was the man who discovered how planets orbit while living in a war zone, or the woman who figured out what the stars were made of but couldn't graduate from college because of her gender. For a long time, astronomers themselves failed to appreciate the full diversity of the people who contributed and are now contributing to their field, an oversight that is sadly reflected in textbooks. This book is a step toward understanding astronomy—and understanding science comprehensively—as one of many wonderful things that humans do.

In each chapter of this book, you'll find several sections, ending with a short paragraph or two called "Wrap-Up." These segments summarize the chapter contents and get you ready for the next chapter. You can use them to check yourself. If the topics mentioned in the Wrap-Up aren't quite clear in your mind yet, then go back a few pages and review the relevant sections briefly before continuing on. You can also check your comprehension using the thought-provoking "Reflection Questions" at the end of each chapter. These usually don't have one right answer, but they incorporate the concepts you just learned and give you a chance to take those concepts in a new direction of your own choice.

In most chapters, you'll also see sections labeled "Do Try This at Home." In these, I'm asking you to set down the book for a moment and do something. You might be making a model of the Earth-Moon system or trying to create rainbows in your home. I really hope you'll try these activities. Research has shown that if you engage in a topic by creating something with your hands, then you'll understand it better. I also have sections that will help you to clear up common misconceptions about astronomy.

What's up with astronomy? Well, the sky is up ... it will always be available for everyone on Earth, regardless of background and location and regardless of what happens here on Earth. Long after you read this book, you will be observing the sky as people always have. So, welcome to the study of astronomy. Not everybody gets the opportunity to ponder the universe, so congratulations. But those who do often find it intriguing, enriching—and even amazing.

CYCLES OF OUR LIVES

Knowing where you came from is no less important than knowing where you are going.

—Neil deGrasse Tyson

Before we start, get out your calendar. If you are reading this book as part of a college course, you'll want to mark the date and month (and year) of your **final exam** on the calendar. You don't want to miss it. Same with mid-term exam(s). But now that you have your calendar out, take a closer look. You might have a wall calendar, a datebook, or an electronic calendar of one type or another. But have you ever wondered how calendars are set up? Why are there 12 months in the year? Why do some months have 31 days, but not all? And what's up with leap years?

Whenever you keep track of days, months, and years on a calendar, you are measuring astronomical cycles involving the Earth, Sun, and the Moon. You're doing astronomy! So, to begin, let's start with something very familiar and ask, "What's up with that?" Exploring deep questions about ordinary things will lead you to new insights and may challenge your preconceived notions. This process is also at the heart of scientific inquiry. Let's start with the simple idea of the **day**.

SECTION 1. Earth's Rotation Gives Us the Day

What is a **day**? "Why, 24 hours of course." But **why** is a day 24 hours? If you answered something like "That's how long it takes Earth to spin once," you'd be close. But it actually takes about 23 hours and

56 minutes for Earth to spin once on its axis. Our concept of one day is based on the **Sun**. Do you like watching sunsets? If you watch two sunsets in a row, the time between sunsets is 24 hours, on average. This is 4 minutes longer than Earth's true rotation period[1] because the Earth has actually ***moved*** *a little* between the first and second sunset. Earth **orbits** the Sun, so when you viewed the second sunset, you were viewing the Sun from a slightly different location. Smaller units of time (hours, minutes, seconds, milliseconds) are just fractions of this "solar day."

The Sun rises and sets because the Earth rotates. While *we* know that Earth is rotating, humans didn't always think this way. Indeed, it doesn't **feel** like Earth is rotating at all. So our ancient ancestors came up with a variety of spiritual explanations for why the Sun rose, crossed the sky, and set each day. The Mediterranean Sun God **Helios** is one example.[2] Back in the day, some people thought that he drove the Sun across the sky in a chariot from east to west. I mention this god only because this name will come up later: anytime you see *helio-*, you can bet that it has something to do with the Sun. These ancient mythological attempts by early humans to understand their observations of the sky constitute the earliest science. Before we scoff at them, we should take a moment to appreciate their thought processes and even ask ourselves how well we can explain our own ideas about what causes the Sun to rise and set. For example, some ancient philosophers claimed that if the Earth were rotating, the clouds would be left behind. What would you say to this idea?

Earth rotates eastward. So, if you live in California, then you are, at this very moment, moving toward New York (at a speed of 700 miles per hour). Of course, New York is moving eastward, too, so you never catch it. This *eastward* motion of Earth makes it *look* like everything else (everything not on Earth) is moving *westward*. Hence, the Sun rises in the east and moves westward until it sets in the west. The Moon also rises in the east and sets in the west, as do the stars.

All stars rotate through the sky all night long. But if you observe the sky for even one full night, you'll see that a few stars in the northern[3] part of the sky **don't** rise and set: they go around in circles, with one star at the center of the circles. This star is called **Polaris**, the Pole Star, better known as the **North Star**. It's a good one to know and easy to find. You start with the well-known pattern of seven stars called the Big Dipper and follow the last two stars of its "bucket" part to get to Polaris, which is part of the Little Dipper. Know this star, and you'll always be able to find which way is north. If you watch the Dippers all night (or set your camera to observe for hours), you'll see the stars tracing out circles around Polaris, which is very near to the part of the sky called the **North Celestial Pole**. If you followed **Earth's rotation axis** directly up into the sky, it would get to the North Celestial Pole and nearly Polaris. It's not a bright star, but you can usually see it even with city lights.

Since Polaris always shows which way is north, it has played an important role in human culture for centuries. For example, it was used by sailors for navigation for centuries before GPS was available. It was also used by people escaping from slavery in the southern United States.[4] The North Celestial Pole (the imaginary point in the sky found above Earth's North Pole) is also a guidepost for astronomers.

---

1   Technically called the sidereal period. *Sidereal* means "relating to the stars."

2   But there are *many* more. See http://www.en.wikipedia.org/Solar_Deity for examples from many cultures.

3   Or the southern part of the sky if you live in the southern hemisphere. Some parts of this discussion are written for an observer in the northern hemisphere, but most distinguish both perspectives.

4   This use is recounted in the folk song "Follow the Drinking Gourd." Drinking Gourd was another name for the Big Dipper.

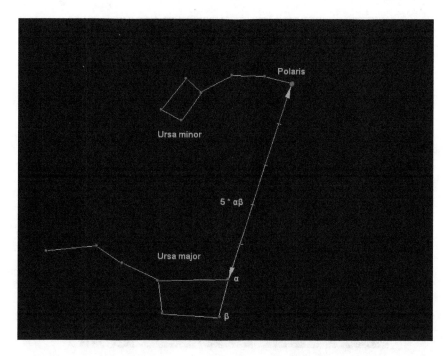

FIGURE 1.1   The last two stars in the Big Dipper (also called Ursa Major) point to the North Star, Polaris, and show you which way is north.

Similarly, the Earth's equator provides us with a reference line in the sky; the **Celestial Equator** is an imaginary line in the sky above Earth's equator. It divides the sky in half. Just as some cities are in the northern hemisphere and some in the southern, some *stars* are either in the northern hemisphere of the sky and some southern. If you live in Earth's northern hemisphere, it is easier to see the stars to the north of this Celestial Equator. There is also a **South Celestial Pole**, directly above the Earth's South Pole.

People living in different parts of the Earth have differing views of these two hemispheres in the sky. If you lived at the North Pole (90 degrees latitude), for example, you could look straight up and see Polaris, whereas for people living in most of the United States, it is about 30–40 degrees above the **horizon**. From the southern parts of the Earth (e.g., Argentina, South Africa, or Australia), Polaris can't be seen at all, but the people there see stars that people in the north have never seen.

SECTION 2. Astronomy Is Part of Human Culture

The Big and Little Dippers are just two of the many patterns people have found in the stars. In the 3 million years or so that humans have lived on Earth, the stars have captured our imagination in many ways. People from different parts of the world imagined heroes, goddesses and gods, animals, and monsters, each drawn from their own traditions. They brought stars together in their minds to form **constellations**. Do you have a favorite constellation? Can you remember a time when you last saw it?

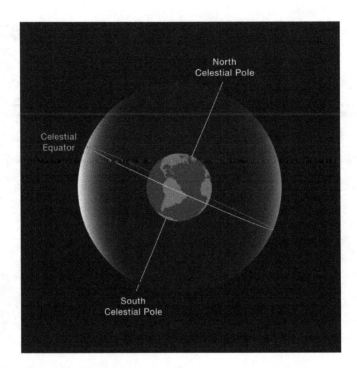

FIGURE 1.2   The Celestial Sphere is an imaginary sphere that surrounds the Earth. Astronomers use it as a reference. The Celestial Equator, which lies above Earth's equator, divides the north from south parts of the sky. The North and South Celestial Poles line up with Earth's rotation axis.

The word *constellation* comes from Latin words meaning "stars together." Latin isn't spoken much these days and is hardly ever taught in school. However, if you grew up speaking Spanish or learned it in school, then you already know that *con* means **together** and *estrella* means **star**. Similarly, when we talk of "solar" and "lunar" eclipses, speakers of languages like Spanish and French will recognize that we are talking about the Sun (*sol, soleil*) and the Moon (*luna, lune*). If scientific terms seem foreign to you, try breaking the word down, and you may find it is made up of parts that you already know.

The diversity of human culture is reflected in the many ways we have viewed even the same part of the sky. For example, the Big Dipper was seen as part of a Great Bear in many of the indigenous cultures of North America and also in those of North Africa, the Near East, and the Mediterranean, where it was called "Ursa Major." But these same stars were traditionally viewed as the "Plough" in the North Atlantic islands, as the "Seven Sages" in India, a lobster or shrimp in Burma, and a traditional sailing ship in Indonesia and Malaysia.

Before the invention of electricity, the skies were much darker and there were no TV, cell phones, and computers to keep humans entertained at night. People could see even the faintest stars and wove wonderful stories about the constellations they saw. A small part of this lore is with us today: astronomers still use old traditional constellation names to refer to different parts of the sky, but we have defined the boundaries of the constellations more carefully. This allows us to communicate with one another better about different parts of the sky, and it also honors some of our ancient predecessors in a small way.

Nowhere is the human connection to the skies more easily seen than in the old traditions of **astrology** and in the ways humans determined which season it was. Both of these depend on the way the Earth orbits the Sun, which is what determines **the year**.

SECTION 3. Earth's Orbit Gives Us the Year

What's your sign? Most people will answer with the name of one of 12 constellations: Aries, Taurus, Gemini, Cancer, Leo, Virgo, Libra, Scorpio, Sagittarius, Capricorn, Aquarius, or Pisces. But why *these* and not some of the other better-known constellations like Orion? And how do these constellations connect with the date of one's birth in order to determine someone's characteristics, as astrologers claim? What's up with astrology?

Let's start with what we can observe. Have you ever seen the large constellation Orion? What month was it when you saw it? I bet it wasn't June. You can't see Orion in June. You can't see Leo in August. Most constellations are invisible for part of the year. Why? Do the stars in these constellations go out for a few months? No, those stars gradually move through the sky when viewed night after night until those stars are in the same part of the sky as the Sun, which makes them hard to see. When you realize that you need the **Sun to be down** to see the stars, then you realize that the stars you were observing at *midnight* are the stars *opposite* to the Sun. Just as Earth's daily rotation creates the apparent motion of the Sun and the constellations move through the sky, Earth's annual **orbit** around the Sun creates the apparent ***annual*** motion of the constellations through our sky every year.

When you were young, did you ever stick glow-in-the dark stars to your ceiling? Look around the room you are in now and imagine that such stars are stuck on the ceiling, the walls, and even the floor. Now find an object near the center of the room and pretend it is the Sun. Turn toward it and imagine the Sun's rays lighting up your face. Looking beyond the Sun, there are stars on the wall, but you won't be able to see them; the Sun is too bright. To see stars it must be nighttime. Now turn your head (which represents the Earth), to face away from the Sun. Your face is now in darkness and it is night. The stars now in front of you would be visible at night. You can even group these stars into constellations (and give them names you like). Now, turn back to face the Sun. From your location, if you look carefully, you can imagine that the Sun falls right in the middle of one constellation, located on the far wall.

Earth *orbits* the Sun. So walk around the room, circling the Sun. Its position with respect to the stars will appear to change, as it gets in front of different constellations. Of all the stars and constellations throughout the room, however, the Sun will *only appear in front of a few,* those that are at eye level. In ancient times, people recognized 12 constellations that the Sun passed "through" and called them the *zodiac*.[5] Amazingly, people knew which constellation the Sun was in front of *even though* they couldn't see that constellation. But they believed that if the Sun was "in" a certain constellation on the day you were born, then you would have the attributes of that animal or being. This is the origin of astrology.

---

5   Several of these constellations are animals; "zodiac" is a collection of animals, like a zoo.

As we discuss in the next section, Earth's axis has a tilt to it, which causes the seasons every year. But the angle of this tilt is changing very slowly. Like a spinning top, Earth is not only spinning but also **precessing**. This slowly changes Earth's orientation with respect to the stars. But since most human calendars sync up with the Sun, the calendar dates when the Sun entered one constellation or another have been slowly changing too. For some reason, most astrologers these days haven't accounted for this adjustment. So, if you are into astrology, I have a surprise for you: your sign is not your sign! Take a look at the chart. Most people find that the Sun was really in the previous sign on the day they were born.

Many people scoff at astrology; others swear by it. Astrologers make money by describing aspects of a person's life based on their birth sign.[6] But different astrologers disagree as to how someone's horoscope should read on any given day. Their statements are always vague and cannot be clearly disproven. For this reason, astrology is not a science. Every scientific theory makes clear-cut predictions that can

TABLE 1.1   CONSTELLATIONS OF THE ZODIAC

This table shows which constellation the Sun is "in" throughout the year. The dates associated with these astronomical signs differ from those given by most astrologers due to precession, the slow turning of Earth's axis. However, in the thousands of years since astrology began, precession has caused a change of almost one whole zodiacal sign. In 1930, astronomers defined constellation boundaries, including "Ophiuchus" in the zodiac. (The dates below specifically correspond for the year 2000. Precession is very slow; as long as you were born within a decade or so of 2000, you can use this chart to see where the Sun was on your birthday.)

Dates	Constellation the Sun is "in" on those dates
January 20–February 16	Capricornus
February 16–March 11	Aquarius
March 11–April 18	Pisces
April 18–May 13	Aries
May 13–June 21	Taurus
June 21–July 20	Gemini
July 20–August 10	Cancer
August 10–September 16	Leo
September 16–October 30	Virgo
October 30–November 22	Libra
November 22–November 29	Scorpius
November 29–December 17	Ophiuchus
December 17–January 20	Sagittarius

Data for this table were kindly provided by Guy Ottewell of the Universal Workshop (http://universalworkshop.com/).

---

6   Other factors are taken into consideration, including the positions of the planets and Moon.

be tested. If the predictions are wrong, then the theory is false. So, if we realize that astrology is not a science, then we can have fun with it … assuming you can figure out which sign is yours and … whose horoscopes to read. To be fair, we should acknowledge that the roots of astrology are the same as those of astronomy—humanity's desire to understand the heavens and see how they are connected to our life on Earth. Possibly the most important such connection is the seasons.

SECTION 4. Earth's Tilt Gives Us Seasons

As we discussed before, it is 24 hours from sunrise to sunrise on average. However, the number of hours the Sun is up in the sky varies widely throughout the year, especially if you live away from the equator. Another **annual** change is the direction the Sun rises and sets throughout the year. You may have noticed that while the Sun always sets somewhere in the west, sometimes it sets in the Northwest and at other times in the Southwest. The point on the horizon at which the Sun *rises* also varies annually.

Another change you've probably noticed is that the Sun is higher in the sky in the summer than in the winter. To many people nowadays, the beginning of summer or the onset of winter might mean vacations, a chance to see family, or a different work or school schedule. But in the earliest times, the changing of the seasons was a life-or-death matter. Early humans migrated seasonally, following sources of food. Crops had to be planted and harvested at just the right times to avoid starvation. So, perhaps it is not surprising that our ancestors expended huge efforts to create different ways of predicting the

FIGURE 1.3   Nabta Playa. More than 8,000 years ago, people in Africa built a circular arrangement of large stones that can be used to track the seasons and movements of celestial bodies. Created thousands of years before the more famous Stonehenge, Nabta Playa may represent humanity's first astronomical observatory. Such monuments may have served as ancient calendars and may have been used for ceremonial or other purposes.

changing seasons. But the enormous size of some of these monuments they created is stunning, as is the sophistication that ancient peoples must have had.

Take, for example, an archaeological site in northeast Africa called Nabta Playa. Over nine thousand years ago (around 7500 BCE), Nubians, the people of this region, constructed a "calendar circle" by erecting large stones in a circular pattern that may have been used for astronomical observations. This monument was created *much earlier* than the pyramids found in Sudan to the south *and* the pyramids of Egypt, which are well north of this site. It also predates Stonehenge, a stone circle built around 3000 BCE–2000 BCE on the island that would later be called Great Britain. Clearly, these ancient peoples saw great value in building these enormous constructions.[7] But what was this value? Archaeo-astronomers have found alignments between the stones and the Sun on important days of the year, allowing seasons to be predicted. There are also alignments with the Moon and the stars. These sites may well have also served for ritual and religious ceremonies. There are hundreds of other such stone monuments around the world, including a huge domed rock building in Ireland called Newgrange, whose central passageway aligns with the rising sun on the shortest day of the year. Such sites are not even part of recorded history because they were built before written records were kept, even before the invention of writing.

Numerous ancient sites of astronomical significance are found in the Americas as well. One is called Bighorn Medicine Wheel in Wyoming.[8] Centuries ago, high on a hill in the Bighorn mountains, an unknown group of Native Americans built a large circular structure with 28 "spokes" using thousands of stones. Farther south, the ancient Mayan civilization had built structures, among their many cities, temples, and observing platforms from which they charted the skies and developed complex astronomical systems and calendars. The Temple of Kukulcan and El Caracol observatory in the city of Chichén Itzá are excellent examples.

These sites are but a few of hundreds that are known where our ancient ancestors sought a connection to the skies. There must be hundreds more that have been lost to time and still others yet to be discovered. For all the changes that humans have experienced over the centuries, in nations, religions, politics, style, arts, music, and especially technology, one thing has stayed the same: we can still look to the sky and see the same patterns playing themselves out, with the Sun and stars guiding the seasons of our lives, while the Moon and planets provide both regular and mysterious cycles to awe and inspire our scientific and spiritual curiosity.

COMMON MISCONCEPTION

Misconception: Earth is closest to the Sun in summer.

Fact: Earth is closest to the Sun on **January 4**, which is **winter** in the northern hemisphere and summer in the southern hemisphere.

In any case, Earth's distance from the Sun barely changes!

Okay, quick, find a friend nearby and ask them (or email/text them) this question: "Why does it get hotter in the summer?" What did they say? What did *you* think of their answer? Can you provide a different explanation? Take a moment to reflect on your own ideas about what causes the **seasons**, perhaps even write them down. It is good to be aware of your own ideas as you integrate new information.

---

7   The stones that make up Stonehenge are twice as tall as a person and weigh some 25 tons. They were hauled about 200 miles (320 km) before being set up!

8   The site was designated Medicine Wheel/Medicine Mountain National Historical Landmark in 2011.

Getting to the bottom of the question "What causes the seasons?" is not simple. One *plausible* answer is "Earth is closer to the Sun in summer, so it gets more of the Sun's light and heat." Why don't you investigate this idea on your own? For example, if this idea is true, then, logically, which day of the year would the

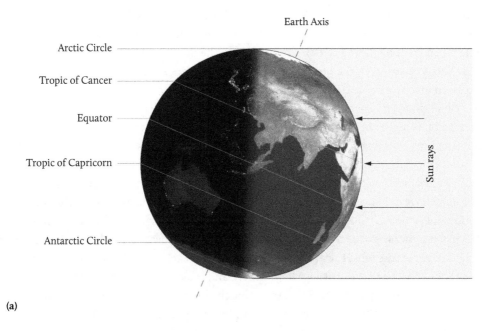

(a)

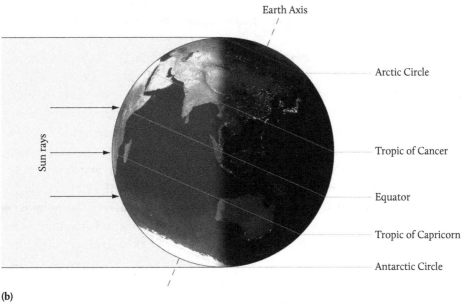

(b)

FIGURE 1.4   The seasons: (a) On June 21st, the Sun's light shines most directly on the northern hemisphere, so people in the north call this the summer solstice. (b) On December 21st, the Sun's light shines most directly on the southern hemisphere. People in the north call this the winter solstice. The seasons are reversed for people living in opposite hemispheres. At the spring and autumn equinoxes, both hemispheres of the Earth are illuminated equally. These changes are caused by the fact that Earth's axis of rotation (which always points toward the North Star) is tilted by 23.5 degrees with respect to Earth's orbit.

Earth be closest to the Sun? And according to **your own experience**, when is it hottest? Now here's a fact for you: Earth is actually closest to the Sun on January 4th. Does this fact support or refute your idea?

This process of checking whether a fact supports or contradicts an idea or theory is a fundamental part of the scientific method. It requires us to use our critical thinking skills and reject ideas that are not supported by actual observations. We'll discuss this process more later. But for now, the fact that Earth's northern hemisphere is **coldest** when Earth is **closest** to the Sun means that our first idea must be false. You may have heard that Earth's orbit around the Sun is not a circle ... but in fact, it nearly is! Even when Earth is closest to the Sun, it is only 1.6 percent closer—not enough to cause the dramatic temperature changes we see between summer and winter.

Above we mentioned two phenomena that you may have observed: the Sun rises and sets farther north in summer, and it is higher in the sky at noontime. Both of these have the same cause: the Earth's axis of rotation is tilted. When we say "tilted," we mean with respect to Earth's orbit. If you imagine a table with several coasters for drinks on it, all sliding in circles around a dish in the center of the table, then you have a very rough model of the solar system. Earth and all the planets orbit around the Sun pretty much in the *same plane,* not above or below. We call this the **ecliptic plane**. So the Earth's axis is tilted with respect to this ecliptic plane; it doesn't point straight up, but tilts over by 23.5 degrees. Because of this tilt, the North Pole of the Earth sometimes tilts toward the Sun, while at other times the South Pole tilts toward the Sun.

Earth's North Pole tilts most toward the Sun on **June 21st** each year.[9] This date is called the **summer solstice** by those who live in the northern hemisphere and is usually regarded as the first day of summer. It's not that this tilt causes part of the Earth to get much closer to the Sun. No, it is the **angle of sunlight** that matters. Direct sunlight is more *intense* than indirect, or glancing, light. The high Sun in summer delivers more energy to the Earth's surface than the feeble low Sun of winter. (You may have noticed solar panels on roofs of buildings propped at different angles; they are trying to maximize the amount of solar energy captured.)

On the summer solstice, the Sun rises very early and sets very late. You may experience 15 hours of daylight, and night will only last for 9 hours. This effect is most dramatic the farther away from the equator you are. So, at the North Pole (and above the Arctic Circle), you'll experience the midnight Sun, which doesn't set, but just goes around in the sky as Earth rotates. The additional hours of sunlight that the land around you experiences in summer allow more energy to be delivered to the land, warming it further. These two effects—the more direct light and the extra hours of light—cause the seasons. But *their* cause is the same, the fact that **Earth's rotation axis is tilted**. If Earth rotated straight up, then we wouldn't have seasons. To explore the seasons further, let's follow the Earth as it orbits the Sun.

As Earth orbits the Sun, it keeps rotating. The axis of the Earth remains fixed, pointing at Polaris. But that axis no longer points directly toward the Sun. So, after the summer solstice, there's less sunlight each day for the northern hemisphere observers. By September 21st, the axis of the Earth points neither toward nor away from the Sun, but perpendicular to it. The Sun's light shines equally on the northern and southern hemispheres. The entire Earth experiences 12-hour days and 12-hour nights, which is responsible for the name of this time: **equinox**, or equal night. So, September 21st is regarded as the first day of fall, or autumn, and called the **autumnal equinox**.

But Earth keeps orbiting. As it does, its polar axis comes back into alignment with the Sun, but this time it is the southern half of the Earth that is angled toward the Sun, not the north, which is increasingly

---

9   In leap years, the date falls on June 20th.

shaded. December 21st is the winter solstice for the northern hemisphere and the shortest day of the year (also regarded as the start of winter). But people in Australia, Argentina, and South Africa are basking then under the most direct Sun of the year. Incidentally, it is called *sol-stice* because observers watching the Sun rise night after night would see it getting farther and farther north (or south) until it stops (*-stice* = stop),[10] turns around, and begins to rise from points farther out.

It helps to view things from different perspectives. This description of the seasons imagines us floating out in space looking down on the Earth as it orbits the Sun. But we experience seasons from Earth. So let's shift back to our usual perspective here on Earth to see how the changes look to us. At summer solstice, the Sun rises in the northeast part of the sky, climbs high overhead,[11] and sets in the northwest part of the sky.

By the way, other planets are also tilted with respect to the ecliptic plane but not by 23.5 degrees. Uranus is tilted by over 90 degrees. If Earth had this tilt, our seasons would be wacky; there would be half a year of darkness in which we never saw the Sun, then half a year of light in which the Sun never set! The planets all have somewhat different tilts because that's how they originally formed. There was no plan in place to line everything up. Similarly, the Earth's rotation period (1 day) is not synchronized with its orbital period (the year). The time it takes the Earth to orbit is, in fact, 365.2422 days. While this doesn't match up with one 365-day year, it is close to 365 and a quarter days. So, if we have four years of 365 days, these four quarters will add up to one extra day,[12] which we account for by having a 366-day year, or a leap year. We could put that day anywhere in the year, but for historical reasons we give it to the shortest month, February.

SECTION 5. The Moon's Orbit Gives Us the Month (and Eclipses!)

In one night, the Moon rises and sets due to the Earth's rotation. But if you decide to observe the Moon for three nights in a row, you'll notice two things. First, you'll find yourself staying up later and later because the Moon rises 48 minutes later each night. The second thing you'll notice is the familiar change in the Moon's shape, from a thin **crescent** to half illuminated a few nights later, then growing larger, or **waxing**, until it is **full**. If the Moon was already full when you started observing, then you'll see it **wane,** or get smaller. At first it appears nearly full, or **gibbous**, but by one week it is half full again. Still waning, it becomes a thin crescent visible just before sunrise. The Moon then moves to the same part of the sky as the Sun, becoming too hard to see. This is called a **new moon**. The Moon's cycle (the lunar month) is divided into 4 quarters, each of 7 days. This is why we have *7 days in a week,* not 8 or 10. If we start with a new moon, as is customary, then the phases in order are new moon, waxing crescent, first quarter, waxing gibbous, full moon, waning gibbous, third quarter, waning gibbous, and new again.

---

10   This can be seen in *armistice*, when people stop using arms (weapons). Same root as *stasis* and *stationary*.

11   The Sun never gets directly overhead unless you live in the tropics.

12   Well … almost. Since a year is 365.2422 days and not 365.25 days, this pattern gets off by one day every 100 years, so century years like 1900 are **not** leap years. To improve further, we *do* add an extra day every 400 years. So 2000 *was* a leap year, but 2100 won't be.

It takes about 29 and a half days for the Moon's phase to go from full moon to full moon.[13] This is called the **synodic** period of the Moon. This period is the basis of our concept of the *month*; indeed, the word *month* comes from "moon." A calendar whose months are *perfectly* synchronized with the Moon's phases is called a lunar calendar. But most calendars also synchronize with the year and the seasons, so are called solar calendars. People all over the world have found elegant and sophisticated ways of keeping track of time. Check out a few of them in the calendar box.

CALENDARS

Keeping track of time has always been important, so creative humans around the world have devised a bewildering array of calendars. Here are just a few of them, along with an example date ("Ex.") in each. Were different calendars traditionally used in the cultures of your family?

The most commonly used calendar in the world is the Gregorian calendar. It was implemented by Pope Gregory in Rome in 1582 and later elsewhere. It's an improvement over the Julian calendar, which had been used since 45 BCE. The Julian calendar was implemented by the Roman emperor Julius Caesar and based on ancient calendars in Egypt, but it was slightly flawed, causing dates to get out of sync with the seasons. So, to correct this, **10 days were deleted**. They never happened! The day after October 4, 1582, was October 15, 1582! An example of a date on the Gregorian calendar is **April 8, 2024**.

The Maya civilization in Central America used three different calendars[1] to keep track of time and record numerous astronomical events. Lunar months alternated between 29 and 30 days. Days were arranged in groups of 20, in line with the Mayan mathematic system, which used base 20 instead of base 10. Ex.: **9 Kimi, 9 Pop, 13.0.11.8.6**.

The Muslim calendar has 354 days, not 365. There are 12 lunar months of either 29 or 30 days. A purely lunar calendar, it is not synchronized with the Sun or the seasons. So, a month such as *Ramadan* may occur in summer, winter, spring, or fall. Ex.: **29th of Ramadan, 1445**.

The Jewish calendar has 12 lunar months of 29 or 30 days. This adds up to 354 days, which is less than one solar year (365.25 days). To compensate, a ***leap month*** is added periodically, which keeps *Rosh Hashanah* (New Year's Day) in the same season. Ex.: **29th of Adar II, 5784**.

The Thai Buddhist calendar and several related calendars are used throughout Southeast Asia. Like the Jewish calendar, it is both lunar and solar and includes leap *months*. Year 1 in this calendar is the year people once thought the Buddha became enlightened. People in Thailand also follow the practice, common throughout Asia, of associating years to one of 12 animals. Ex.: **8th of Mes'ayn, 2567, Year of the Dragon**.

---

1   The Mayan calendars were called the *Tzolk'in*, the *Haab*, and the Long Count calendars. On December 21, 2012, the Long Count calendar reached an interesting date: 13.0.0.0.0. In the years leading up to this day, many silly people predicted that this would cause the end of the world or some other disaster. Such predictions happen all the time and are usually intended to scare people and sell books and other products. The frantic "2012 phenomenon" badly misrepresented the culture of the ancient and modern Mayan peoples.

(continued)

---

13   It takes 29.53 days, to be precise. Why not a whole number of days? Because the Moon, which is orbiting 239,000 miles away from Earth, doesn't care what time it is down here on Earth. The Earth's spin, which is what gives us the concept of one day, has little impact on the way the Moon **orbits** way up there.

The Persian calendar, widely used in Iran and Afghanistan, is the only solar calendar to begin with an astronomically important date. The Persian New Year (*Nowruz*) always falls on the spring equinox, around March 21st. The original form of this calendar, devised by poet/astronomer Omar Khayyam, synchronized with the Sun without needing leap years. Ex.: **20 Farvardin, 1403**.

The Celtic calendar may have been the first calendar widely used in western Europe. It was organized by priests called Druids. Its details are still uncertain because the culture that used it was displaced, first by Roman invaders and later by Christians. One 1,800-year-old artifact, the *Coligny Calendar*, shows that this calendar was lunar and solar and included leap months. Some holidays from this tradition are still celebrated today in different ways, including *Samhain* (October 31, from which we get Halloween), *Imbolc* (February 2nd), from which Groundhog Day originates, and *Beltane* (May Day).

The dates shown above all correspond to April 8, 2024 (the date of a total solar eclipse in North America).

One final note: as you can see above, the simple question of "what year is it?" depends on when your calendar starts. Christians using the Gregorian calendar have used AD for years after the birth of Jesus on their calendar. (*Anno Domini* means 'year of the Lord'). They also used BE to mean "Before Christ." Modern scholars prefer the less religious terms: CE and BCE meaning "Common Era" and "Before the Common Era." Either way, the calendar is based on an event that is not well dated. When historians attempt to ascribe a date to the birth of Jesus, then come up with a range of dates of 6 to 4 BCE. If you were to create your own calendar now, when would it start? Would it be lunar or solar or both?

But *why* does the Moon take on these appearances? There is a simple activity you can do to visualize what you see in the sky. You can find it below in the box labeled "Do Try This At Home." These are a series of activities I've created that you can try out with simple household items.

DO TRY THIS AT HOME: MOON MODEL

Turn out all the lights in the room except one desk lamp (a bright bulb works best, but you can use a flashlight or even a bright cell phone light). Get out any round ball—you can even use your fist if you don't have one, but a smooth ball like a racquetball is better. The ball represents the Moon and your head represents the Earth. The light, of course, is the Sun. First, get close to the light and notice that it lights up half of your head; perhaps your whole face is lit or maybe the back of your head, half of each. The part of your head facing the light represents where it is noontime on Earth. The opposite side is experiencing midnight.

To start, hold the Moon-ball in your left hand almost directly in front of the light but just a little to the left. What shape does the lit-up part of the ball make? Can you see a crescent? You might need to fidget with your lamp and make sure the ball gets enough light on it. Next, move the ball so that your arm makes a right angle with the Sun. This is the **first quarter** phase. Can you see that the ball is half illuminated? As you move your ball a little farther to the left, you'll see more and more of it getting lit up, making a **gibbous** phase. At the back side of your head, there's a problem: your head blocks the light on the ball. So, hold the ball a little higher than your head. You'll now see the fully illuminated side of the ball facing you, a full moon. The full moon is always opposite the Sun. As you continue this process, switch the ball to the other hand and move the Moon in a circle around your head. You'll see the Moon wane, with the phases repeating in reverse order. The reason the Moon has phases is simply that it is a sphere with light shining on it. You can sketch what you see if that helps.

The activity above works well to visualize the phases shown in Figure 1.5. This model, of course, is not exact; in fact, it gives the false impression that the Moon is very close to the Sun, as shown in many books. To make a **scale model,** try using a typical globe for the Earth, or just a soccer ball, and a tennis ball or baseball for the Moon, which is about four times smaller than the Earth (in diameter). What's surprising about this model is where you need to put the Moon. Before I tell you, take a guess: should it be three times the Earth's diameter away? Five away? 10? In fact, the Moon is much farther away: 30 times the diameter of Earth! You'll have to put it outside the room! When astronauts landed on the Moon in 1969, they had to fly through space for *three days* to get there. You can make your own sketches if it helps.

When you held the Moon directly behind you to simulate a full moon, you may have noticed that your head blocked the light from hitting the Moon. This actually happens—it is called a **lunar eclipse**. As the Moon is orbiting its way toward becoming full, it drifts into the shadow that the Earth is always casting. But real lunar eclipses are much less common than our simple model would suggest. In part, this is because of how far away the Moon is, which makes a perfect alignment hard. It's also because the Moon's orbit is tilted (by about 5 degrees) with respect to the ecliptic plane, meaning that it is usually above or below the plane that contains the Earth and the Sun. It only crosses the ecliptic plane twice a month and usually not while the Moon is full or new.

We can now see where the ecliptic plane gets its name: the Moon must be in this plane for an eclipse to occur. The Earth's orbit around the Sun brings the Moon into the right position for an eclipse twice every year. When this happens, the results are stunning. If the Moon is full at this time, then everybody who can see it is in for a treat. First, the full moon seems to have a bite taken out of it—a **partial lunar**

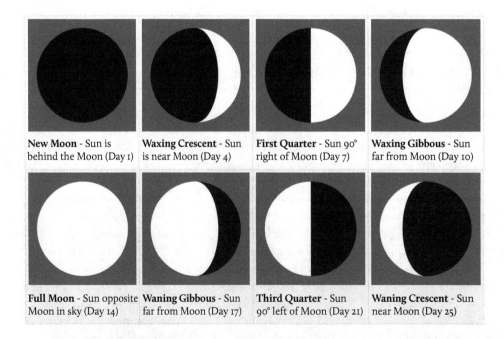

FIGURE 1.5 Phases of the Moon: The Moon's apparent shape, its *phase*, constantly changes, returning to the same phase after 29.5 days. You can visualize why phases happen by shining a light on a ball in a dark room. Can you create each of the phases shown here? Since the Moon orbits the Earth, we see the Moon in a different place every night (or day). This lets us see more or less of the lit-up part of the Moon (the part facing the Sun).

eclipse. Then, as the hours progress, this bite becomes bigger until the entire Moon goes dark! This is called **totality**. Sometimes the Moon can be faintly seen in totality bathed in an eerie red glow from stray light that has managed to leak through Earth's atmosphere. This lasts for about an hour until the Moon, always moving as it orbits the Earth, moves slowly out of the shadow. Lunar eclipses are a sight to behold, but aren't as hard to see as you might think. When they happen, half of the Earth can watch the spectacle (the half that can see the Moon then). And they happen every year. Check Table 1.2 for upcoming lunar eclipse dates.

COMMON MISCONCEPTION

Misconception: The Moon is close to the Earth, just a few Earth-diameters away.

Fact: The Moon is over **30** Earth-diameters away. Here's the math: Earth's Diameter = 12,000 km. Moon's distance: 384,000 km. 384,000/12,000 = 32.

As remarkable a spectacle as lunar eclipses are, there's an even more impressive sky show waiting for those who are lucky or motivated to see it: a **solar eclipse**. As the name implies, a solar eclipse consists of the Sun disappearing, not the Moon. But it is the Moon that blocks the Sun's light, throwing a dark shadow onto a small part of the Earth (and graying out a much larger area). The astronomical cause is the same: the Sun, Moon, and Earth have come into perfect alignment. A solar eclipse occurs because the Moon passes directly in front of the Sun. While a lunar eclipse requires a full moon to occur, *a solar eclipse can only happen at new moon.* You can see this by holding up a ball in front of a lamp.

Not every new moon causes a solar eclipse. Once again, the reason is that the Moon doesn't orbit Earth in the same plane as the Sun (the ecliptic plane). To cast a shadow on the Earth, the Moon must cross the ecliptic plane. Even then, because the Moon is four times smaller than the Earth, this shadow is small: a dark spot about 100 km wide, which glides across the Earth's surface at great speed. But if you are inside that small spot, the sight is stunning. First, the Sun appears to have a bite taken out of it, then this dark area grows until the Sun takes on a crescent shape. The crescent gets thinner and thinner until the moment of perfect alignment (**totality**) occurs and the Sun is *gone*. The surrounding area is suddenly plunged into darkness, and it instantly gets about 10 degrees colder. Looking up, you are amazed that you can now see *stars* in the sky in the middle of the day! Where the Sun was, you'll instead see a shimmering circle of light called the **corona**. This remaining light comes from very hot gases just outside the Sun, whose light is not blocked by the Moon. You have just witnessed a **total solar eclipse**! This experience is so stunning and moving that it cannot be put into words.

People have been awed by solar eclipses for thousands of years. The earliest record of one is from 1223 BCE,[14] but they must have been observed much earlier than that. Eclipses frequently appear in myth as an ominous sign. In one example from India, there is a myth about Rahu, a sort of demon, devouring the Sun with his disembodied head, but the Sun returns because Rahu is unable to swallow it. A solar eclipse back in 585 BCE even stopped a war.[15] This eclipse was actually predicted in advance by the Greek scientist Thales of Miletus. Remarkably, you don't need advanced science or math to predict an eclipse ... you just need to be able to keep track of the days since the last eclipse, which could add up to years. Another

---

14   In the Mediterranean city of Ugarit (in modern-day Syria) on March 5 (see https://www2.hao.ucar.edu/Education/solar-physics-historical-timeline-1223-BC-250-BC).

15   This occurred on May 28, 585 BCE, between armies of the kingdoms of Lydia and Media in modern-day Turkey.

ancient astronomer, Meton of Athens, realized that 19 years after an eclipse, another eclipse would occur on the same day of the year.[16] But these Greek scientists based their theories on centuries of observations made by Babylonian, Sumerian, and other Middle Eastern scientists whose names we do not know.

TABLE 1.2   SOLAR AND LUNAR ECLIPSES

To see a total solar eclipse, you'll need to be on the path of totality. This will require you to travel, but it will be worth it! During annular solar eclipses, the Sun turns into a ring because the Moon appears too small to block it. Lunar eclipses are easier to see, since they are visible over half the Earth. But you should check the day before to learn the timing of the eclipse in your local area. You may need to set an alarm clock to see one.

Date	Type of Eclipse	Visible in ...
May 16, 2022	Total Lunar	Americas, Europe, Africa
Nov. 8, 2022	Total Lunar	Asia, Australia, Pacific, Americas
Oct. 14, 2023	Annular Solar	North, Central, and South Americas
April 8, 2024	Total Solar	Mexico, United States, Canada
March 14, 2025	Total Solar	North, Central, and South Americas
Sept. 7, 2025	Total Lunar	Europe, Asia, Australia
Mar. 3, 2026	Total Lunar	North America, East Asia, East Australia
Aug. 12, 2026	Total Solar	Spain, Iceland, Greenland
Feb. 6, 2027	Annular Solar	Chile, Argentina
Aug. 2, 2027	Total Solar	Spain, North Africa, Arabia
Jan. 26, 2028	Annular Solar	North and South America, Europe
Dec. 31, 2028	Total Lunar	Europe, Asia, Australia
July 22, 2028	Total Solar	Australia, Southeast Asia
June 26, 2029	Total Lunar	Eastern United States, South America, Africa
Dec. 20, 2029	Total Lunar	Europe, Africa
Jan. 14, 2029	Partial Solar	North and Central America
June 1, 2030	Annular Solar	Europe, North Africa, China
Nov. 25, 2030	Total Solar	Southern Africa, Australia

So let's end this first chapter the same way we began: with your calendar. Get it out and make a plan to see an eclipse! Remember that lunar eclipses are easier to see: anyone on the night side of Earth who can see the Moon can catch it. Solar eclipses are only *total* over a small strip, called the path of totality, so you'll need to travel to get there. But they can be seen as partial over a wide area. The total solar eclipse on August 21, 2017, was viewed by hundreds of millions of people; the first total solar eclipse in the

---

16   This is called the Metonic cycle. It also means that on your 19th birthday, the Moon has (for the first time) returned to the same part of the sky, with the same phase as the day you were born.

FIGURE 1.6   Path of totality for the April 8, 2024, solar eclipse. This eclipse represents the last chance in 20 years for people throughout the United States to see a total solar eclipse without leaving their country. Those in the path of totality will see a total solar eclipse. The skies will darken, and the stars will come out. Those outside this zone will see a partial eclipse.

continental United States in 38 years. Did you see it? Was it total where you were? Another opportunity for US observers is April 8, 2024. As you can see from the map in Figure 1.6, people along a path extending from Texas to Maine on that day witness the last total solar eclipse in the United States for over 20 years.

WRAP-UP

The stunning spectacle of a solar eclipse thrilled, stunned, and impressed ancient viewers just as much as it does us today. In this chapter, we saw how careful observations allowed our human ancestors to harmonize their lives with the natural cycles of the universe. They charted the Sun's movement through the constellations and created complex calendars using the Moon to keep track of time. We humans have always been observers of the sky. In the next chapter, we will explore how very careful observations, made a few hundred years ago, allowed us to get a deep understanding of what planets are and how they really move. This understanding would then revolutionize the world of science.

REFLECTION QUESTIONS

1. What's *your* astronomy connection? Have you seen an interesting astronomy event like an eclipse? Or do you have a ritual of watching the sunset from a special place? Do people in your family celebrate holidays using a calendar different from the widely-used Gregorian calendar? Are you interested in science fiction stories involving space travel, or perhaps you're familiar with astrology?

2. We mentioned that sunrise and sunset are caused by Earth's rotation, but that ancient people thought that Earth did not rotate. Imagine that you have time-traveled and meet a person from the distant past who believes that the Sun moves through the sky on its own. How would you convince this person that the Earth is, in fact, rotating? What evidence could you give? Would it help to make that *person* rotate (e.g., on a merry-go-round) and then ask them to describe what they see?

BIBLIOGRAPHY

Betz, Eric. "Nabta Playa: The World's First Astronomical Site Was Built in Africa and Is Older than Stonehenge." *Astronomy Magazine* (2020). Retrieved March 13, 2021. https://astronomy.com/news/2020/06/nabta-playa-the-worlds-first-astronomical-site-was-built-in-africa-and-is-older-than-stonehenge

Burnham, Andy. *The Old Stones: A Field Guide to the Megalithic Sites of Britain and Ireland*. London: Watkins, 2017. https://www.megalithic.co.uk/

Fraknoi, Andrew. *Unheard Voices, Part 1: The Astronomy of Many Cultures*. Los Altos: Foothill College. (Available in PDF format at: https://multiverse.ssl.berkeley.edu/multicultural)

Krupp, Ed. *Beyond the Blue Horizon*. Oxford: Oxford University Press, 1992.

For More Information About Calendars and Dates:

Islamic calendar: https://www.islamicfinder.org/islamic-date-converter/

Jewish calendar: https://www.hebcal.com/converter/

Mayan calendar, *Chac*: https://www.chacapp.com/Chac.html

Persian calendar: http://www.iranchamber.com/calendar/converter/iranian_calendar_converter.php

Various others: http://www.webconversiononline.com/

Eclipses:

http://www.mreclipse.com/Special/SEnext2021.html

https://eclipse.gsfc.nasa.gov/eclipse.html

You can find videos on eclipses, moon phases, and much more on the author's YouTube channel. The link to it can be found under "Videos" at this page:

http://www.physics.sfsu.edu/~chris/

The triple spiral motif used throughout this book was created by Wikipedia user AnonMoos and represents the triple spiral pattern found in prehistoric astronomical sites, including Brú na Bóinne in Ireland. An example can be found on the front cover of this book, which shows a large stone at the entrance to the Newgrange site.

CREDITS

Fig. 1.1: Copyright © by Bonč (CC BY-SA 3.0) at https://commons.wikimedia.org/wiki/File:Ursa_Major_-_Ursa_Minor_-_Polaris.jpg.

Fig. 1.2: Source: https://solarsystem.nasa.gov/bosf/docs/BOSF_02_06v2_Celestial_Sphere.jpg.

Fig. 1.3: Copyright © by Raymbetz (CC BY-SA 3.0) at https://commons.wikimedia.org/wiki/File:Calendar_aswan.JPG.

Fig. 1.3a: Copyright © by Przemyslaw "Blueshade" Idzkiewicz (CC BY-SA 4.0) at https://commons.wikimedia.org/wiki/File:Earth-lighting-summer-solstice_EN_-_corrected.png.

Fig. 1.3b: Copyright © by Przemyslaw "Blueshade" Idzkiewicz (CC BY-SA 2.0) at https://commons.wikimedia.org/wiki/File:Earth-lighting-winter-solstice_EN.png.

Fig. 1.4a: Copyright © by Daniel Kmiec (CC BY 3.0) at https://commons.wikimedia.org/wiki/File:Moon_phase_0.svg.

Fig. 1.4b: Copyright © by Daniel Kmiec (CC by 3.0) at https://commons.wikimedia.org/wiki/File:Moon_phase_1.svg.

Fig. 1.4c: Copyright © by Daniel Kmiec (CC by 3.0) at https://commons.wikimedia.org/wiki/File:Moon_phase_2.svg.

Fig. 1.4d: Copyright © by Daniel Kmiec (CC by 3.0) at https://commons.wikimedia.org/wiki/File:Moon_phase_3.svg.

Fig. 1.4e: Copyright © by Daniel Kmiec (CC by 3.0) at https://commons.wikimedia.org/wiki/File:Moon_phase_4.svg.

Fig. 1.4f: Copyright © by Daniel Kmiec (CC by 3.0) at https://commons.wikimedia.org/wiki/File:Moon_phase_5.svg.

Fig. 1.4g: Copyright © by Daniel Kmiec (CC by 3.0) at https://commons.wikimedia.org/wiki/File:Moon_phase_6.svg.

Fig. 1.4h: Copyright © by Daniel Kmiec (CC by 3.0) at https://commons.wikimedia.org/wiki/File:Moon_phase_7.svg.

Fig. 1.5: Source: https://commons.wikimedia.org/wiki/File:SE2024Apr08T.png.

WANDERERS OF SCIENCE

Not all those who wander are lost.

—J. R. R. Tolkien

What's your favorite day of the week? If you celebrate Fridays, then you are celebrating Frigga, the goddess of love and wisdom from Norse mythology, for whom Friday was named ("Frigga's Day"). Unless, of course, you speak a language other than English. For example, if you speak Spanish, you know Friday as *viernes*, named for Venus, also a love goddess, and a planet. Have you ever wondered where the days of the week come from? And why are there seven of them and not, say, thirteen or just four? Venus isn't the only planet to lend its name to a day of the week. In fact, *all* the days of the week are connected to planets or celestial bodies.

The word ***planet*** means wanderer.[1] Indeed, some of the stars you see when you look up in the sky *wander* from one constellation to the next. They are not, in fact, stars at all: they are the planets. It just takes a few nights' observation to notice this motion,[2] so people have been aware of these wanderers throughout human history. In most ancient cultures, they were thought of as gods and goddesses in the sky and named accordingly. In this chapter, we will see how the quest to understand the motion of these wanderers led humans down a long and wandering path that eventually led to modern science.

---

1 A related term from biology is *plankton*, wanderer of the sea.
2 Another way to distinguish them is that planets do not twinkle; stars do.

SECTION 1. The First Five Wanderers

You have the ability to observe the planets and ponder what you are seeing. There are five planets easily visible without a telescope: Jupiter, Saturn, Mars, Venus, and Mercury, the faintest. If there happens to be a planetarium near where you live, you'll be able to see the star patterns and planet positions above your home right now. If not, you can find a planet in the sky by looking for a "star" that doesn't fit into a known constellation. Or nowadays, you can cheat a bit by downloading a computer program that will tell you where to spot planets in the sky above your home. Try searching online for "planetarium software" for computers or "stargazing apps" for cell phones. If you observe the same planet again a week later, you'll start to see why ancient people called them wanderers.

TABLE 2.1

Day of the Week	Spanish	French	Astronomical Body
Monday	Lunes	Lundi	Moon
Tuesday	Martes	Mardi	Mars
Wednesday	Miércoles	Mercredi	Mercury
Thursday	Jueves	Jeudi	Jupiter (also called "Jove")
Friday	Viernes	Vendredi	Venus
Saturday	Sabado	Samedi	Saturn
Sunday	Domingo	Dimanche	Sun

The days of the week are named for the five planets visible to ancient people along with the Sun and Moon, for a total of seven. This pattern can be found, with interesting variations, in many languages.

Together with the Sun and the Moon, the planets made up seven moving bodies in the skies (in contrast with the "fixed" stars). In fact, this is why we have seven days in a week! The connections between planets, gods, and days (see Table 2.1) become clearer if you use Spanish or French.[3] While all seven of these bodies move with respect to the stars, only the Sun and the Moon move smoothly. Night after night, both move **eastward** in the sky, with the Sun taking a year to go around, and the Moon, a month. But the planets are strange. Not only do they speed up and slow down as they move, sometimes they reverse direction! This motion, called **retrograde motion**, was regarded by ancient astrologers as particularly odd and worrying.[4] For example, Figure 2.1 shows Mars's motion over the time span of a few months. After moving toward the east for several months, Mars changes direction and begins to "go retrograde." What's up with that?

Retrograde motion is not real. It is an illusion of motion. There are many such illusions. Have you ever been in a car, stopped at a light, and watched cars on either side of you move forward as the light turned green? For a moment, it seems like you are moving backward. The illusion of Mars's backward

---

3   The English language is related to German, and some of its day names derive from Norse mythology. Can you guess which days of the week were named for Thor and Odin (also called Woden)?

4   Even today, astrologers blame disturbances (e.g., with electronic equipment) on the retrograde motion of Mercury.

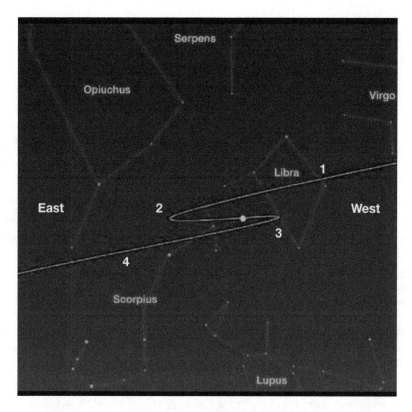

FIGURE 2.1   Path of a planet over several days. The backward, or retrograde, motion of the planets seemed perplexing and perhaps ominous to ancient observers. Ptolemy explained retrograde motion using a geocentric model. However, we now know that this model was wrong.

(retrograde) motion is caused by the fact that Earth is moving. But it doesn't *feel* like Earth is moving, so ancient people had to come up with another explanation. By the year 140 CE, they had one.

SECTION 2. The First Model Was Geocentric

In those days, the northeast corner of Africa was home to the greatest center of learning in the world. The famous Library of Alexandria, a port city in Egypt, housed about 100,000 books (in the form of scrolls) and an institute of learning, where people studied music, literature, poetry, mathematics, geography, medicine, zoology, astronomy, and many other arts and sciences. One of those people was named **Ptolemy**,[5] who wrote books on music, geography, astronomy, astrology, and other subjects. Combining the work of earlier scientists, Ptolemy found a way to explain the retrograde motion of planets, consistent with the common belief at that time that the Earth was at the center of the universe.

---

5   Pronounced "Tall-a-me," Claudius Ptolemy lived c. 100–170 CE.

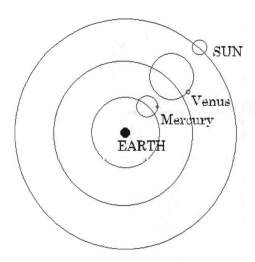

FIGURE 2.2 Geocentric model of the inner solar system. In this simplified version of Ptolemy's model, the planets Mercury and Venus are shown moving on their epicycles, which themselves orbit the Earth, as does the Sun. The full geocentric model also included the Moon (orbiting closer than Mercury) and Mars, Jupiter, and Saturn, orbiting farther out. In this model, the epicycle would sometimes cause the planet to move backward, thus "explaining" retrograde motion.

His **geocentric model**[6] looked like this: the Moon moved around the Earth every month and the Sun moved around every year, passing through each of the constellations. Both objects moved in circles. For some reason, Ptolemy and his contemporaries thought that circles were a perfect shape. So, he also used circles to explain how planets moved. But because planets sometimes go backward, he used two circles: one riding on top of the other. Take the planet Mars, for example. In Ptolemy's model, Mars moved along a small circle called an **epicycle**.[7] But this epicycle itself moved on a larger circle around the Earth. This way, Mars would sometimes swing forward and sometimes loop backward, as these two circles interacted. The same thing applied to the other planets, but the circles they rode on had different sizes. This model worked—it could explain why Mars showed retrograde motion: it swings inward (toward us) and backward on its epicycle. More distant planets, like Jupiter and Saturn, which moved more slowly, also had epicycles of different sizes.

But there was one small oddity, which I'll return to later. It is a fact that Mercury and Venus are never seen at midnight; to find them, look near the Sun, just after sunset or before sunrise.[8] So, Ptolemy just *assumed* that the epicycles of these two planets were centered on the line between the Earth and the Sun (shown as a dotted line in Figure 2.2). He had no explanation for why these two planets behaved differently, but without this *ad hoc* assumption, his model would falsely predict that we could see these planets at midnight.

This geocentric model of the universe[9] held sway, more or less, for over 1,400 years. But as I'm sure you know, it is wrong. As we discussed in Chapter 1, the Earth goes around the Sun, not the other way around. Why wasn't this theory challenged earlier? Part of the reason is the authority that many people conferred on Ptolemy and other scholars from the classical era (like Aristotle or Plato). While Ptolemy was undoubtedly a genius, anyone can make a mistake. But since his books, particularly one called the *Almagest*, were used as university textbooks for centuries, few people thought to question him. And how would you even go about challenging an accepted theory?

Centuries later, an answer to this question was provided by **Alhazen**,[10] an Arabian astronomer, mathematician, and scientist who lived in the same part of the world as Ptolemy (Cairo, Egypt). Alhazen read

---

6   *Geo-*, as in geology; geography means Earth. The word originally comes from the Earth goddess *Gaia*.

7   *Epi-* means "on top of," so **epicycles** are circles on top of circles.

8   This is why Venus is sometimes called the morning star and sometimes the evening star.

9   Nowadays, we refer to the Sun, the Moon, and the planets as the solar system. But back then, these *were* the whole known universe, together with the stars, which were thought to reside just beyond the last planet, Saturn.

10   He was also called Ibn al-Haytham, born in Basra c. 965 CE.

the books of Ptolemy carefully, criticizing errors he found. When two theories disagreed, he said they should be put to the test. A theory that made wrong predictions must be discarded, regardless of how authoritative its author is. We now credit Alhazen for providing the earliest known example of what would later be called the scientific method. Unlike Ptolemy, he also insisted that the planets were physically real things and should move in realistic ways. So, while he did not overturn Ptolemy's geocentric theory, Alhazen showed later astronomers exactly how to do it.

SECTION 3. The Next Model Was Heliocentric

The theory that did overthrow Ptolemy's work is called the **heliocentric** theory.[11] It proposes that the Sun—and not the Earth—is at the center, and that all planets orbit the Sun. This idea was published in 1543 by Nicolaus Copernicus, a Polish astronomer who also worked for the Catholic Church as an administrator, or *canon*. In fact, Copernicus was not the first to come up with the idea, so perhaps he gets too much credit. Way back in the second century BCE, Aristarchos, a Greek astronomer living on the island of Samos (near modern Turkey), suggested the Sun was at the center. Alternatives to Ptolemy were also proposed by Aryabhata in India (c. 500 CE) and Nasir al-Tusi (c. 1250 CE) in Persia.

In any case, Copernicus's idea would trigger a revolution in human thinking, as more and more people began to consider the idea that our home, the Earth, was not at the center. Copernicus didn't live to see this, however; his book was published just before his death. He may have held off publishing deliberately; he probably realized that the book would get him in trouble. Why? Well, at that time, the Catholic Church had accepted the scientific ideas of Ptolemy and earlier scholars such as Aristotle.[12] In particular, they interpreted certain Bible verses as evidence that the Earth was at the center of the known universe. Anyone who taught otherwise was seen as challenging the authority of the Church. It's hard to imagine how much influence the Catholic Church and the newly created Protestant Church had at that time. The countries of Europe did not have

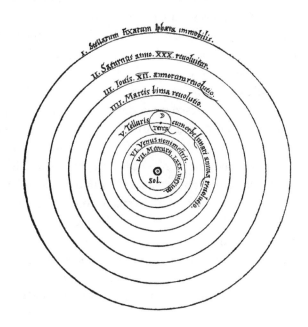

FIGURE 2.3 The heliocentric model of the solar system proposed by Nicolaus Copernicus in 1543. The Sun is at the center, and each of the planets orbits it, including the Earth (*Terra*), which itself is orbited by the Moon. This model was a radical change from the geocentric model.

---

11   Named for Helios, the god who represented the Sun.

12   Ironic because these two scholars predate Christianity.

the principle of separation of church and state, so these churches could impose their doctrines on the people by force of law. For example, the **Inquisition** was the arm of the Catholic Church that enforced violations of Church law, called heresy. They became notorious for their use of torture and could execute accused heretics by burning them at the stake. While Copernicus never got in trouble for advocating that the Sun was at the center of our solar system, another scientist, living in Italy, did. His name was Galileo.

SECTION 4. A New Device, the Telescope, Provided Evidence for the Heliocentric Model

Sometime in the late 1500s, somewhere near the Netherlands, somebody (probably a glassmaker) combined two glass lenses and found they could then see things very far away, as if they were close. This new invention, the **telescope**,[13] began to spread throughout the world. They were used to look at people or birds miles away or to spot ships at sea. But the first person, as far as we know, to turn a telescope upward and look at the sky was an Italian scientist from a city in Italy called Pisa. Galileo studied many fields of science. In one experiment, he is said to have dropped two balls from the famous Leaning Tower of Pisa, one heavy, one light. Both fell at the same speed, which contradicted the old teachings of Aristotle, who said the heavier object should fall faster. But this was just the warm-up for his experiments that would contradict an even more deeply held idea: that the Earth is the center of the universe.

Galileo built a telescope by combining two lenses. Apparently, no one had pointed a telescope to the sky yet, so when he did, the discoveries rolled in. He found that the surface of the Moon was scarred with craters, which challenged the common idea that everything in the heavens should be perfect. He was stunned when he looked at Jupiter, because it seemed to have four little "stars" near it. Jupiter is a planet, so it should "wander" from one constellation to the next, leaving the stars behind. But these stars followed Jupiter! In fact, Galileo eventually realized that they were orbiting Jupiter. Today we recognize them as the moons of Jupiter. This discovery also challenged the idea that everything orbits the Earth.

When Galileo observed Venus, he saw something that no one had seen before. Through the scope, he saw a crescent shape, just as the Moon sometimes appears. In a way, this made sense. Remember that a crescent is seen when the Moon is between the Earth and Sun. Whether one used the heliocentric or geocentric model, Venus could be found *between* the Earth and the Sun (see Figure 2.4). But what Galileo saw next completely *disproved* the geocentric model.

Waiting a few months, he observed Venus to now look more than half full (gibbous). This simply would never happen if the Earth was at the center. However, the reason is not obvious. Remember that the geocentric model had this quirk where Venus[14] orbited on an epicycle that was "glued" to the line between the Earth and the Sun. This meant that if the Earth was the center, Venus could *never* be more than half full. But observations show that, in fact, sometimes it is.

---

13 *Tele-* means far away; *scope* means to see.
14 And Mercury as well.

Now, you might think that at this point the geocentric theory was nearly dead. Unfortunately, instead it would be *Galileo* who was nearly dead! After these discoveries, he published a provocative book that strongly criticized the geocentric model. Remember that this model was Church doctrine at the time. The book offended the pope, and Galileo was put on trial for heresy. This was potentially life threatening: some people convicted of heresy were put to death. Historians tell us that Galileo was unlikely to be executed. However, he was forced to recant, stop teaching the geocentric idea, and placed under house arrest for the rest of his life. His books were banned.

The story of Galileo is sometimes portrayed as a Church-versus-science clash, and not without reason. But the details of his case are more complex. At this time, many scientists still accepted the long-held geocentric idea. And some scientists who agreed with Galileo (such as the Jesuits) were priests in the Church. Galileo deliberately provoked the Church by writing a book that mocked the pope, who happened

FIGURE 2.4   The heliocentric and geocentric models both predict that Venus will move between Earth and the Sun. So, in both models, Venus should appear as a crescent when observed through a telescope, as in the photo of Venus above, or like how the Moon looks crescent when it is between Earth and the Sun. However, if the planets are orbiting the Sun and not the Earth, then sometimes Venus will get *behind* the Sun and appear as gibbous. (See Figure 1.4.) According to the old geocentric model, this should never happen. Galileo showed that it *does*.

to be his old friend. After his death, the Catholic Church changed its views on Galileo, "unbanning" his books in 1835. By 1992, the pope admitted that the Church had made an "error" in the case. Nowadays, many people still regard religion and science as being in conflict. Indeed, some people use religious arguments to reject well-established scientific theories like evolution, even as they rely on scientific theories for their health, for safe travel, etc. But there are also many scientists whose practice of religion does *not* interfere with their scientific inquiry. How do you come down on the issue? Can scientific theories be reconciled with your spiritual or religious traditions (if any), or do you find them in conflict? Does this lead you to learn more about those traditions about the universe?

In any case, the idea that the planets we see at night are moving around the Sun, not the Earth, began to spread. Copernicus's book was widely published, even if it was hard to read. In some places, the book was censored by the Church, but the heliocentric idea spread. There was a problem though; Copernicus's predictions for the planets were close but not exact. The old geocentric theory also made roughly accurate predictions, so the observers of the day couldn't tell which was better. These two problems would be solved by two astronomers who could not have been more different from each other.

SECTION 5. Kepler and Tycho Were an Odd Couple

Tycho Brahe (1546–1601) was a man of privilege in European society. He was born in Denmark into a family that was well connected to royalty. The king gave him an island near Copenhagen to rule over. He made money by taxing the peasants who worked the land there. But instead of just building a castle, he built an **observatory** to study the skies.[15] You see, he had been inspired to study astronomy by watching an eclipse as a child. At this observatory, he made the most precise measurements of the wandering planets that had ever then been made. Tycho made valuable measurements and a few important discoveries, such as a "New Star" that appeared in 1572. He called it *Nova Stella*, and from this we get the words *nova* and *supernova* for different types of exploding stars. We now know that Tycho had witnessed a supernova (see Chapter 8 for more on why stars explode). But Tycho maintained an elite lifestyle I can only describe as pompous and bizarre. A few highlights included wearing a fake gold nose (after his nose was cut off in a duel), having a "dwarf" who served as his court jester,[16] and a pet moose that got drunk and stumbled down a staircase.[17]

Johannes Kepler (1571–1630) was completely different. Far from royalty, he was born into a poor family in Germany. His father was a mercenary and disappeared when he was five years old, possibly killed in one of the many wars Europeans were fighting at that time. However, in the next few years, Kepler observed a great comet and a lunar eclipse, events which would spark an interest in astronomy and guide the rest of his life.

This was a hard time to live in. The disease smallpox (which now has been eliminated from Earth) was common and fatal. He survived it, but his arms were somewhat disabled. Two of his children died in infancy. In the span of one year, three of his surviving children got smallpox, one died, and then his wife, Barbara Müller, died of a different disease. He did remarry, but three of the children of his second marriage also died. Meanwhile, the world around him was insane. Most of Europe was divided into Protestant and Catholic areas. Members of these two religions[18] fought endless wars against each other. When armies of one group conquered a town, they could expel all people who didn't convert to their religion. Living in a border region, Kepler had to move several times in his life and sometimes lived in a battle zone. He even had to defend his mother, Katarina, in court after she was accused of witchcraft.[19] Remarkably, though, Kepler overcame these challenges and worked out amazing new ideas about how the planets orbit.

Kepler's first idea, however, was completely wrong. Like others in this time, Kepler read the books of ancient writers. From these, Kepler knew about the five geometric solid shapes shown in Figure 2.5. Since there were only five known planets,[20] he figured that the planets orbited the

---

15   Actually, the observatory was like a castle. He named it after the goddess of the heavens, Urania. Although it was extremely expensive, he built another one next door when he realized the first observatory's instruments jiggled too much. Tycho just couldn't give up the royal lifestyle.

16   For a fictional account of this exploited little person, see *Jepp, Who Defied the Stars* by Katherine Marsh.

17   https://mentalfloss.com/article/50409/tycho-brahe-astronomer-drunken-moose

18   Ironically, both groups are followers of Jesus, the so-called "Prince of Peace."

19   Persecution of women who practiced traditional medicine or some form of folk healing was common in Europe at the time. Over 40,000 women were put to death after being found guilty in "witch trials."

20   The five known planets were Mercury, Venus, Mars, Saturn, and Jupiter. Uranus and Neptune were not discovered until 1781 and 1846, respectively.

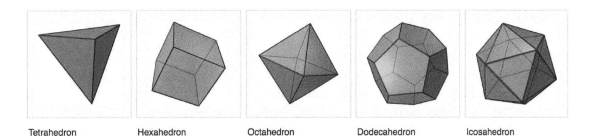

| Tetrahedron | Hexahedron | Octahedron | Dodecahedron | Icosahedron |

FIGURE 2.5 The five perfect solids. They are called perfect because for each one, the faces are all identical, AND each face is a shape whose sides are also identical. (For example, all the triangles that make up a face are perfectly symmetric equilateral triangles.) It turns out there are only five ways to do this. The only solids that work are: tetrahedron (4 sides), cube (6 sides), octahedron (8 sides), dodecahedron (12 sides), and icosahedron (20 sides). Some modern gamers use these solids as dice.

Sun in circles that were arranged according to these geometric shapes. It was an inspired guess, and Kepler tried to make it work for many years. While it turned out to be wrong, Kepler's (almost fanatical) drive to understand how planets moved led to his discoveries. I mention this odd but elegant idea of Kepler's to show how scientists work. We may get an inspiration, follow up on it, and then find it doesn't work. But this may allow us to wander down another path that does work. Similar approaches are used by artists, musicians, writers of literature, etc.

Both Tycho and Kepler became wanderers. Tycho left Denmark after a new king came to power who didn't like him as much. Kepler and his whole family were deported from their home by a new wave of religious intolerance. Traveling as refugees in 1600, they arrived in Prague, the capital of Bohemia (in the modern-day Czech Republic), where Tycho was now employed by King Rudolph as the royal mathematician. Tycho hired Kepler as his assistant. From the standpoint of science, it was a perfect match: Kepler could devise theories of how planets moved and Tycho could make the observa-

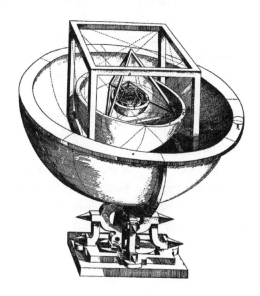

FIGURE 2.6 Kepler's first model of the solar system, connecting the five known planets with the five perfect solids. He actually built this model. The beauty of these shapes inspired Kepler to figure out how the planets orbit the Sun.

tions to test them. But from the standpoint of personalities, it was terrible. They clashed from the beginning. Tycho assigned Kepler the hardest task he could think of: figure out the orbit of Mars, which was known to move oddly. But Tycho would not give Kepler the hundreds of observations he had carefully made of Mars's position in the sky. Without these data, Kepler could not check any of his ideas! It seems like Tycho was more interested in living the royal lifestyle: he threw many parties and had dinner with the king. After one such event of heavy eating and drinking, Tycho fell deathly ill and died a few days later.

SECTION 6. Kepler Discovered How Planets Move

Ironically, the death of the best observational astronomer of his time, Tycho, was great news for astronomy. That's because Kepler, who took Tycho's place, now gained access to his data. But Kepler's work was just beginning; he then set about to figure out exactly how the planets orbited the Sun. Even though the heliocentric model of Copernicus made more sense to him, it didn't correctly predict Mars's motion, so there must be something wrong with it. But what? He persistently pursued this question for *10 years*. His general process was like this: make a slight change to the heliocentric model;[21] then, using geometry, trigonometry, and algebra, calculate where Mars would be seen in the sky at each of the times Tycho had observed. If these matched the observations, then the change should be kept in the model.

But they didn't match. Time after time, model after model—none of Kepler's additions to the heliocentric theory worked. It was painstaking work; hundreds of pages of calculations ... all done without an electronic calculator! Once, he thought he was done: the position of Mars in his current model matched 10 of the observations of Tycho, but was off for two observations, but only slightly off (1/8th of one degree in angle). Most scientists would pat themselves on the back and say, "That's good enough." But not Kepler. Knowing the precision of Tycho's measurements, he had the humility to realize that these observations were valid, and it was Kepler's model that was wrong. He threw away that model and the years of work that went into it and started over. Along the way, he made some algebra errors, as we all do from time to time, which slowed him down more.

It is much harder to unlearn a wrong idea than it is to learn a correct one.[22] Eventually, Kepler became willing to abandon the idea that planets orbited in **circles** only and considered other shapes for the orbit. After several more tries, he returned to a shape he had considered before but skipped over—an **ellipse**. Looking like a flattened circle, an ellipse is an elegant, symmetric shape with one long axis. When Kepler calculated where Mars would appear in the sky *if* its orbit was an ellipse, he found a perfect match to Tycho's observations. The ellipse shape works for all other planets too. Kepler had finally figured out how the "wanderers" of our solar system move! Today we call this discovery **Kepler's First Law**.

Kepler didn't invent the ellipse shape. Its properties were well known and similar to those of a circle. We measure a circle using its **diameter** or its **radius**, which is just half the diameter. But an ellipse has *two* diameters. The long diameter is called the *major axis*. Half of the major axis, which is like the radius of an ellipse, is the *semimajor axis*. We'll use this semimajor axis to measure the size of a planet's orbit around the Sun and abbreviate it using the letter *a*. Try making an ellipse of your own: attach a piece of blank paper to a piece of cardboard using two thumbtacks. Tie a string in a loop and stretch it out with a pencil.

FIGURE 2.7   Examples of ellipse shapes. A circle is actually a kind of ellipse (just as a square is a kind of rectangle).

---

21   For example, Kepler considered the idea that planets orbited the Sun in circles but also moved in epicycles, as in the Ptolemaic model.

22   You may have noticed this in your own learning. For example, if you had ideas about what causes seasons (Chapter 1), it may have been difficult to add new information to those ideas without first challenging your old ideas.

As the pencil loops around, it will trace out an ellipse. The location of each thumbtack is called a **focus** of the ellipse.

The ellipse shape of Mars's orbit explains why people before Kepler couldn't understand its motion: they assumed it moved around the Sun in a circle. But, in fact, it sometimes comes closer to the Sun. Its distance of closest approach is called **perihelion**,[23] and it farthest distance is called **aphelion**. The Earth's orbit is also an ellipse, and some people think this is what causes the seasons. But remember from Chapter 1 that Earth's ellipse is, in fact, almost a circle. We only get 1.6 percent closer when Earth is at perihelion, and the *entire* Earth gets closer—both northern and southern hemispheres, which have opposite seasons. Perihelion occurs January 4th, but it doesn't affect Earth's overall temperature much. Seasons are caused by the tilt of Earth's axis.

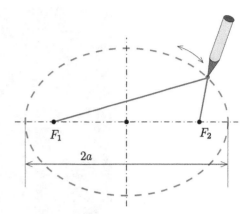

FIGURE 2.8   An ellipse is drawn by stretching a string around two thumbtacks stuck in cardboard. The line made by the pencil is an ellipse, and each of the two points, F1 and F2, are called a focus of the ellipse (plural *foci*).

Kepler also noticed something else about how Mars orbited: it sped up when it got closer to the Sun and slowed down when it was farther from the Sun. He expressed this in geometric terms in his **Second Law** (see Figure 2.9). But we can state this law simply as, "Planets move fastest when they are closest to the Sun (perihelion)."

Take a moment to ask yourself, "Why would a planet move faster when closer to the Sun?" What did you come up with? Does it seem at least plausible to you that the Sun's gravity might be stronger when the planet is closer? Kepler didn't think gravity was responsible. Kepler *couldn't* think gravity was responsible. This idea, gravity, which is common knowledge for ordinary people today, **didn't exist** in Kepler's life. In fact, it was Kepler's own work to understand how planets move that led to the theory of gravity, some 60 years later. Personally, I find it bewildering to try to think of the motion of planets around the Sun without ever thinking of gravity.

Kepler continued. Using the times that Tycho had recorded for the planets' positions, he figured out how long it takes them to orbit the Sun. This amount of time is called the planet's **period (P)**. Of course, Earth's orbital period is one year. Kepler found that the period of each planet is related to how far that planet is from the Sun, or to put it another way, the size of the planet's orbit. So, let's first discuss how we measure the size of a planet's orbit.

As mentioned above, we measure the size of an ellipse using its semimajor axis (a). Most planets' orbits are actually quite close to being circles, so you can think of a as the radius of the circle. The radius of Earth's orbit is 150,000,000 km, or 93 million miles. But instead of dealing with these large numbers, we'll make things simpler by defining a new unit, the **astronomical unit, or AU**. One AU = 150,000,000 km = 93 million miles = Earth's distance from the Sun (on average). So Earth's period and semimajor axis are: P = 1 year, a = 1 AU.

---

23   *Peri-* means close to, and *helios*, you will remember, means Sun.

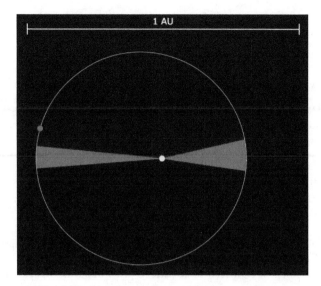

FIGURE 2.9   Kepler's Second Law. The orbit of the planet Mercury (red dot) is an ellipse, with the Sun (yellow dot) at one focus (not the center), as shown in Fig. 2.8. To see how Kepler's Second Law works, look at the red wedges. Each shows the area swept out by Mercury in 4 days as it orbits the Sun. The long wedge on the left is skinny because Mercury moves more slowly when farthest from the Sun (perihelion). The short on the right is much wider because Mercury is moving faster when it is closest to the Sun (aphelion). Kepler's Second Law says that planets sweep out "equal areas in equal times." A simpler way to say this is to say: "A planet moves faster when closer to the Sun."[1]

DO TRY THIS AT HOME: SKETCH THE PLANETS

To visualize the planet's orbits, get out a sheet of paper and make a simple sketch. Put a dot in the center and label it "Sun." Draw a small circle[1] around the dot, and mark the radius of this circle "1 AU." That's the Earth's orbit. Now, try Jupiter: draw a circle that's five times larger than Earth's circle. This is Jupiter's orbit, and its radius is "5 AU." You could try to draw the whole solar system, but it might not fit. Pluto's orbit is about 40 AU in radius.

Now, let's return to the timing of the orbits. Look at your sketch. If the time it takes Earth to orbit (P_{Earth}) is one year, how long do you think it takes Jupiter to orbit? Did you guess five years? That's a logical guess and would be correct if the planets all moved at the same speed.[2] But Jupiter's observed period is actually about **12 years**! What's up with that?

---

1   While Earth's orbit is an ellipse, it only differs from a circle by a tiny amount.
2   To see how fast planets actually orbit, check this animation produced by NASA: https://www.youtube.com/watch?v=Jxri2rBqs-U

---

1   I made this figure by using the app on this page: http://physics. unm.edu/Courses/Rand/applets/kepler_2. html and selecting the planet Mercury, which I chose because its orbit is the most elliptical. (Even still, its orbit looks like a circle. For a more dramatic ellipse, choose Halley's Comet or increase the "eccentricity.") You can see that the Sun is not at the exact center of the ellipse. The two highlighted wedges show the area swept out by Mercury's motion in the same amount of time (around four days). Thanks to Richard Rand (University of New Mexico) for creating this app.

Kepler figured out a connection between a planet's orbital period (the time it takes to orbit once) and the size of its orbit (*a*, the semimajor axis). This connection is called **Kepler's Third Law**. If you multiply the period, P, by itself you get $P \times P = P^2$ (pronounced "P squared"). This turns out to be the same as: $a \times a \times a = a^3$ (*a* cubed). You can see this in the table of planets' orbital periods.

TABLE 2.2

Planet	Period (P)	Semimajor axis (*a*)	a^3	P^2
Mercury	0.241	0.387	0.06	0.06
Venus	0.615	0.723	0.38	0.38
Earth	1	1	1.00	1.00
Mars	1.88	1.52	3.51	3.53
Jupiter	11.9	5.20	140.61	141.61

Period, P, and semi-major axis, *a*, for five planets. Periods are in years, and SEMIMAJOR axes are in AU. Kepler found that while the period and orbit sizes (SEMIMAJOR axes) differed, there is a relationship between their cubes and squares: $P^2 = a^3$

Humans had been curious as to the wandering planets' paths through the sky for thousands of years. At long last, Kepler provided three rules that would tell you exactly where to find any planet at any time in the future. Not only that, but they were later found to correctly predict the movements of planets that had not even been discovered in Kepler's day. They also predict the movement of *moons* like those Galileo had found orbiting Jupiter.

KEPLER'S LAWS

1. A planet moves in an *ellipse* with the Sun at one focus.

2. A planet moves fastest when it is closest to the Sun. (Original version: A line from the planet to the Sun will sweep out equal areas in equal times.)

3. A planet's orbital period *squared* equals its semimajor axis *cubed*: $P^2 = a^3$.

You may notice that this book spends more time discussing Johannes Kepler. This is not just because he's my personal favorite astronomer. Kepler radically changed astronomy from speculations about the skies to a genuine science about real physical things. Whereas people in those days still referred to the planets as wandering gods, Kepler envisioned them as real worlds, and even predicted that humans would travel in space to them![24] His life also offers an important lesson to us today. He lived in a time of intense political polarization, religious intolerance, and violence. A victim of several injustices, he did not get caught up in the violence but was able to stay focused on his personal dream: to find beauty and order in the movement of the planets.

---

24   Kepler wrote the world's first book of science fiction, *Somnium*, in which a kid travels to the Moon with the help of his mother, who is a witch, and a demon. Bizarrely, Kepler's own mother was accused of witchcraft by a mayor who had already executed eight women for the "crime"! Kepler spent years defending her.

SECTION 7. Gravity

Kepler's Second Law says that a planet orbits faster when closest to the Sun (perihelion). As a planet approaches, the Sun pulls it in and whips it around. The Third Law implies that planets that are closer to the Sun, like Mercury and Venus, orbit at a faster speed. You may have already deduced the reason for both laws: the Sun's gravity gets stronger the closer you get to it. But as mentioned above, Kepler didn't have the idea of gravity available to him. He realized the Sun must exert a force on the planets, but couldn't quite describe it.

Half a century later, Isaac Newton, a scientist living in England, described it. He proposed that the same force of gravity that we feel on Earth keeps the planets orbiting the Sun. But it took a lot of work for him to come up with that idea. At first, he wasn't studying planets at all. He noticed that every time something moves, it moves in certain ways, and not in others. For example, a marble rolling down a flat surface will roll in a line, not curve, unless something is pushing it (like a strong wind). Observations of seemingly mundane, obvious things like this are at the core of science. When a scientist sees something happen, she or he asks: "Why?" And that is the beginning of a new scientific idea.

Newton noticed that moving things seem to always follow three "laws" of motion (see box below). First, like the marble above, they move in straight lines unless acted upon by some force outside themselves. The second thing he noticed concerns how quickly things accelerate; that is, change their speed. The more force you apply to something, the faster it will end up going. For example, you can hit a ping pong ball with a paddle softly, or, to make it fly away faster, hit it hard. But if you try to hit a *bowling ball* with a paddle, it will hardly move at all. That's because it has higher **mass**. These observations are all encoded in Newton's Second Law of Motion. His Third Law explains how scooters and skateboards work. First, there is an **action**: a skateboarder *pushes the ground* backward. Then there is a **reaction**: the skateboard moves forward. While these actions may seem simple, the process of understanding how and why things move led us to everything from trains to rockets to the Moon.

NEWTON'S LAWS OF MOTION

1. An object in motion will remain in motion, *moving in a straight line*, unless some force acts on it.

2. If a force is applied to an object, it will accelerate, but more massive objects will accelerate less.

3. For every action, there is an equal and an opposite reaction.

We'll only concern ourselves with the First Law, since it led to Newton's most famous inspiration, the falling apple. But this inspiration might never have happened if it weren't for a horrible disease. The bubonic plague, a bacterial infection carried by fleas on rats, killed around 100,000 people in London.[25] Universities were closed and students like Newton were sent away. At his family home, there was an apple orchard, and Newton observed an apple falling to the ground. He wondered why apples fall down, and not, say, sideways. At the same time, he had been thinking about the Moon. It clearly moves around

---

25 An earlier outbreak of plague in Europe was far worse: around 100 million people died—over 30 percent of the population!

the Earth in a near circle. But according to Newton's First Law, it **should** move in a straight line … unless some force is acting on it.

At this point, he thought of the falling apple and wondered if the Earth could exert a force on the Moon just like it did on the apple. It is hard for us to appreciate what a radical idea this is. We naturally think of gravity when we talk about planets, the Sun, and the Moon. But back then, gravity was thought of as an "earthly" phenomenon and didn't apply to "heavenly" bodies in the sky. When people looked to the skies, or the heavens, they thought of the pure, divine, spiritual idea of "heaven," which was quite a contrast to the Earth, with its wars, diseases, rats, and fleas. Newton proposed that the **laws of nature are universal**: they apply equally here on Earth as they do out in space. But does this work? If gravity pulls the Moon toward the center of the Earth, why doesn't the Moon crash into Earth?

Newton imagined a cannon on top of a large hill. If it fired cannonballs at greater and greater speed, they would travel farther and farther before they hit the ground. But if a cannonball was still airborne by the time it had traveled halfway around the world, it would *stay airborne* and encircle the entire Earth! Assuming the cannonball didn't hit the cannon that fired it, it would just keep going around and around; **it would *orbit* the world**! In fact, this is exactly what modern satellites do: they "fall" in orbit around the Earth, without consuming any fuel at all. This explains how the Moon can orbit the Earth without crashing—it is moving fast enough (and far enough) that gravity allows it to just swing around the Earth. Newton next applied this new idea of gravity to the **planets'** orbits around the Sun, which Kepler had previously mapped out. Could gravity also explain Kepler's Laws of Planetary Motion?

Eventually, Newton showed that, yes, all the motions the planets make can be explained by the Sun's gravity. To *prove* this requires some mathematical tools that today we call calculus. But calculus didn't exist at this time; in fact, Newton invented it[26] in order to solve this problem! When he was done, he found that if the force of gravity pulled on the planets, they would orbit the Sun in ellipses and speed up when close to the Sun, as Kepler had found they do. Newton proved all three of Kepler's Laws of Planetary Motion. This new scientific theory, gravity, could be used to predict how not just planets, but comets, asteroids, and even spaceships move. There are over 1,000 satellites in orbit around the Earth today, including those that communicate with your cell phone's GPS receiver, to tell you where you are. So-called **geostationary** weather satellites deliver images of hurricanes and storms, and communication satellites allow people from all over the world to be in touch. None of these would be possible without Newton's realization, way back in the 1600s, that the same force that pulls an apple to the ground makes the Moon orbit the Earth.

SECTION 8. Modern Science

While people all over the world have engaged in science at all times in human history, we can say that **modern science**, in the sense that we practice it today, came into being in the 1600s and 1700s. Of course, far more people contributed to this process than I have discussed in this book. In the modern sense, science can be characterized by these attributes:

- All valid scientific theories must be confirmed by observations. These observations must be repeatable by other researchers throughout the world, not just one group in one place.

---

26   German mathematician Gottfried Leibniz also shares credit for the independent invention of calculus.

- Scientific theories must make specific predictions that can be checked. If these predictions don't hold up, the theory is not valid. (If your friend says they have their own theory about something, ask them, "What evidence could prove your theory wrong?" If they can't come up with anything, then they don't have a theory!)

- No scientific theory is ever "proved true." Scientists accept that new and better observations may invalidate their current theories.

This last point might surprise some people, especially people who trust in scientific theories, which, actually, we all do. The reason is that most people would like to think that if something is very *reliable*, then it's a sure thing.

While science provides the most reliable way to predict what will happen next, scientists do not claim to have found absolute truth. Our willingness to replace old ideas that are not supported by observed facts is what gives scientific theories their strength. And here I have to admit that sometimes scientists cling to their cherished ideas, even as evidence mounts against them. But all good scientists must, like Kepler, have the humility to reject disproven ideas and seek out a better explanation. Indeed, scientists are often excited to see if they can find an error, however small, in a current theory and propose a better one. As we will see later in this book, the theory of gravity, as laboriously worked out by Isaac Newton, was later proved wrong and replaced with a new theory that correctly predicted all observations. Modern scientists have made tremendous use of the understanding of planetary orbits provided by Copernicus, Kepler, and Newton. Once we knew how planets and the Moon orbit, we could figure out how to make *anything* orbit, including spaceships. Here is an example of just one such scientist. Katherine Johnson (1918–2020) was a mathematician who worked for NASA calculating orbits. She worked on some of the most important space missions, including the first American in space and the first American to orbit the Earth. Space travel is high-risk and such calculations are life-or-death. However, as a Black woman in the early 20th century, she faced many challenges. In fact, the college she attended for graduate school did not even allow people of color to attend until she and two other Black students enrolled in 1939, following a Supreme Court ruling prohibiting discrimination. Working at NASA, she became the first woman to be an author of a technical report (on the details of launching a satellite into a selected position). Her achievements were eventually recognized after she appeared in a book and movie called *Hidden Figures*. Katherine Johnson was awarded the Medal of Freedom by US president Barack Obama.

FIGURE 2.10 Katherine Johnson working at NASA.

Because they can be tested, scientific theories are very reliable. So reliable, in fact, that you can bet your life on them ... literally. Would *you* bet your life on a scientific theory, like, say aerodynamics? Too late, you already have! This theory predicts that an airplane's wings will allow it to lift off once the plane reaches a certain speed. If this theory is wrong, the plane will crash. Every time you fly, you are betting your life on a scientific theory. Indeed, you can't even cross the street at a busy intersection without trusting your

COMMON MISCONCEPTION

Some confusion comes from the way we use the word *theory*. Most people use the word to mean a speculative idea or guess. (For example, if one student says, "If I get enough sleep, I'll ace this mid-term," another may reply, "Well, that's just your *theory*.") But a **scientific theory** is a general organizing principle that can explain many different and even unrelated facts, which makes clear-cut predictions that can be tested, that *have been* tested, and which have *passed* the test *every time*.

life to a scientific theory, specifically **electromagnetism**. This scientific theory explains the working of electric circuits[27] in everything from cell phones to stop lights. Are people who travel in airplanes or who cross intersections with a green light foolish to trust their lives to a scientific theory? Certainly not. Theories are so reliable, you can bet your life on them. It might seem strange to trust your life to a scientific theory when scientists admit that any theory can be disproven if a new and different set of observations invalidates it. But that vulnerability to testing is what gives scientific theories their strength. If we weren't willing to discard ideas that are disproven by observed facts, we would still be stuck with the idea that everything moves around the Earth or the ridiculous notion that the Earth is flat.[28]

SECTION 9. Culture and Science

This is a good time to briefly discuss science and culture. A simple way to state the connection is: **science influences culture and is influenced *by* culture**. The first fact is clear to nearly everyone. Just think of technological devices that modern culture depends on (satellite-based GPS maps, airplanes, etc.), all of which were enabled by scientific discoveries. But in a deeper sense, science influences culture in some of the same ways as art or music, inspiring people, questioning social norms, challenging government policies. Photographs of deep space from the Hubble Space Telescope make us wonder, while NASA satellites showing us images of the shrinking Amazon rainforest or rising ocean temperatures allow us to question our current mode of living. Scientific research into the cause of global warming reveals threats that span the globe and can unite humanity in finding solutions.

But "science" does not just happen by itself. It is a creative process made by people. Both the joys and the problems that people everywhere face are the joys and problems of science. In this chapter, we discussed the lives of some scientists who lived up through the 1700s, some of whom faced political intolerance based on religious ideology, which interfered with their work and lives. Even now, hundreds of years later, there are plenty of other societal problems that also impact science. They are rarely discussed in books

---

27   It also explains what light is, as we will see in the next chapter.
28   Don't even get me started on Flat-Earthers.

on science. For example, did you notice that the historical scientists whose groundbreaking work was discussed in this chapter were male? A critical thinker would ask, "Why were no contributions by women presented?" One reason is that the role of women was heavily restricted in historical times. Another is that the histories we have from back then may well have excluded the contributions of those women courageous enough to defy social pressures and pursue science.

The challenges faced by women were clearly still present even in the 20th century, as we saw with the case of Katherine Johnson above. In recent decades, opportunities for women in science have become much better. In the following chapters in this book, we will cover a number of discoveries made by women, including some who have been excluded from other textbooks. Sexism isn't the only problem to impact science. In my field of astronomy, people of color are still underrepresented at the top levels, such as professor and department chairperson.[29,30] My colleague in the field of exoplanet research, Harvard professor John Johnson, observed, "The further I went in my field, the fewer and fewer black people I saw."[31] In addition to racism, students wishing to embark on a career in science face economic challenges ranging from large student debt to high housing costs to expensive textbooks. There are many other societal challenges, as you might know from your own personal experience. The progress of science is hindered whenever a person interested in the field is unable to make their contribution for these reasons.

But old ways of thinking change, sometimes gradually and sometimes quickly. As we have seen in this chapter, a revolution in people's thinking can occur as old ideas are displaced by new ones that actually match up with observed facts. The change that took place in the 1600s, from thinking of the Earth as the center to thinking of the Sun as the center of our solar system (called the "Copernican Revolution"), is just one of a number of scientific revolutions in people's thinking. Such revolutions are similar to the huge changes that have occurred regarding social issues: the abolition of slavery, women's suffrage, and the legitimacy of same-sex relationships, just to name a few. Scientists can play a role in creating positive change in our cultural and societal ideas and science itself will benefit *from* that change.

WRAP-UP

This is one of the longest and most important chapters in the book. The modern methods of science developed as we discussed, and they are basically what we still use today. Science is reliable because it is based on evidence that many people can check, not just one person's opinion. One of the reasons I teach astronomy is to help people understand what science is, what it isn't, and why it is reliable. While I love my career as an astronomer, I realize that most people won't become scientists. Still, it is important for everyone to understand the role of science in society. Science can't solve all problems (and it may even contribute to some), but in a world facing issues like pandemics and global warming, science has an important role to play in human society. Your understanding of science means that *you* have an important role to play as well. In the next chapters, we will apply these scientific methods to allow us to interpret the light we get from things in space, to help us understand what they are.

---

29   https://www.aip.org/sites/default/files/statistics/faculty/africanhisp-fac-pa-12.pdf

30   http://womeninastronomy.blogspot.com/2017/02/women-people-of-color-and-people-with.html

31   https://www.smithsonianmag.com/science-nature/how-can-we-give-black-and-latino-astronomers-foundation-reach-stars-180960213/

REFLECTION QUESTIONS

1. As described above, the 1500s and 1600s were a chaotic and difficult time for scientists (and others) in Europe. Kepler was forced to flee his hometown as religious wars raged on. Galileo faced persecution by the Church for sharing his observations challenging the geocentric idea. People who rejected science were in positions of power. Compare this era to today. How is our era different from then, and what are some ways that the two time periods are similar?

2. To get a feel for how planets move, try tracking a planet over a week or two. You can use online software like Stellarium to see which planets are visible in your night and morning sky. Go outside and sketch the location of the planet in relation to some nearby stars, and see if the planet has moved much after a week. Remember that Kepler rejected one idea because it predicted planet positions that were off by 8 arc minutes. This is about 1/3 the width of the full Moon or 1/6 the width of your finger held at arm's length. Could you make measurements with a similar precision?

BIBLIOGRAPHY

Gingerich, O. *The Book Nobody Read: Chasing the Revolutions of Nicolaus Copernicus.* London: Heinemann, 2004.

Gutman, David. "West Virginian of the Year: Katherine G. Johnson." *Charleston Gazette-Mail*, 2015. Archived from the original on August 27, 2017. Retrieved from https://www.wvgazettemail.com/news/west-virginian-of-the-year-katherine-g-johnson/article_a8da210c-3071-5a8b-ab5e-c6d345591e32.html

Marsh, Katherine. *Jepp, Who Defied the Stars.* New York: Hyperion Books, 2013.

Melfi, Theodore, dir. *Hidden Figures.* 2016; Los Angeles, CA: Fox 2000 Pictures.

Shetterly, Margot Lee. *Hidden Figures*, p. 129. William Morrow, 2016. ISBN 9780062363596.

———. Official NASA Biography of Katherine Johnson, 2020. Retrieved from https://www.nasa.gov/content/katherine-johnson-biography

Regarding Kepler:
Kepler, Johannes (1609). *Astronomia Nova* (New Astronomy). English translation by William Donahue. Santa Fe, New Mexico: Green Lion Press, 2015.

For an excellent biography of Kepler's trials and tribulations, see "The Watershed," by A. Koestler, which is an excerpt of a larger book:

Koestler, Arthur. *The Sleepwalkers: A History of Man's Changing Vision of the Universe*. London: Hutchinson, 1959.

For a fictional account of the trial of Kepler's mother, see:

Galchen, Rivka. *Everyone Knows Your Mother Is a Witch*. New York: Farrar, Straus and Giroux, 2021.

Play Online:
You can play with Kepler's laws (and other principles) using the fun apps at the University of New Mexico's site: http://physics.unm.edu/Courses/Rand/applets/

You can fire Newton's cannon at this site: https://physics.weber.edu/schroeder/software/NewtonsCannon.html

3

OBSERVING

You can observe a lot by watching.

—Yogi Berra[1]

Theorizing, speculating, pondering, and even dreaming are all part of science. But as we saw in the last chapter, an idea cannot be considered part of a scientific theory unless it has been confirmed by observed facts. In principle, one observation is enough to refute a theory if that theory's predictions clearly differ from the observed fact. In practice, many measurements made by different people in different countries are used to challenge and refute scientific ideas, as happened to the geocentric theory. In most sciences, like chemistry, physics, or microbiology, experiments can be conducted in a lab to test out new ideas. Indeed, experimentation is often taught as a crucial part of the scientific method. But in astronomy, we can't put stars or planets in a lab to study them. For astronomers, the way to figure out what the universe is really like is not experiments but observations, like the ones Tycho Brahe made of the planets' positions in the sky or the detailed studies Galileo made with his telescope.

But a skeptical person might ask, "How do we know these observations are reliable?" Indeed, the only way you can see the Moon or the stars is for light to come from these objects and be focused in your eye. So, it is not surprising then that several researchers, including Alhazen and Kepler, took time to try to understand how the human eye works and how light interacts with it. After the invention of the telescope, it became important to understand how this new device focused light and produced such useful images.

---

1 A 20th century baseball player and coach, known for his witticisms (1925–2015).

In this chapter, we'll explore what light even is, how it can be focused, and how modern astronomers observe using a variety of different cameras and other devices.

SECTION 1. What Is Light?

In the first chapter, we looked into the common notion of one *day*. Now, let's consider the equally common notion of *light*. For example, when you turned on the lights in a dark room, what just happened? Of course, you can see better, but what physically happened to the room? Did something come out of the light bulb and land on the floor, walls, and furniture in the room? If so, what is that something? A liquid? A solid? And why isn't it still there when you turn off the lights? Take a moment to ponder this and even write down ideas and concepts you already have about light. Just for fun, why not call or text a friend and ask, "Quick question: In 12 words or less, what is light?" See how their responses compare to yours. After you've done this, continue reading.

Of course, humans have observed light for as long as we've had eyes. But it took quite a long time to come to our modern understanding of it. One early idea was that light starts in our eyes, then moves out to the world around us, allowing us to see. But then how would we be able to open our eyes and instantly see the stars, which are very far away? Galileo was curious about light and came up with a clever way to measure its speed. He took a lantern to the top of a hill and turned it on. The light traveled to another hill, about two miles away, where his friend saw it and turned on another lantern. Suppose light traveled at the same speed as humans walking, 3 miles per hour (5 km/h). Then it would take six hours for light to go between the hills and another six hours to get back. In fact, it took hardly any time at all. Galileo concluded that light moves "very fast." Later experiments measured light's tremendous speed precisely. Light can travel 186,000 miles, or 300,000 kilometers, in **one second**! We can also express this in meters per second (m/s), given that 1 kilometer is 1,000 meters.

THE SPEED OF LIGHT

Light travels at a constant speed. It doesn't move instantly from one place to another, but it is very fast. It is common to use the symbol "c" to represent the speed of light. The speed of light is:

$$c = 3 \times 10^8 \text{ m/s} = 3 \times 10^5 \text{ km/s} = 300{,}000 \text{ km/s} = 186{,}000 \text{ miles/s}$$

Knowing its *speed* doesn't tell us what light is. If you had trouble articulating exactly what light is, you're not alone. The greatest minds of science struggled with the question also. Isaac Newton had an idea that light is made of particles that pour out from any light source, including the Sun. Newton's idea was wrong, but as often happens, it was accepted for many years, possibly because of his fame and stature. In 1801, an experiment[2] was performed by Thomas Young that proved light has properties of a

---

2   For an excellent video on this "double slit" experiment, see *The Original Double Slit Experiment* by Veritasium. https://www.youtube.com/watch?v=luv6hY6zsd0

wave. But what kind of wave? On the ocean, waves travel through water. *Sound waves* travel through air. What's up with **light waves**? They come to us from distant stars, and there's nothing but empty space between Earth and the star—no water, no air, nothing for the wave to *wave* in.

A solution to this dilemma came about through a slow series of steps in the 1800s. The first clues, surprisingly, came from magnets. A magnet creates a force field all around it. This just means that if you hold another magnet close by, you will feel the **force** created by the first magnet. Small bits of iron will also respond to this **magnetic field**. At the same time, a different force, **electricity**, was known to create its own fields. **Electric fields** show up when substances like hair are rubbed or when static electricity makes small sparks. Chemical batteries (which were new in the 1800s) also make electric fields. The real breakthrough came when researchers, including Michael Faraday in England and H. C. Oersted in Denmark, discovered that these two types of field are related. They found that if the electric field changed, then a magnetic field was produced, *and vice versa*. By the late 1800s, J. C. Maxwell in England had shown mathematically that this allowed a new type of phenomenon, **an electromagnetic wave**.

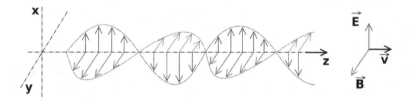

FIGURE 3.1   Light is an electromagnetic wave. It consists of magnetic fields (red arrows) that are constantly changing. This change produces electric fields (blue arrows), which also change. These create magnetic fields, and the process repeats. The wave moves along at the speed of light. This is what happens every time you turn on the lights!

Instead of moving water or air, like other kinds of waves, an electromagnetic (or EM) wave consists of a changing electric field and a changing magnetic field. We can use sound waves as an analogy for light waves. Sound waves consist of changes in the pressure of air. Specifically, if a singer sings a single note, then the air between you and the singer will consist of a pattern of air pressure that oscillates: higher, lower, higher, lower. If you graphed the pressure, you would see a long series of peaks and valleys. Do you play an instrument? Most instruments have a range of notes, from high to low. How are these notes different from each other? Well, in a high-pitched note, the distance from one peak to another is shorter. High-pitch instruments, like a violin or piccolo, make shorter waves. Low-pitch instruments, like a bass, tuba, or pipe organ, make longer waves. The **wavelength** of a sound wave is what determines its pitch. Our *ears* hear different wavelengths of sound and perceive them as different notes.

Different light waves each have their own wavelength as well. When these waves enter our *eyes*, we perceive the different wavelengths as **color**. So, if you see a rainbow, then many different light waves, each with a different wavelength, are entering your eyes. As a matter of fact, there are many more types of light wave than our eyes can see. These forms of light are invisible to us but are an important part of our everyday light. Each type of light has a different wavelength. Infrared light, microwaves, and radio waves are all types of light with a longer wavelength than **visible light**. Other types, including ultraviolet, X-rays, and gamma rays, have shorter wavelengths. Shorter wavelength waves have more energy and can be more dangerous.

PROPERTIES OF WAVES

All waves have three properties:

1. **Wavelength** is the distance between one wave and the next. Ocean waves breaking on the beach have a wavelength of perhaps 10 meters. Light waves are much smaller. The Greek Letter *lambda* (λ) is often used to represent wave*length*.

2. **Frequency** (f) is the number of waves that pass by per second. Frequency is measured in waves per second, or Hertz (Hz). For example, the note musicians designate as *A* vibrates the air 440 times per second, so its frequency is f = 440 Hz.

3. **Speed:** All waves travel with a certain speed, designated "c." For light waves, c = 3×10^8 m/s.

These properties are related. High-frequency waves have small wavelengths, and low-frequency waves have long wavelengths. Wavelength and frequency are *inversely* related. These three are connected mathematically by the relationship:

$$c = f \times \lambda$$

Alternatively, we can measure **how many waves** pass by us in one second. If many waves pass by us each second, then we describe these waves as **high frequency** (whether they are light or sound waves). High-frequency waves have short wavelengths because many of them must pack into the same space. The highest frequency light that we can see is violet-colored light. It also has the shortest wavelength we can see. Visible light waves are so small that we need smaller units to measure them. One **nanometer** (nm) is 1 billion times smaller than a meter (10^9 nm = 1 m, or 1 nm = 10^{-9}m). Violet light has a wavelength of about 400 nanometers. The red light you see on the other side of the rainbow is made of waves that are almost twice as long. The waves of red light are about 700 nm long. We can symbolize wavelength using the Greek letter[3] *lambda* (λ). So, the above information can be written λ_{violet} = 400 nm & λ_{red} = 700 nm.

We can now see "light" in a broader context. The visible light that illuminates the room when we turn on an electric light is just one type of an electromagnetic wave, with a range of wavelengths our eyes can detect. While *light* technically means all forms of EM waves, most people use "light" to mean visible light. Electromagnetic radiation[4] is another word for EM waves or light. All different types of light, considered collectively, are called the electromagnetic spectrum. But most such EM waves are not detectable to us. Our eyes don't *see* microwaves, infrared waves, gamma rays, etc., but the *universe produces them* naturally. To understand the universe, astronomers would like to see these waves too. So we have built a variety of different devices to detect the different types of light to which our eyes are blind.

Incidentally, ideas about light continued to evolve. In the 20th century, for example, it was realized that in addition to being a wave, light can also behave like a particle, depending on how we set up the experiment. Particles of light are called **photons**; you can perhaps think of them as atoms of light. While we won't go into this topic in this book, if you are curious about it, you may find that modern physics

---

3   By the way, we use Greek letters for many purposes, often because we've run out of letters like x, y, and z. The first two Greek letters are alpha (α) and beta (β), from which we get "alphabet"! The letter lambda (λ, or capital Λ) is Greek for *L* and has been used to represent Einstein's "cosmological constant" as well as to symbolize LGBTQ rights.

4   It is different from **nuclear** radiation, although both "radiate" out from a single location.

is stranger than you expected. For example, every particle, such as an electron or proton, can also be thought of as a wave. This curious situation, called the wave-particle duality,[5] is essential to the modern science of quantum physics. Odd as this may sound, the ideas of quantum physics have been tested, and the theory is extremely reliable. In fact, we now build and sell electronic devices that rely on quantum physics to observe and measure photons of light. One such device is the digital camera on your cell phone.

One limitation astronomers face is Earth's atmosphere. It blocks several types of light that come from space and prevents us from seeing them on the surface of Earth. X-rays, gamma rays, and to some extent ultraviolet (UV) and infrared (IR) light are all blocked. Actually, this is a good thing! If our atmosphere didn't block UV and X-rays from the Sun and from space, they would damage our bodies. The only types of light that pass easily through air are visible light, which we can see, and radio waves, which are used extensively for communication. Not only do radio stations and TV stations transmit their signals via radio waves, but cell phones communicate with towers using radio waves. If you are calling or texting someone with your cell phone, then you are transmitting EM waves like the one shown in Figure 3.2, but with a wavelength of about 1 foot (30 cm). Since astronomers want to observe everything in the universe, regardless of what type of light it emits, we need to get above most of Earth's atmosphere. These days we either launch a telescope on a satellite into orbit or fly an airplane at great height.

DO TRY THIS AT HOME: SEEING THE INVISIBLE

Next time you are using a computer video camera, try this trick. First, get out a TV remote control. These have a small light bulb in front that sends light signals to the TV. Look at this bulb and try pressing some buttons. Do you see any light? Hmm. Now, point the remote into the video camera. While you are looking at the live video feed, now press some buttons. Did you see a light?

What's up with that? Well, your remote must be producing some light in order to send signals to the TV. The fact that you couldn't see this light implies that its wavelength must be out of the visible range. Remotes use infrared (IR) light for communication. Video cameras are able to see some IR light, so light from this bulb shows up on your screen, even though it's invisible!

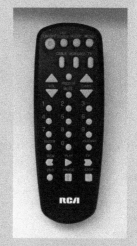

FIGURE 3.2   A handheld remote control for a television emits infrared light that we cannot see to tell the TV to change channels.

SECTION 2. Telescopes

Telescopes have been an essential part of astronomy since the 1600s, when Galileo showed how useful they can be in seeing things the human eye cannot. Galileo's telescopic observations of Venus utterly refuted the geocentric theory, and it had to be discarded in favor of the heliocentric theory. One reason

---

5   This radical, revolutionary idea was first suggested by a college student, Louis de Broglie, in 1924.

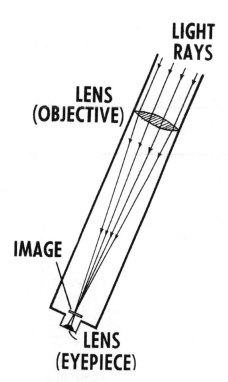

LIGHT RAYS

LENS (OBJECTIVE)

IMAGE

LENS (EYEPIECE)

FIGURE 3.3   A refracting telescope uses two lenses. The first (called the objective lens) brings light to a focus, like a magnifying glass. But to see this light, another smaller lens is used called the eyepiece because you put your eye there to look through the telescope.

people were slow to reject the old geocentric theory is that they weren't sure if they could trust observations from Galileo's new device. If we are going to rely so much on the new views of the universe that telescopes give us, then we should at least explore these powerful devices that might perhaps seem magic when they produce detailed images of things that humans have never been able to see before.

No one knows who invented the telescope.[6] But by the early 1600s, telescopes were being used in western Europe, probably to observe ships on the horizon or distant mountains. The first telescopes used **lenses**. Since a lens, such as a magnifying glass, works by bending or **refracting** light, telescopes that employ lenses are called **refracting telescopes**. Light from a faraway *object* goes through the first lens (called the *objective lens*) and comes to a focus. But to see this light clearly requires another lens, called the *eyepiece*, since it is held close to your eye. That's all you need to build a telescope! If these two lenses are held at the right distance, then when you look through both of them, you will see distant objects magnified and in more detail.

Lenses aren't the only way to build a telescope. **Mirrors** also change the direction light is traveling when it reflects off them. Have you ever put on makeup or shaved your face using a *curved mirror* to magnify the image of your face? You could also use that mirror to build a telescope! It would be called a **reflecting telescope** because mirrors reflect. But you would still need an eyepiece, as with a refracting telescope. The problem is where to put the eyepiece. If you line it up with the mirror, as was done with the lens of a refracting telescope, then your head will block the incoming light. A solution, which, as it turns out was discovered by Isaac Newton, is to place a small flat mirror in the telescope tube. Light from a star will first bounce off the curved primary mirror, then bounce off this small flat mirror to the eyepiece and finally into your eye. This type of telescope, the Newtonian design, is quite popular with amateur astronomers.

Modern astronomy research telescopes are much larger than those used by Newton. Why? It turns out that telescopes become more powerful if we increase the size of the mirror or lens the telescope uses. There are three things telescopes do for us: they gather light, resolve small details, and magnify images. A telescope's **light-gathering power** is its most important ability and depends on the **area** of its lens or mirror.

Before we discuss this, let's think about pizza! Imagine that you and your friends are very hungry and go out for pizza. You have two options at this restaurant:

8-inch diameter pizza for $10 or
16-inch diameter pizza for $25.

---

6   The word comes from *tele-*, meaning "far" (as in telephone, television) and "scope," meaning to see.

Which should you buy? Think about it for a while (and even ask your friends what they think) because you are going to buy several pizzas and you don't want to waste money. Once you've picked an option, read on.

If you and your friends bought the 8-inch pizzas, you wasted money. Did you reason that two 8-inch pizzas are cheaper than one 16-inch? That is true. But one 16-inch pizza is as large as *four 8-inch pizzas*! To see why, we need to determine the **area** of each pizza. Perhaps you recall that the area of a circle (A) depends on its radius (r). The formula is A = πr^2, where π = 3.14. The pizzeria gave us the diameter (D) of the pizzas, but that is just double the radius. Since radius is half of diameter (r = D/2), the area of a pizza is

$$A = \pi \, (D/2)^2 = \pi \, D^2/4.$$

The fact that a circle's area depends on its diameter **squared** means that a pizza whose diameter is two times larger will have an area four times larger (2^2 = 4). A pizza with three times the diameter will be *nine times bigger* (3^2 = 9)!

A telescope is a light bucket. The bigger the bucket (the mirror or lens), the more light can be collected. This is why astronomers build larger and larger telescopes. They can gather more light and see fainter and farther things in space. We've come a long way since the days of Newton. Modern telescopes are *huge*. The twin Keck Telescopes in Hawai'i each have mirrors that are 10 meters across (33 feet), and newer telescopes are larger. A large telescope also delivers better **resolution**, which is the ability to see fine details. For example, the human eye cannot distinguish the moons of Jupiter or the phases of Venus, observations that allowed Galileo to disprove the geocentric theory.

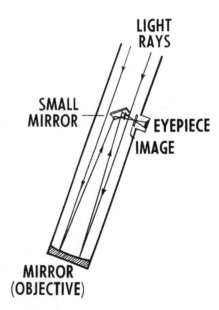

FIGURE 3.4   A reflecting telescope uses a mirror instead of a lens. Light from a star first strikes the large objective mirror. Before it can be viewed by a human eye, the light passes through an eyepiece, just as with a refracting telescope. There are different types of reflector. This diagram shows a Newtonian design, in which a small flat mirror is placed inside the telescope tube to bounce light out through the eyepiece.

COMMON MISCONCEPTION

A common misconception about telescopes is that their main purpose is to magnify things. In fact, a telescope's magnification is the *least* important of its three powers. By using a different eyepiece, the magnification of a telescope can be changed to any value, even 5000x. But having images 5,000 times larger doesn't help you see them if the images are blurry to begin with. A telescope's **resolution**, determined by the size of its mirror, determines how clear or blurry the image is. The **light-gathering power** related to the area of the mirror is also more important than magnification.

A third power of telescopes, which you may have heard of, is their **magnification**, the ability to make images seem larger. If you ever decide to buy a telescope, the magnification factor will be advertised (e.g.,

"100x" or "200x"). You should *ignore* this information! Magnification doesn't help if you can't see the details ... you just get a large image that is blurry. Instead, you should look at the telescope's **aperture**. This is the size of the primary lens or mirror. If you can get a 20 cm (~8 inch) lens for your refracting telescope, that's better than 10 cm (~4 inch). Also, try to get a good mount for the scope; this will prevent it from wiggling while you adjust it, which can be frustrating. Of the three powers telescopes have, magnification is the least important.

FIGURE 3.5   The Keck Telescopes in Hawai'i. Perched on 4,261-meter (13,9792-foot) high Mauna Kea, they are two of the best research telescopes in the world. They both are reflecting telescopes with mirrors that are 10 meters (33 feet!) in diameter.

BIGGER AND BIGGER AT WHAT COST? CONTROVERSY ON MAUNA KEA

Astronomy is an aspect of human culture. It is affected by the culture we live in and also impacts human culture. One of the best sites in the world to observe the skies is **Mauna Kea**, a tall (13,796 ft = 4205 m) volcanic mountain on the island of Hawai'i, that is largely free of light pollution. Over the years, 13 observatories have been built there. Their construction has led to many scientific discoveries but has also impacted a unique high-altitude, snow-covered tropical natural environment. Furthermore, Mauna Kea ("White Mountain" in the Hawai'ian language) is regarded as a holy site by native Hawai'ians. From this cultural perspective, continued construction there is desecration of a sacred place. In the 2010s, astronomers attempted to build one of the largest telescopes on Earth near the summit of Mauna Kea. While initial plans received government approval, large protests in 2015 by native Hawai'ians and others blocked construction. The project was halted by the governor and its permit invalidated by the state supreme court.

SECTION 3. Telescopes in Space

This isn't a quiz, but just for fun, take out a piece of paper and write down (or type out) in a sentence or two your best answer to this question:

Why is the sky blue?

Before you read on, try asking one other person this question. If there's no one in the room with you right now, send a message to a friend and see what they say. Do they agree? If not, how is their explanation different? Take two minutes to critique their idea (and your own) scientifically. For example, if your explanation had something to do with, say, the ocean, then consider places far away from the ocean, like Kansas or Mongolia. If the sky is blue there, then the ocean can't be the cause. Where is the sky's blue light coming from?

People have observed the blue sky since the earliest times. So, have people always understood *why* it is blue? Nope. Then don't feel bad if you didn't have a clear explanation. When Abe Lincoln was elected president of the United States in 1860, not one scientist on earth could explain why the sky is blue. Well, actually just one—John Tyndall. He had just done an experiment[7] by shining a white light into a tank full of water with some flour particles thrown in. Amazingly, when viewed from the side, the water looked blue. This is because blue light is more easily scattered than red.

Color is wavelength, so light's ability to shine through air depends on wavelength. The blue light we see in the sky *comes from the Sun*. It is scattered into our eyes by air molecules. This also explains why the setting Sun is red. As its light shines through a greater length of air, blue waves are lost, but orange and red waves are left behind. In fact, some wavelengths of light can't pass through air at all. Our atmosphere absorbs many types of light that we don't see. **Infrared light** is absorbed by certain gases in our atmosphere, including carbon dioxide. This is what causes the greenhouse effect. **Ultraviolet light** (UV) is partially absorbed, which is a good thing for those of us wishing to avoid sunburn. However, when I climb a high mountain, I need extra sunscreen because there is less air to absorb that UV light. X-rays and gamma rays from space are also blocked by Earth's atmosphere.

From humanity's point of view, this is a good thing—those rays can damage our bodies.[8] But from an astronomer's point of view, this is a sad thing. It means that any telescope we build on Earth to observe UV light won't work; those waves of light will never get to the telescope because they are blocked by the atmosphere. Our human eyes are keenly adapted to detect precisely the kind of light we get here on Earth from our Sun (thanks, evolution!). Since normal human vision relies on this type of light. we call it **visible light**. But that doesn't mean that the rest of the universe only produces this visible light.[9] Here's a breakdown of what happens to different kinds of light in our atmosphere, starting with the shortest wavelengths, gamma rays.

Gamma rays—*extremely short wavelength* entirely absorbed by Earth's atmosphere

X-Rays—*very short wavelength* entirely absorbed by Earth's atmosphere

Ultraviolet—*short wavelength* partially absorbed by Earth's atmosphere

---

7 For more information, search for the "Tyndall effect."

8 For example, if UV light hits the DNA in a skin cell, it can cause skin cancer.

9 While humans are restricted to visible light, other animals are not. Bees can see ultraviolet, and snakes can detect infrared.

Visible—*"normal" wavelength*: not absorbed; passes through the atmosphere

Infrared—*long wavelength* partially absorbed by Earth's atmosphere

Microwaves—*very long wavelength*: partially absorbed

Radio waves—*extremely long wavelength*: not absorbed; passes through the atmosphere

As you can see, a lot of light from space is blocked before it can get to Earth. In fact, only visible light and radio waves are completely unhindered. That's why astronomers have designed and launched several **space telescopes** that observe the universe above Earth's atmosphere. Numerous discoveries have been made by observing the light that is otherwise blocked.

Here are a few quick examples of discoveries made using nonvisible light:

The **Chandra X-ray telescope** captured images of exploding stars that produced high-energy light.[10]

The **Spitzer** infrared telescope observed the atmosphere of an "exoplanet"—a planet outside our solar system.[11]

The **Fermi Gamma-ray Telescope** discovered a strange dead star that fires off bursts of high-energy light three times a second.[12]

In 2022, NASA's **James Webb Space Telescope** began to observe the universe using infrared light. You will probably hear more about its discoveries soon![13]

You can learn more about the exciting discoveries made by NASA by checking NASA's science news page: https://science.nasa.gov/science-news.

With large telescopes on Earth and satellites in space, astronomers are now well equipped to explore the universe and to answer questions that have challenged us for years: do other planets exist that could support life? How long do stars, including our Sun, live? What makes a star die? And even, what is the fate of the universe? The answers to these questions can be found in the light that stars, planets, and galaxies are sending to us. We just need to interpret that light. In the next chapter, we will explore how to read these messages in starlight and figure out what's going on in space.

WRAP-UP

This chapter and the next both concern the ways astronomers use light to understand what is in space. I'm sorry if these chapters don't seem necessary to you. Perhaps you just want to learn about stars, galaxies, black holes, etc. But it is very important for me to share with you *how we know* what we know. You

10   https://chandra.harvard.edu/photo/2019/tycho/

11   https://exoplanets.nasa.gov/news/1588/atmosphere-of-midsize-planet-revealed-by-hubble-spitzer/

12   https://www.nasa.gov/mission_pages/GLAST/news/gr_pulsar.html

13   https://www.jwst.nasa.gov

should never simply accept a scientific idea, regardless of how authoritative the person sharing it seems. You have the right to ask, "Where does the evidence for this idea come from?" and then compare that evidence with other evidence that may support alternate ideas. (To be clear, this process is very different from simply rejecting a scientific idea because you don't like it without looking at *any* evidence.) Hopefully, after reading this chapter, you can see why we astronomers make a huge effort to build very large telescopes that can collect faint light of many different wavelengths coming to us from the universe.

REFLECTION QUESTIONS

1. Try to find different kinds of waves around your home, and your neighborhood, including sound waves with light waves. Remember that light waves includes the entire electromagnetic spectrum: visible light, infrared, microwaves, radio waves, etc. Make a list of the different devices in your home and the types of waves they produce or receive.

2. After reading the box above on Mauna Kea, what do you think about conflicts like this? Look up the current status of the "Thirty Meter Telescope" and write a report on what you find. (You can find articles with a range of viewpoints online.) Can you think of aspects of astronomy (or other sciences) that might be judged as having a negative impact? In general, should the public support science with funding, and occasional use of land? What limits would you place on such support?

TURNING LIGHT INTO KNOWLEDGE

Do not undertake a scientific career in quest of fame or money. There are easier and better ways to reach them. Undertake it only if nothing else will satisfy you; for nothing else is probably what you will receive. Your reward will be the widening of the horizon as you climb. And if you achieve that reward you will ask no other.

—Cecilia Payne

A picture is worth a thousand words. But sometimes a picture isn't enough. Take a look at the image in Figure 4.1. What is it? Go ahead take a guess at what it might show ... Could it be an explosion? Or does it show something that's collapsing on itself? Is it extremely hot? ... or icy cold? What is it made of? Is it coming toward us? Could it be a threat to Earth? Just looking at the picture, it's hard to say, isn't it?

Instead of just looking at a picture, astronomers have a strategy to answer questions like these. Specifically, for any star (or galaxy or mystery object in space), we can figure out its:

1. temperature
2. composition
3. motion

The strategy involves studying the light from the object *one color at a time*. The color, or colors, of an object tell us a lot about it. Take a look at the colors of the things in the room you are in now. To perceive those different colors, different **wavelengths** of light must enter your eye. For example, the waves of light from red objects are longer than those from blue objects. But most of these objects don't *emit* the light you are seeing; they reflect the light emitted by a light bulb or the Sun. Objects that *emit their own visible light* are hot and glowing, like the Sun or an incandescent bulb. Light from hot glowing things, like stars,

FIGURE 4.1 A mystery object. This is a genuine astronomical photograph made using special filters that only transmit certain wavelengths of light. What do you think it is?

is called thermal radiation. In this chapter, we will learn how to find out what stars are like by looking at what colors of light they emit. This strategy is called **spectroscopy**.

SECTION 1. Measuring Temperatures

Temperature is an important quantity to measure for everyone from doctors who want to see if you are sick, to chemists, to ecologists measuring temperatures of ocean waters around the world. The most commonly used scale to measure temperatures is the Celsius (C) scale. On this scale, water freezes at 0 degrees (C) and boils at 100° C. Scientists normally measure temperature using a closely related scale, the Kelvin (K) scale. Zero Kelvin isn't the point at which water is frozen; it is the point at which *everything* is frozen, or "absolute zero." (The old, outdated Fahrenheit temperature scale is not used by any country on Earth except the United States.) Using thermometers, we can measure temperatures here on Earth. But how would you measure the temperature of a star?

You can learn about the **temperature** of a glowing object by observing the colors of light it gives off. For example, if you heat up a piece of metal, it glows red-hot. But if you heat it *more*, it starts to glow *orange* and then *yellow*. It can even emit some blue light, which combines with the other colors to make a white-hot object. We can precisely measure *how much* of each color of light is emitted *if* we can separate out light by color and measure each color separately. You probably already know about a way to do this: a piece of glass, such as a **prism**, produces an array of colors when light shines through it. Droplets of water also do this to form a rainbow. Similarly, you might have seen rainbows produced when light is reflected off computer or music discs (CDs or DVDs) or other surfaces with many grooves. Anytime you see a rainbow of light, it means that something has "spread the light out" by color; that is, separated the light waves according to their wavelengths with the short waves (violet light) on one side and long waves (red) on the other. This is called a **spectrum**.[1]

DO TRY THIS AT HOME: CREATE A SOLAR SPECTRUM OF YOUR OWN

You can create a spectrum of the Sun by letting sunlight pass through a glass of water. Fill a clear glass with water and hold it up in the sunlight. See if you can see a rainbow on the floor or wall. That's what we call a solar spectrum. If you let the rainbow shine into your eye, you can see each of the colors individually. A similar effect can be created with an old CD or DVD disc. Both devices spread out white light into its many colors, each with a different wavelength.

When you hold a piece of glass in sunlight and see a rainbow, you have just produced a **spectrum** of the Sun. You can then clearly see that not all the Sun's light is yellow; many other colors appear, some more than others. Astronomers can precisely measure the amount of light of each color produced by the Sun or any other star. Since color is wavelength, this spectrum is often presented as a graph showing "amount of light" versus "wavelength." Figure 4.2 shows a spectrum in this format. But the information in the graph is the same as what you see in a rainbow.

Let's take a look at this spectrum of the Sun. To read this graph, note that it's measuring the amount of light as a function of wavelength. Imagine 100 waves of light coming from the Sun. Some of them will be red light with long wavelength, and some will be violet with short wavelength. This graph tells you *how much* of the light comes from each wavelength category. So, the right part of the graph, with wavelengths over 1000 nanometers (nm), tells us that not many of these long waves of light (infrared, or IR) come out of the Sun. Also, because the left part of the graph is low, we can tell that there aren't many short waves of light, which is good because these ultraviolet (UV) waves cause skin cancer. But there is a lot of light with wavelengths between 400 and 700 nm in the **visible** part of the spectrum. The light output of other stars is different, but there is one pattern they all follow. Their spectrum has a "peak" at a certain wavelength, meaning that the star produces *more light at this wavelength* than any other.

We call this the **peak wavelength** and label it λ_{max} (pronounced "lambda-max"). Peak wavelength just tells us, in a precise way, what color a star is. The Sun produces more yellow light, with wavelength 570 nm, than any other color. So for the Sun, λ_{max} = 570 nm. This is just a scientific way of saying the Sun looks yellow.

But other stars are different. **Rigel**, for example (a bright blue star in Orion), emits a lot of UV light. Its **peak wavelength** is roughly twice as small as the Sun's, meaning that it mostly emits smaller waves of light, including UV. This brings us to the whole reason we are discussing peak wavelength. It turns

---

1   In general, *spectrum* means any phenomenon that has a wide range of possibilities. For example, doctors refer to the autism spectrum because this condition has many possible manifestations. We previously referred to all possible forms of light as the electromagnetic spectrum. Here, we use **spectrum** to refer to a readout of the light emitted by, say, a specific star.

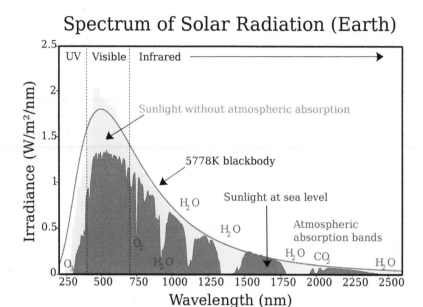

FIGURE 4.2   A full spectrum of the Sun, showing the amount of light produced of all types: Ultraviolet, Visible, and Infrared. The graph shows the amount of light energy the Sun delivers at each different wavelength. Wavelengths of light are measured in nanometers. The Sun produces more visible light (the kind our eyes can see) than other types. The colors in this graph don't represent the colors of the rainbow. The yellow graph shows the spectrum emitted by the Sun, and the red shows the spectrum of sunlight that hits the ground on Earth. The difference between them is caused by absorption of light by molecules in our atmosphere. (As discussed in Chapter 13, these molecules, such as CO_2, are called greenhouse gases because they cause the greenhouse effect.)

out that there's a direct connection between a star's peak wavelength and its **temperature**: *Rigel*[2] is twice as hot as the Sun, and the light waves it generates are twice as small as the Sun's. The **hotter** the star, the *shorter* the light waves it emits. Since short wavelengths of light correspond to bluer colors, we can conclude that blue stars are hotter than red stars. The way astronomers can measure the **temperature** of a star is to first measure its peak wavelength.

Mathematically speaking, peak wavelength (λ_{max} measured in nm) and temperature measured in Kelvins (T_K) are **inversely** related. When one is large, the other is small. This connection was discovered in the early 1900s by W. Wien, so it is called Wien's law:[3]

$$T_k = \frac{300,000 \text{ nm}}{\lambda_{max}}.$$

---

2   T_{Rigel} = 12,100 K.

3   This version of Wien's law works for temperatures measured in Kelvins and wavelengths in nanometers (nm), the standard units. If you measured using different units, the equation would be the same, but the constant of proportionality (which just happens to be about 3,000,000) would change.

So, to find a star's temperature, you don't need a thermometer. You need a *spectrograph*, like a prism, that measures the *spectrum* of the star. Looking at that spectrum, you can determine the peak wavelength, then find the temperature using Wien's law. For example, if the star's spectrum peaks at 1000 nanometers (λ_{max} = 1000 nm), then you divide 3,000,000 by 1,000 to get a temperature of 3,000 K. (Remember, we always measure temperatures using the Kelvin scale.)

By the way, Wien's law is also used to measure the temperature of things here on Earth. The most common example is a temporal thermometer, a device that measures the infrared light coming from a person's forehead and uses Wien's law to calculate human body temperature, based on the peak wavelength of that light. These became widely used in 2020 during the COVID-19 pandemic because they allow temperatures to be measured without much physical contact.

So, these are the steps to measure the temperature of a star: make a spectrum of the star, find λ_{max}, then use Wien's law to calculate the temperature, T. If you are thinking, "So much work just to take the temperature of a star!" you're right. That's the challenge of being an astronomer and studying things that are light-years away. But this also shows you the power of spectroscopy (the analysis of light)—you get to learn what things are like far, far away. Not only does a spectrum tell us how hot a star is, it can also tell us what the stars are made of.

COMMON MISCONCEPTION

Misconception: Red is hot, blue is cold.

Fact: If you look at weather maps or other graphs showing temperature, you will often find that the hot areas are colored red and colder areas colored blue. Perhaps this is because the glowing coals of a warm fire are red, while ice and cold water sometimes appear blue. But if those coals got hotter, they would start to turn blue. In fact, you can see a blue color in the hot flame of a stove's gas burner. As we showed above, if a star is hotter (high T), it will emit the most light as shorter wavelengths (low λ), according to Wien's law. Since the wavelength of blue and violet light is lower than red, this means that the hottest stars we can see must be blue or violet, not red. By the way, there are things in space so hot that they emit mostly ultraviolet light or even X-rays—light that is invisible to our eyes.

SECTION 2. What Are Stars Made Of?

Are you health-conscious? When you eat (processed) food, do you look at the ingredients label to see what it's made of? How do we know what's in our food, anyway? Independent government inspectors check the composition of food, which isn't very hard to do, actually. They can just take a piece of the food and use some standard chemistry experiments to determine its composition (that is, which atoms and molecules it is *composed* of). That way we know our food is safe ... whether or not it's healthy!

But how would you figure out what a *star* is composed of? You don't have a sample to work with; it is located many light-years (trillions of miles) away. One fact helps us. The laws of nature are **universal**. The properties of any element—say, carbon—that we measure here on Earth, will be true of carbon out in space. So, experiments we've already done in labs on Earth can help us figure out what the stars are made of. The simplest such experiment is the one we've mentioned already: pass light through a glass prism to get a rainbow.[4] This basic type of spectrum is called a **continuum.** A bright white light bulb will produce a continuum spectrum.

But scientists found that something interesting happens if this same light *first passes through a gas*: some of the light gets absorbed. You wouldn't notice this absorption easily because *only a few very specific colors* are absorbed. If you first pass the light through a narrow slit (before it goes into a prism), then you will see small dark **absorption lines** in the spectrum (as shown in Figure 4.3). This type of spectrum is called an **absorption spectrum**. It is like a continuum spectrum with some light missing. The spectrum of the Sun is an absorption spectrum.

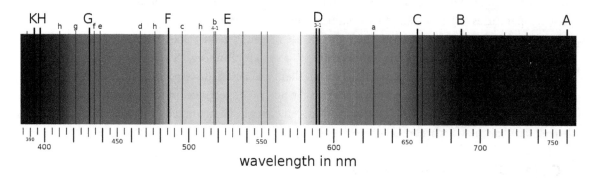

FIGURE 4.3   Detailed spectrum of the Sun. Sunlight passes through a small opening, or slit, then a glass prism and disperses into a rainbow that is missing light at certain wavelengths/colors. This is an example of an absorption spectrum. Light at those colors got absorbed as it was leaving the Sun by atoms in the Sun's outer layers.

The third type of spectrum can be seen when we analyze light coming from a very hot gas. Fluorescent light bulbs and neon lights seen in the windows of some restaurants and bars are an example of this type of light source. When this light is analyzed with a spectrograph, we don't see a rainbow; in fact, we only see light emitted at a few distinct colors, which we call an **emission spectrum**. Spectra of these objects can be used as comparisons for astronomical objects, including nebulas and the Sun's corona, which also show an emission spectrum. Figure 4.4 shows an emission spectrum. As you can see, most colors are not there, only a few bright emission lines.

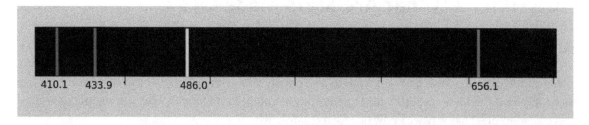

FIGURE 4.4   Light from a hot nebula or a fluorescent light bulb only comes out at a few wavelengths. The rest are dark.

---

4   Isaac Newton first did this in 1666.

But *why* do stars, nebulas, and other things in space have those spectra? For example, why does the Sun have an absorption spectrum? To figure out how the Sun generates a light spectrum that is missing certain colors, we need to think about what the Sun is made of. The Sun is made of **atoms**, so to answer the question "What is the Sun made of?" we need to first explore what atoms are so we can find out *which* atoms make up the Sun and other stars.

SECTION 3. What's Up with Atoms?

At some point you probably learned about **atoms**, but you may not have stopped to think about how *strange* they really are. You probably learned the basics—that atoms have a center, or **nucleus**, containing positively charged **protons** and neutral **neutrons**. And that there are **electrons** that orbit the atom's nucleus at quite a distance away, almost like planets orbiting the Sun. This analogy is strangely accurate because the distance between the Sun and the planets is similar, *proportionally*, to the distance between the nucleus of an atom and its electrons. That is, **atoms are mostly empty space**. Try feeling a table or chair near you now, or even your own body. Isn't it strange that the atoms that make us up are almost entirely empty? I call this a "freaky fact."

You may wonder, "What, then, holds atoms together?" Well, the particles that make them up are held together by powerful forces. The electrical force, for example, makes the negative electrons attracted to the positive protons in the nucleus, much like the way the force of gravity keeps the planets in orbit around the Sun. But this doesn't explain something very strange about atoms. This same electrical force should make the positive protons in the nucleus repel other protons in the nucleus. So why doesn't the nucleus explode? Did your high school chemistry class cover that? The answer again is a type of force, but not the electrical force. There is another, stronger force called simply the "strong nuclear force" that holds nuclei together. It controls **nuclear reactions**, which, we will later see, are what power the Sun and other stars.

But the nucleus isn't what concerns us now. Let's turn to the electrons. The number of electrons usually matches the number of protons in any normal atom. The negative and positive charge of these particles cancels out and the atom as a whole is **neutral**. The number of protons is important because that's what determines which element the atom is. For example, all atoms with six protons are carbon, and all carbon atoms have six protons. Hydrogen, the simplest element, only has one proton in its nucleus. Because carbon atoms also have six electrons, they all react the same way with other atoms. An atom's chemical properties are determined by the number of electrons, which is determined by the number of protons.

Are you ready for another freaky fact? We thought of an atom as a miniature solar system. But there are some differences. Atoms are held together by electricity, not gravity. Also, while planets are big, electrons follow the laws of **quantum physics**, the modern theory governing extremely small things. This is the reason for our second freaky fact: *electrons can only orbit at specific distances from the nucleus.* Each of these stable orbits is like a lane that an electron must stay in as it goes around the center of the atom. They can switch lanes but can't be found between lanes. Since each of these lanes has a different energy, they are called **energy levels**.

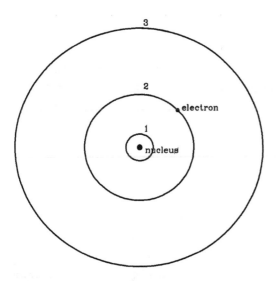

FIGURE 4.5 Bohr model of the atom. Electrons can only occupy certain energy levels, labeled "1,2,3." Higher levels have higher energy, so when electrons fall to a lower level, they give up this energy in the form of light. The color of this light (its wavelength) depends on how far the electron falls. The electron in this diagram in Level 2 could fall to Level 1 and emit light. Or, if some light passes through the atom with just enough energy, the electron could absorb the light and jump up to Level 3.

We can understand what's up with atoms using a simple model created in the early 20th century by Danish physicist Niels Bohr. According to this **Bohr model**[5] of the atom, electrons orbiting *close* to the nucleus have *lower* energy than those orbiting farther away. Imagine if someone lifted a bowling ball to the top of a staircase. It would have more energy there than one at the bottom. So, in Figure 4.5, the circles show the energy levels where electrons can be found in the atom. "Level 1" is the lowest level; an electron on this level would need extra energy if it wanted to jump up to "Level 2" or to "Level 3," which has the highest energy of the levels shown (but there are even higher levels not shown).

What can provide the energy to lift an electron to a higher level? *Light* has energy, with shorter waves of light having more energy than longer. This means that each **photon**, or unit of blue light, has more energy than a photon of red light. If light enters an atom, it can be **absorbed by electrons**, which jump up a level or two. This light, with a specific wavelength, is now gone. But the other wavelengths/colors of light will not be absorbed because they don't have just the right energy to bump an electron up to one of the stable levels. If these atoms are in the outer layer of a star, then the result will be an **absorption spectrum**. Light of most colors will get out of the star, but a few colors will be absorbed, producing dark lines in the spectrum. This is why dark lines appear in the spectrum, as shown in Figure 4.3.

But the reverse can also happen. Imagine that bowling ball on top of a flight of stairs. If the ball rolls down one step, it will hit with a thud and make a loud sound. The sound waves you hear represent energy changing form: first the ball had "potential" energy on a high step, then it lost this energy but created sound waves of equal energy. Electrons do the same thing when they jump **down** to a *lower* energy level in an atom. But instead of emitting sound waves, they emit light waves. Remember that bowling ball that someone lifted to the top of a staircase? It took considerable effort to place it there. Someone put a lot of energy into that ball.

The same kind of thing can happen out in space. A huge amount of energy might shine out from some very hot star and energize a cloud of gas. The electrons in its atoms are lifted up to higher energy levels. The gas starts to glow because those electrons eventually fall down to lower energy levels giving off light, in the same way that the bowling ball gave off sound.

---

5   Bohr's model is relatively simple, but it was the first to be able to explain spectral lines. Later it was replaced with more sophisticated models. If you ever took a chemistry class in which s-orbitals and p-orbitals were discussed, then you've already seen this more sophisticated model. For our purposes, the simple model is all we need.

There's one difference, however. When a bowling ball falls, it makes a thud, not a pure note. But when electrons in a particular atom fall (say from Level 2 to Level 1), they all produce light with exactly the same wavelength. That's because the energy of light is determined by its wavelength. High-energy light (such as ultraviolet or X-rays) has a shorter wavelength than low-energy light (such as infrared or radio waves). Visible light is between these. So, when we look at a neon light or a fluorescent bulb *with a spectrograph*, we don't see a rainbow showing every color as we do with a continuum spectrum. Instead, we just see a few bright **emission lines**. Each emission line has a different color/wavelength/energy and so represents electrons falling from one particular energy level to another. For example, an electron falling from Levels 3→1 has more energy than an electron falling from 2→1. We see more than one emission line because any given atom may have several electrons, each in a different energy level, so there are a few possibilities for how they can jump from level to level. The number of possible jumps increases with more electrons. So atoms of **carbon**, which has six electrons, show more emission lines in their spectra than atoms of **hydrogen**, which has only one. In fact, **by examining these patterns of emission lines, we can figure out what something is made of**.

Let's summarize. All atoms of a particular element (such as carbon) have the same number of protons and the same number of electrons (six of each in the case of a carbon atom).[6] Those electrons can only be found in specific energy levels, but they can jump from one level to another, either gaining or losing energy. Energy *lost* by electrons is **emitted** as light whose color is determined by the energy difference. To *gain* energy, an electron **absorbs** light of the right color to bump it up to a higher level. Each different element has a different pattern of energy levels for its electrons and thus a different pattern of light emitted or absorbed. That's how astronomers can figure out what elements make up the stars: we look at the spectrum of a star and find patterns that are characteristic of certain elements. If we see the pattern of spectral lines that goes with carbon, it means that there is carbon in that star.

If all this sounds complicated, then imagine what it was like to be the first scientist to figure out what stars are made of. Now, imagine that you had made this discovery, but that other scientists, including your own mentor, told you something must be wrong with your discovery and that you should keep it quiet. Unfortunately, that's exactly what happened.

Around 1925, **Cecilia Payne** was getting ready to publish her PhD dissertation at Harvard University in Boston after studying the spectra of stars for years. She had been raised by a single mom in England, but went to Harvard because the colleges in England wouldn't accept women for PhD programs. In fact, she wasn't even allowed to graduate from Cambridge (outside of London), even though she

FIGURE 4.6 Cecilia Payne (1900–1979), also called Payne-Gaposchkin, discovered what stars are made of by analyzing their spectra. She overcame severe sexism and became the first woman to lead Harvard Observatory.

---

6   If a carbon atom loses an electron, it becomes a carbon ion. But it is still carbon.

met all the requirements, because Cambridge didn't allow women to graduate.[7] For years, astronomers had guessed that stars were made of the same heavy elements as Earth, such as silicon, iron, and carbon. Payne found instead that while stars contained those elements, they were mostly made up of the two *lightest* elements, **hydrogen** and **helium**. Because this result contradicted the conventional understanding so much, she was encouraged to dismiss her discovery as spurious. But she was right: stars are made of mostly H and He. In spite of these challenges, Payne went on to become the first female science professor at Harvard and the first female director of Harvard Observatory.

Because of pioneering work by astronomers like Cecilia Payne, we can now know what any star is made of, just by looking at its spectrum. The absorption lines tell us how much of each element is present—and it turns out, they also tell us how fast the star is moving.

SECTION 4. How Fast Do Stars Move?

Do you like fast cars? What is the fastest speed you've ever traveled? Have you ever been pulled over by the highway patrol for driving too fast? Whatever your top speed is in a *car*, you certainly have gone faster than that traveling in an *airplane*. Planes travel about 10 times faster than cars, perhaps 600 mph versus 60 mph for cars. The abbreviation *mph*, of course, stands for miles per hour (also written miles/hour or mi/h), which is a **unit of speed**. We need these *units* to measure how fast things are going, just like we need units (such as **meters**) to measure distance and seconds to measure time. To measure *speed*, you need two things: **distance** *and* **time**. A car going 100 miles/hour will be able to travel 100 miles in one hour. Actually, it won't … because the driver will be pulled over for speeding! Driving 100 miles/hour is not safe.

But in most of the world, the speed limit signs on the road (see Figure 4.7) allow you to go 100. That's because most of the world measures speed in **kilometers per hour** (km/h), and driving 100 km/h (= 61 mi/h) is pretty safe. Astronomers measure the speed, or velocity, of stars using kilometers, not miles. But since stars move so fast, we usually use kilometers per **second** (abbreviated km/s; that's kilometers *divided by* seconds, just to be clear). Strange as it may seem, the method to see how fast *stars* are speeding along is the same method the highway patrol uses to measure the speed of cars. It is called the **Doppler effect**, and here's how it works.

FIGURE 4.7   A speed limit sign on a road in Mexico. Speed (*velocidad* in Spanish; *velocity* in English) is measured in metric units (km/hour) in Mexico and nearly every other country on Earth.

---

7   Amazingly, this sexist policy continued all the way until 1948.

First, let's imagine you are on a hill, looking down on a lake. You see a duck bobbing up and down, making ripples in the lake. They might look like this:

Based on this alone, would you say that the duck is moving? Which way, left or right? For fun, try showing this image to someone near you and tell them **why** you think the duck is moving that way. Do they agree? And here's the important question. *How did you know* which way the duck was moving? What were you noticing in this image? (Please try to answer this question before reading on.)

If you noticed that the waves on the left side are closer together than the waves on the right, then you detected a Doppler effect. The **wavelength** of the waves on the left is smaller because the duck is moving to the left. Of course, if the duck *weren't* moving, the waves would be the same on both sides. So, wavelengths change if something is moving. The same thing is true of all types of waves: *they are closer together (shorter wavelength) if the thing making the waves is **moving toward** you and farther apart if the waves are **moving away***.

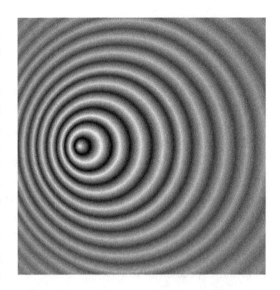

FIGURE 4.8   This image shows waves that would be made in a pond by a moving (but unseen) duck. Can you tell which way the duck is moving? How do you know? When a moving object emits waves, they get bunched up or compressed in the direction of motion. This is called the Doppler effect.

The same applies to **sound waves**, which also have different wavelengths. Our ears interpret different wavelengths as different musical notes, or different pitches. Have you ever heard a fast car drive past you while you stood on the sidewalk? The sound of the car changes in two ways. It gets louder when the car is closer, but that's not a change in pitch. The "note" that the car seems to be playing also changes, making a sound like *eeee-ooow*. The *eeee* sound, heard when the car is coming closer, is a high-pitched sound. These *high* notes are produced by *short* sound waves. The sound waves you hear when the car comes toward you are like the water waves on the left side of the duck—they are scrunched together. But when the car zooms past and moves away from you, the sound changes to *ooow* ... that's a low note. These sound waves have been stretched out because the car is a little farther away from you with each successive wave it emits. If you had your eyes closed, you could tell whether the car was moving toward you or away from you, just based on the changes in its pitch. You could even tell if it was a very fast car because the change in pitch would be more dramatic. **The change in wavelength tells you the speed.**

This is the **Doppler effect**, and it applies to *all* waves, even light. Changing wavelengths of light can be used to measure the speed of a moving car and even a moving star! Highway patrol officers use Doppler "guns" to measure how fast cars are going. These devices shine microwave light on a car. The **change in wavelength** of the reflected light waves tells them how fast the car is going. They know the **original wavelength** of the light their devices emit, so to measure the change, they just subtract the new wavelength from the old. If a car were not moving (or at rest), then the wavelength of the reflected waves would be the same as the emitted wavelength. This is called the **rest wavelength**.

Similar Doppler devices also measure how fast a baseball is thrown. In astronomy, we use the Doppler effect to see *how fast stars are moving*. Like the highway patrol, astronomers need a rest wavelength, the wavelength of light we expect to see if the star isn't moving at all. Luckily, the spectrum of the star provides that to us. As mentioned above, every element has **spectral lines** that can be found at specific wavelengths or colors. (The element sodium always produces a yellow spectral line, for example.) This **rest wavelength** is designated λ_0 and pronounced "lambda-zero" or "lambda-naught."[8] (The "0" subscript just means zero velocity.) The rest wavelength of a spectral line caused by a certain element is usually found by studying that element in a lab.

The next task is to measure the actual light waves we are getting from the star and compare them to λ_0. Again, we use a spectrograph to spread the light of a star out into each of its colors. Typically, this spectrum will show absorption lines, whose wavelength can be measured. We'll call these **measured** wavelengths simply λ. Remember that it is the **change in wavelength** that tells us the speed. To get this, we just subtract $\lambda - \lambda_0$. Scientists often use the Greek letter Δ (delta) to mean a difference in something. So, we write this *difference* as $\Delta\lambda = \lambda - \lambda_0$. It is important because it tells us the speed (or velocity) of the star, which we write as **v**. If we put all this together, we come up with an equation that can be used to find the speed a star is moving:

$$\frac{v}{c} = \frac{\Delta\lambda}{\lambda_0}$$

Putting this in words, the change in wavelength divided by the rest wavelength (of a spectral line) equals the star's velocity divided by c, the speed of light. The speed of light is always constant, and we normally know the rest wavelength, so we just need to measure the wavelength that a certain spectral line appears at in our star, and we'll know how fast the star moves. Just as the Doppler effect changes the **tone** of sound waves, it also changes the **color** of light waves. Since red light has longer wavelength than blue light, we say that a star's light has been **redshifted** if the Doppler effect stretches it out to longer wavelengths as the star moves away from us. Conversely, when the waves are compressed to a smaller wavelength (because the star is moving toward us) we say that the light from this star was **blueshifted**.

Let's see this equation in action in an example. One of my favorite stars is called Barnard's Star; it is one of the *fastest* stars in the sky. I've observed its spectrum many times. Suppose the spectrum of Barnard's Star has a spectral line with a wavelength $\lambda = 500.2$ nm. And assume that previous lab experiments have found that this same line has a rest wavelength of $\lambda_0 = 500$ nm. From this information, can you figure out how fast the star is moving?

Yes, you can. Here's how. First, let's ask ourselves: is the star moving toward or away from us? The measured wavelength (500.2 nm) is **longer** than the rest wavelength (500 nm). Think about why waves get stretched out to longer wavelength. If you remember the duck, you'll recall that the waves in the pond are longer when the duck is moving **away**. Or think of the car driving past you on the street. When it makes that low-pitch (long wavelength) *oooow* sound, it is moving **away**. So, this star must be moving away from us because the waves of light from the star have been stretched out from 500 to 500.2 nanometers in length. This doesn't seem like much of a stretch, so you might think the star isn't moving very fast. Let's calculate how fast it moves using the Doppler formula. The change in

---

8   *Naught* is another word for nothing or zero.

wavelength is just 0.2 nm: $\Delta\lambda = \lambda - \lambda_0 = 500.2 - 500.0$ nm = 0.2. This lets us figure out the star's speed (*v*). Here are the steps:

$$\frac{v}{c} = \frac{\Delta\lambda}{\lambda_0}$$

$$\frac{v}{c} = \frac{0.2}{500}$$

$$\frac{v}{c} = 0.004$$

$$v = 0.004 * c$$

$$v = 0.004 * 300{,}000 \text{ km/s}$$

$$v = 120 \text{ km/s}$$

In the last two steps, we multiplied both sides of the equation by c, the speed of light, which equals 300,000 km/s. So, this star moves 120 kilometers (about 72 miles) in *one second.* If you traveled this fast, you could get from San Francisco to Los Angeles in about 7 seconds! If your car traveled this fast, you *wouldn't* get pulled over by the highway patrol—they couldn't catch you!

So, even though stars are trillions of miles away from us, we can learn a great deal about them by looking at the light they send us. When we spread out that light into its component colors, this spectrum reveals the star's secrets. We can first find the star's temperature—by noting which wavelength it peaks at (Section 1). The second thing we can figure out about what a star is made of—its composition—is by comparing the dark absorption lines in its spectrum with similar lines made in a lab by known substances (Section 3). This is how we figured out that stars are mostly hydrogen and helium. Finally, as we just saw (in Section 4), we can measure how fast a star is moving—its velocity, or speed—using the Doppler effect.

Please take a glance back at the image that began this chapter. To me, it almost looks like a giant space jellyfish on its way to swallow the Earth. But using spectroscopy, astronomers have figured out what it really is. It is a large cloud created by an old dying star, or rather two stars.[9] We'll discuss what happens when stars die in Chapter 8. We are now equipped with some powerful techniques for studying stars or anything in space really. Whatever's out there, we can figure out its temperature, its composition, and how fast it is moving … all just by looking carefully at the light it emits. So, let's explore the entire universe and discover what's up out there. We'll start relatively close to home with the nearest star to us and the source of energy for all of us here on Earth, the Sun.

WRAP-UP

In the Wrap-Up section of Chapter 3, I said it is important to understand *how we know* what we know. Based on what you read in this chapter, you now have a clear idea of how astronomers can measure the temperature of something, its composition, and how fast it is moving (its velocity). These techniques

---

9   To learn more about this image, visit https://noirlab.edu/public/images/noao-hfg1/

are also used here on Earth, for measuring human body temperatures to check for sickness, and finding out which cars are driving too fast. But there's another reason for me to share this information: to let you know how the process of scientific discovery happens. I have made several discoveries, and I can tell you that there is a real thrill when you know that you are among only a handful of people on Earth who are aware of a new insight. But as we saw in the case of Cecilia Payne, the process of discovery can sometimes be a painful one, depending on how well other scientists accept the new ideas and the people who discover them.

REFLECTION QUESTIONS

1. Go outside on a dark night and look at as many bright stars as you can. Wait 15 minutes for your eyes to become adapted to the darkness. Can you see colors in any of the stars? It's not easy—because stars are so far away. But you might be able to notice some color differences, especially if you are looking at the winter constellation Orion and the stars near it. Make a list of the colors you see, and sketch the location of those stars (or look them up electronically). Each of the different colors you see corresponds to a star of a different temperature.

2. Put yourself in Cecilia Payne's shoes. You've just made an important discovery. But if you publish it, other scientists *might* attack you, some based on their scientific opinion of your work, others based on bigotry. Your career might be impacted. Would you publish the contentious result?

BIBLIOGRAPHY

Rector, Travis. *Coloring the Universe: An Insider's Look at Making Spectacular Images in Space*. Anchorage: University of Alaska Press, 2015.

Cecilia Payne:
A brief, online biography of Cecilia Payne can be found on the following webpage:

https://www.salientwomen.com/2020/05/17/biography-of-cecilia-payne-british-astronomer/

Cecilia Payne also wrote an autobiography, published posthumously:

Payne-Gaposchkin, Cecilia. *An Autobiography and Other Recollections*. London: Cambridge University Press, 1996.

Spectral Lines:
To learn more about how spectral lines were first discovered, see "Hiding in the Light," the fifth episode of *Cosmos: A Spacetime Voyage*, hosted by Neil deGrasse Tyson. (First aired in 2012 on National Geographic Channel and Fox.)

CREDITS

5

THE SUN

The Sun is a mass of incandescent gas.

—They Might Be Giants[1]

What do you do on sunny days? Some people like to go to the beach, others take a walk, or play sports outside. Of course, some people don't like the Sun and heat and would rather say indoors. Either way, I'm sure you know that without the Sun's light, we'd all be dead. Not only does this light nourish the plants that make up our food chain, but without the Sun's heat, we would all freeze. The Sun has been appreciated—and indeed, *worshipped*—since the earliest days of human history (see sidebar for one example).

We take the Sun's light for granted, but have you ever thought about where it comes from? A fun way to do science is to just think about some ordinary phenomenon and ask, "What's up with that?" as we saw in Chapter 3 when we pondered the question "What is light?" So, what's up with the Sun? What, exactly, is it, and how does it make the light that we need to live? Even though people have been thinking about the Sun and its light for thousands of years, it is only recently in human history that people have understood how it works. I was surprised to realize that when my own father was born, there was no one on Earth who could tell you why the Sun shines.

The Sun is a star. In fact, it is nothing special; it's just an average star. Some stars are larger than the Sun, but many are smaller. Some stars are much older than our Sun, but others are younger. And some

---

1 To hear this awesome and scientifically accurate song about the Sun, search for "They Might Be Giants Why Does the Sun Shine?" or follow this link: https://www.youtube.com/watch?v=23e-SnQvCaA

HYMN TO THE SUN GOD ATEN

Your rising is beautiful on the horizon, O Aten.
You shoot up in the East and fill every land with your beneficence.
You are beautiful and great and sparkling, exalted above every land.
Your rays envelop everywhere all the land which you have made
—by Egyptian pharaoh Akhenaten, 1340 BCE

FIGURE 5.1 Pharaoh Akhenaten and Queen Nefertiti (14th century BCE) are shown with their daughters worshipping the Sun. Sun worship in many forms is found in cultures all over the world.

stars produce much more light and heat than our Sun, while others' output is much more feeble. The only reason the Sun *looks* brighter than every other star is that it is much, much closer. In this sense, the Sun *is* special to us because it provides the light and heat that our life depends on.

SECTION 1. What We Know and How We Know It

Our understanding of the Sun has evolved over the centuries, from the days when we humans thought of it as a god of some sort. Scientific knowledge of the Sun's properties has come slowly, obtained by a number of different observations. When discussing the solar system, we defined the astronomical unit (AU) as the (average) distance from the Sun to Earth, which we can use to measure other planets' distances from the Sun. And while we've understood the layout of the solar system since Kepler's work in the early 1600s, it took over a hundred years just to figure out what one AU was. But in 1761, during a "transit of Venus," scientists were finally able to compare the size of the solar system to the size of Earth, after a carefully planned series of international observations. They found that the Sun is, on average, about 150 million kilometers away (1 AU = 150,000,000 km).

Once we know the distance to the Sun, it is easy to find the true size of the Sun, using its angular size (about 1/2 of a degree). The Sun is so large that you'd need just over **100 Earths** to span its diameter.[2] Since the Sun's radius is also about 100 times larger than Earth's, its *volume*[3] is 1 million times larger. This means that if you have 1 million Earths, you could fit them all in the Sun! The Sun

---

2 109 to be precise: $R_{Sun} = 109\ R_{Earth}$.
3 The volume (V) of a sphere depends on its radius, r, *cubed*: $V = 4\pi R^3/3$.

is *massive*, which, by the way, doesn't mean that it is large. Massive means "having great **mass.**" You might think the Sun's mass should be about 1 million times the Earth's mass, but it is actually less than that: 333,000. The reason is that Earth is made of rock, which is more dense than what the Sun is made of, gas. Astronomers like to use symbols to simplify what we write. For example, we would typically write the sentence "The mass of the Sun is 333,000 times larger than the mass of the Earth" this way: $M_{Sun} = 333,000\ M_{Earth}$.

How do we even know the mass of the Sun? We certainly didn't weigh it on a scale. The answer can be found in Newton's Law of Gravity (Chapter 2, Section 7), which says that the Sun's force of gravity depends on its mass. We know how much force the Sun must exert on the Earth (to keep it in orbit) because we can measure how fast the Earth is orbiting (using the Doppler effect). This tells us the Sun's mass.

Similarly, observations of the Sun's spectrum reveal both its temperature and its composition, as we discussed in the last chapter. The Sun is yellow, or as we would say, its peak wavelength, λ_{max}, is in the yellow part of the spectrum (500 nm). This allows us to calculate its temperature using Wien's law: $T_{Sun} = 5,800$ Kelvins. The surface of the Sun is 10 times hotter than the inside of an oven. In the last chapter, we mentioned Cecilia Payne's discovery that stars are mostly composed of hydrogen and helium. The first hints came from a spectrum made during a total solar eclipse.[4] A strange new element was found in the Sun, which was named helium, for the Sun God Helios. Helium makes up almost 30 percent of the Sun's mass, while hydrogen makes up 70 percent. Many other elements are present, but none of them are more than 1 percent of the Sun's mass.

You've probably heard of the three states of matter: solid, liquid, and gas. If a solid like ice heats up, it first becomes a liquid (water), then a gas (steam). But do you know about the *fourth state* of matter? **Plasma** is a gas that has become so hot that its atoms have begun to break apart. Negatively charged electrons are normally held to the positive nucleus by the powerful electric force. But in plasma, the atoms crash into each other so quickly that electrons get knocked off and float around freely. You've seen plasma before—in the inside of a fluorescent light bulb, a brief electric spark, or a lightning bolt. While plasma is rare on Earth, the entire Sun is made of this strange, hot state of matter. To understand the Sun better, we will first study its outer layers, called its **atmosphere**, and then its **interior**.

SECTION 2. The Sun's Atmosphere Has Three Layers

It may seem strange to say that the Sun has an atmosphere because unlike Earth, the Sun has no solid land to stand on. But like the Earth, we can *see through* the Sun's atmosphere. The layers below the atmosphere are too thick to see through, and we call them the interior. Astronomers usually distinguish three layers to the Sun's atmosphere. The lowest is called the **photosphere**. *Photo* means *light*, and the photosphere is the layer from which the Sun's light comes. If you can look out a window and see the Sun right now, take a (quick!) peek. The circular shape that outlines the edge of the Sun is the photosphere.

---

4   On August 18, 1868.

FIGURE 5.2   The Sun's photosphere is its visible surface. If you catch a glimpse of the Sun's circular disc, you are looking at the photosphere. When viewed through a telescope, sunspots can often be seen. They are cooler regions on the Sun where the magnetic field is strong.

Observing the Sun with a telescope, using special filters that block most of its light, you'll notice something's going on with the photosphere. The Sun's surface is broken up into thousands of small cells, which can be seen to bubble up over the course of a few minutes. This process, called **convection**, is the same one seen on the stovetop when a pot of water boils.[5] Bubbles appear on the surface of the water because the lower part of the pot is on a heat source. Similarly, the lower part of the Sun (its interior) must be a source of great heat (whose cause we discuss in the next section).

The layer above the photosphere is called the **chromosphere**. The chromosphere is thinner than the photosphere, so it doesn't emit as much light. However, it can be seen during a total solar eclipse, when the photosphere is blocked out by the Moon. That's when you can see a colorful red or pinkish glow from this part of the Sun, which is what gives this layer its name (*chromo-* means color).

Farther out from the photosphere, the Sun's plasma gets thinner. But what is surprising is that it also gets hotter. In fact, the Sun's outermost layer, the **corona,** is around 1 million degrees. What's up with that? You would think that the outer layers would be colder because they are farther away from the hot center. Actually, we don't know why the corona is so hot, but we suspect it may have to do with the fact that the Sun has a strong magnetic field. To find this out and learn more about the Sun, NASA launched the *Parker Solar Probe*[6] frighteningly close to the Sun in 2018. The spacecraft's orbit takes it 20 times closer to the Sun than Earth is, and well within the orbit of Mercury.[7] *Corona*, by the way, means crown,[8] named for its appearance during a total solar eclipse.

The atoms that make up the Sun's corona are so far from the Sun that its gravity can't hold them. They are constantly drifting off into space, forming a stream of matter that flows through the solar system called the **solar wind**. This stream is normally harmless, but sometimes an enormous *solar flare* sends out a burst of high-energy particles that just happen to collide with Earth. These particles, mostly positively charged protons, are deflected by Earth's magnetic field, which converges on the North and South Poles of the Earth. When the particles hit the atmosphere, they energize oxygen and nitrogen, which then glow. (Specifically, these particles from the Sun strike electrons in oxygen and nitrogen atoms bouncing

---

5   Convection on the Sun also reminds me of patterns I've seen in a bowl of miso soup.

6   For information on its progress, see https://blogs.nasa.gov/parkersolarprobe/

7   Its perihelion distance is just 0.05 AU, less than 10 times the radius of the Sun!

8   As in *coronation*, when a king or queen is crowned, and also *coronavirus*, which looks crown-shaped when viewed with X-rays.

(a)　　　　　　　　　　　　　　　　　　　　　(b)

FIGURE 5.3   The solar chromosphere (a) is a colorful glowing region just above the Sun's photosphere. The corona (b) is a hotter region above the chromosphere. Both are seen here during a total solar eclipse.

the electrons to higher energy levels. When the electrons fall back down, they emit light.) This produces a lovely, glowing ribbon of light called Aurora Borealis, seen in the skies above the far-north places like Alaska, Scandinavia, or Siberia.[9] Most of the particles are absorbed by Earth's protective atmosphere, but there is some risk to astronauts in space at the time of a solar flare.[10]

The Sun has a magnetic field that is even stronger than Earth's magnetic field that we use to orient compasses and find which way is north. But since the Sun is a gas, it rotates *differentially*. That means its equator rotates at a different rate than other parts of the Sun. This causes its magnetic field to become twisted and tangled. Sometimes, "knots" of magnetic field erupt on the surface of the Sun, producing dark spots called **sunspots**. The magnetic field in these regions is about a hundred times stronger than in the rest of the Sun. Because magnetic fields always form loops, sunspots usually come in pairs. They last for a few days or a few weeks and then disappear. What's strange is that the total of sunspots on the Sun varies periodically. Sometimes there are many, and other times there are none at all. People started noticing sunspots hundreds of years ago, and by now we realize that they come and go roughly every 11 years. The exact reason for this **solar cycle** is still a mystery, but there are some patterns. When the solar cycle reaches a minimum, the magnetic field of the Sun reverses polarity. This has also happened on Earth, but much more slowly. If it happened now on Earth, you would notice all magnetic compasses reversing direction; they would point south rather than north. Whatever the cause of these reversals in

9   A similar phenomenon, *Aurora Australis,* is seen near the South Pole.

10   You can find predictions of solar flares and auroras at http://spaceweather.com

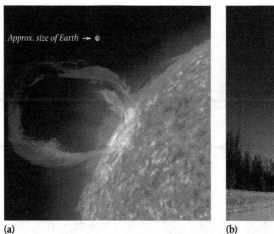

FIGURE 5.4   Solar flares (a) are eruptions of gas from the Sun produced by twists in the Sun's magnetic field. They are enormous! As shown in this NASA image, they are much larger than the Earth. Luckily, Earth is not really this close to the Sun. But the particles produced by solar flares do sometimes reach the Earth and produce auroras (b).

the Sun, they have occurred for years, most recently in 2020. We can thus expect another solar maximum in 2025–2026. This would be a good time to look for auroras in places like Alaska.

SECTION 3. The Sun's Interior

What I find most fascinating about the Sun is the way it generates energy. This energy, particularly visible light, is what our *lives depend on*, here on Earth. Not only does this light allow our food to grow, but increasingly, it provides us with electricity (generated by solar panels and turbines driven by wind). Its heat also creates weather, filling rivers with the water we drink. The Sun also *might* just show us the way to safely generate more energy through nuclear reactions.

Every *second*, the Sun provides Earth with as much energy as 170 million of our nuclear reactors. And that's just a tiny fraction of the Sun's total energy output. Most of the Sun's energy, of course, misses the Earth and just goes into space. The Sun's life-sustaining light takes eight minutes to reach the Earth after leaving the surface of the Sun. But here's a freaky fact that amazed me when I learned it: this same light energy first took thousands of years to go from the center of the Sun, where it was generated, to the surface! Let's see what's going on inside our star, our source of light—our Sun.

The Sun's surface shows bubbles of gas that come and go every five minutes or so. But this convection process also goes deep down into the Sun. In fact, the outer 30 percent of the Sun (by radius) comprises this **convection zone**. Deeper inside, the convection process stops, but light and heat (radiation) can still get out. This **radiative zone** allows energy to transfer outward, but it transfers slowly. That's because the closer we get to the center of the Sun, the *denser* its matter becomes. **Density** is the amount of mass (in kilograms) contained in a volume (measured in, say, cubic meters). Things we think of as "heavy," like metals such as steel or lead, have a high density, whereas feathers have low density. The density of the radiative zone is so high that light can't get out easily; it bounces from one atom to another randomly and only gradually diffuses outward.

That light was generated in the **core** of the Sun. The core is a sphere of hot plasma gas at the very center of the Sun. Its density is higher than anywhere else. It is also *hotter* than anywhere else in the Sun, about 15 million degrees! As you know, when something gets hot, its atoms move faster. In fact, the temperature in the core of the Sun is so hot that the *atoms* there don't just collide with each other. Instead, the **nucleus** of one atom collides with the nucleus of another, creating a **nuclear reaction**. Nuclear reactions are not only essential to making the Sun shine, they are also important when created by humans here on Earth. So, we'll discuss nuclear reactions in general but focus on the ones that power the Sun.

SECTION 4. The Energy of the Nucleus Is Powerful

At some point, you probably took a chemistry class in which you had to balance a **chemical reaction**. For example, this one shows the "burning" of hydrogen gas (H_2) to create water (H_2O):

$$2\,H_2 + O_2 = 2\,H_2O.$$

"Burning" means combining with oxygen (O_2). It was important to balance the reaction because chemical reactions do not create new elements. The amount of hydrogen that went in (two atoms, in this case) is the same as the amount that goes out (in the water). But we're not going to talk about balancing chemical reactions in this book because the Sun is powered by **nuclear reactions**. These reactions are different from chemical reactions because *they create new elements*. Nuclear reactions are also more powerful than chemical reactions, typically a *million times* more powerful.

COMMON MISCONCEPTION

Given its high temperature and the huge amount of light and heat the Sun produces, you might think of the Sun as being an enormous fire. This is a common misconception. **The Sun is not on fire.** As you know if you've built a campfire or learned about fire safety, every fire needs three things: fuel, heat, and oxygen. There is no oxygen in space, so the Sun cannot burn. How, then, does it generate heat?

Most ancient people regarded the Sun as some sort of god or goddess associated with fire, which makes sense, actually. Like a fire, the Sun provides both light and heat. Even scientists in the early 1900s thought the Sun might shine by burning a substance like coal. But a quick calculation proved that if the Sun burned coal, it would have gone out a long time ago. Finally, after the discoveries of Marie Curie, Ernest Rutherford, James Chadwick, and other pioneers of nuclear science, a new possibility arose: reactions involving the *nucleus* of the atom. **Nuclear reactions** can occur in two basic ways called fusion and fission. Although their names are similar, they have the opposite effect. Both types have been used by people on Earth—sometimes for very destructive purposes.

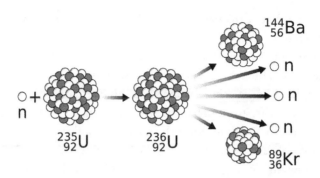

FIGURE 5.5   A nuclear fission reaction. The nucleus of a large and unstable atom (uranium in this case) is struck by a neutron and breaks in half, becoming two different elements (krypton and barium in this case) and some more neutrons. If these neutrons struck other uranium nuclei, then they could start a chain reaction in a reactor or in a bomb. There are many ways a nucleus can split, but we won't study these fission reactions because they don't occur in the Sun or other stars.

Nuclear fission was the first type of nuclear reaction to be discovered.[11] It only happens to atoms with a large nucleus, such as uranium and others you'll find at the bottom of the periodic table. Their nucleus literally splits in half, creating two new atoms each of a different element. It was discovered in 1939 just as World War II was starting. Before the war had ended, humans had made use of the reaction to create atomic bombs. Such *nuclear weapons*, as they are properly called, work by a chain reaction: when one nucleus of uranium splits, it releases two **neutrons**, which each cause another uranium nucleus to split, and the process continues to grow exponentially, with each split releasing energy. The result is a catastrophic, out-of-control energy release—an explosion—that can destroy an entire city. Indeed, the cities of Hiroshima and Nagasaki in Japan were destroyed by nuclear weapons dropped by the United States in World War II.

After that war, even more powerful nuclear weapons were developed by the United States and several other countries. These used **nuclear fusion**, combining small hydrogen atoms together, and so are called H-bombs. Today, nine countries have nuclear weapons; Russia and the United States have over 6,000 each. If used, these weapons could kill half the people on Earth or more. But there is hope they won't be used. Politicians are starting to realize such weapons are not a good idea. Back in 1963, the United States and the Soviet Union realized that exploding nuclear bombs, even just to test them, contaminates the atmosphere. So, this practice was banned. Later, some countries agreed not to conduct underground nuclear explosions, but others still do. A war using nuclear weapons would harm not just the countries involved; the radioactive fallout from these weapons would encircle the globe.

There are also peaceful uses of nuclear reactions. A nuclear power plant uses a carefully controlled fission chain reaction to generate electricity. This almost always works fine, but when it doesn't, the results can be disastrous. Nuclear meltdowns, where operators lose control of a nuclear reactor, have

---

11   It was discovered in 1938 by Lise Meitner. She teamed up with her nephew, Otto Frisch, who named the reaction after a biology term for cell division. They made the discovery by interpreting results from the German lab that Meitner had worked at. As a Jewish scientist, Meitner had to flee that lab and the country to avoid being killed after fascists took over Germany.

happened in the United States, Ukraine, and most recently in Japan in 2011.[12] Because of this risk, very few of this type of power plant have been built in recent decades. There may be an alternative, however. If we could generate energy using nuclear fusion, then there would be no risk of a runaway reaction, and the problem of where to dispose of nuclear waste would also be minimized. It would also be easy to find fuel: just get hydrogen from water. However, fusion reactions are hard to produce. One project (ITER in France)[13] hopes to generate fusion energy before 2026. While humans struggle to generate useful energy from fusion, the Sun has no problem. With its enormous size, it can use gravity to force hydrogen atoms to fuse into helium.

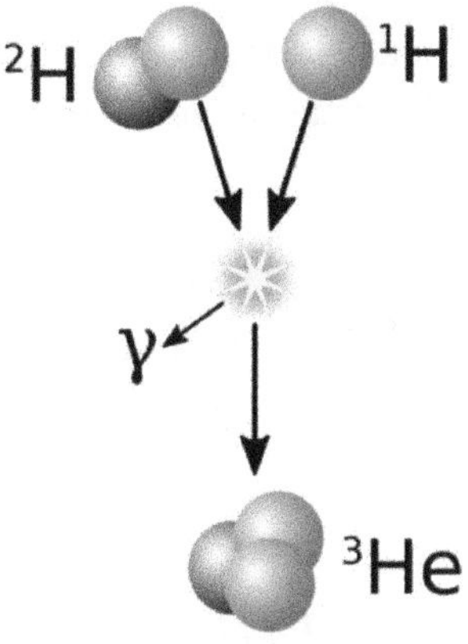

Let's see how that works. To generate energy, fusion must convert one element into hydrogen, into another, helium. Hydrogen's nucleus just has one particle (the proton), while helium's has four: two protons and two neutrons. To make fusion happen, the Sun brings four protons together and then plays a trick. Two of the protons are converted into neutrons. This might seem impossible because protons have positive charge, while neutrons have no charge. But the trick is that this reaction also produces a *positively charged electron*. At this point, you might remember that electrons are negatively charged … so, what's up? Well, this positively charged electron, called a **positron**, is a bit like the electron's evil twin; it is an example of **antimatter**. The reason you don't hear about them is that they don't last long. As soon as a positron touches an electron, KABOOM! both are destroyed. Actually, both are converted into pure light energy in a reaction called *annihilation*.[14]

So, when the Sun fuses two protons together, one of them converts into a neutron producing a nucleus that has one proton and one neutron. This isotope of hydrogen is called deuterium and abbreviated ^{2}H. The "2" means that this flavor of hydrogen has two particles in its nucleus, not just the one proton. Normal hydrogen is written ^{1}H. Thus, this first reaction is usually written:

$$^1H + {}^1H \rightarrow {}^2H + e^+ + \nu.$$

FIGURE 5.6 A nuclear fusion reaction. The red balls represent protons. This means that the two nuclei on top are both from hydrogen atoms because hydrogen only has one proton. The gray balls represent neutrons. In this reaction, two hydrogens fuse into helium. (Specifically, the hydrogen isotope deuterium ^{2}H, with a neutron and a proton, combines with normal hydrogen, ^{1}H.) The gamma symbol, γ, represents gamma rays, high-energy light released in the reaction. This reaction is used by the Sun to generate our light.

where the e$^+$ means the positron. The Greek letter *nu* (ν) represents a **neutrino**, a very light particle with no charge. They don't interact with much of anything, so we'll ignore them for now.[15] The next step

---

12 The Fukushima nuclear power plant suffered multiple meltdowns as a result of the Tohoku earthquake and ensuing tsunami.

13 https://en.wikipedia.org/wiki/ITER

14 There are other "evil twins" out there, types of antimatter that also annihilate matter. Antiprotons, for example, annihilate protons.

15 But neutrinos do play a role in the explosions of stars called supernovae, as we will discuss later. Their role in the Sun only became clear in the early 21st century when the "solar neutrino problem" was solved.

is simpler: as shown in Figure 5.6, our growing nucleus (^{2}H) adds a proton (^{1}H) to become helium-3 (^{3}He), releasing considerable energy in the form of gamma rays:

$$^2H + {}^1H \rightarrow {}^3He + \text{gamma rays.}$$

But the helium produced in this reaction (^{3}He) isn't the standard helium in a kid's balloon at a birthday party. To produce normal helium (^{4}He), we need two protons and two neutrons. The neutrons each come from a ^{3}He nucleus:[16]

$$^3He + {}^3He \rightarrow {}^4He + 2\,{}^1H + \text{gamma rays}$$

To astronomers and astrophysicists, the three reactions above are the answer to the age-old question "Why does the Sun shine?" For everyone else, here is a simpler answer, which can also be written in symbols that represent all the above steps as one single reaction:

The Sun shines by fusing hydrogen into helium and converting mass into energy
$$\textbf{4}\,{}^1\textbf{H} \rightarrow {}^4\textbf{He} + \textbf{energy.}$$

There's one more detail about the reaction above, but it is a big detail. *Why does* this reaction generate energy? The phrase "converting mass into energy" is your clue. The mass of four helium nuclei is ***less than*** the mass of the four hydrogens that made it up. Since we ended up with *less* mass than we started with, where did that missing mass go? The answer was provided in 1905 by Albert Einstein: **mass is a form of energy**. Matter can transform into energy. (So, if you were ever taught that mass cannot be created or destroyed, then sorry, you were taught wrong!) That's right, some number of kilograms of mass (let's call it "m") can *totally vanish* and produce a certain amount of energy (E). Using the speed of light (c = 3×10^8 m/s), Einstein told us *how much* energy would be produced:

$$E = mc^2.$$

In the case of the Sun, the amount of mass lost when nuclear fusion converts hydrogen into helium is about 1 percent.[17] So, if you had 100 kilograms of hydrogen and converted it all into helium, you'd end up with 99 kilograms of helium. The missing 1 kg is completely converted into energy. Einstein's $E = mc^2$ is considered the most famous equation in history, so let's try to understand it better. To measure energy, we'll use the standard metric unit called the **joule** (a 50-watt light bulb uses 50 joules every second). One joule (J) equals one kilogram times 1 meter per second squared: $1\,J = 1$ kg m/s^2. The speed of light, c, is a huge number, but we need c^2, which is enormous: $c^2 = c \times c = 9 \times 10^{16}$ m^2/s^2. Sometimes, I like to write Einstein's equation in a way that better gives me some idea of how powerful it is:

$$E = m \times 90{,}000{,}000{,}000{,}000{,}000 \text{ m}^2/\text{s}^2.$$

---

16   As shown in Figure 5.6, the final reaction requires two helium-3 nuclei to go. So, it happens once while the reactions before it happen twice.

17   The exact figure is 0.007 = 0.7 percent.

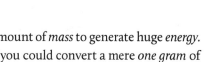

This form, while cumbersome, shows that it only takes a small amount of *mass* to generate huge *energy*. To get a feel for its amazing power, let's see what would happen if you could convert a mere *one gram* of mass into energy. This is roughly the mass of a piece of tissue paper you might blow your nose with. To see how much energy is contained in the tissue, we start with its mass. A *kilo*gram is one thousand grams, so one gram = 0.001 kg. We then multiply this by c^2 to get the amount of energy (E) released:

$$E = mc^2$$
$$E = (0.001 \text{ kg}) \times 9 \times 10^{16} \text{ m}^2/\text{s}^2$$
$$E = 9 \times 10^{13} \text{ kg m}^2/\text{s}^2$$
$$E = 9 \times 10^{13} \text{ J}.$$

What we've just found is that the tiny mass of a piece of tissue paper contains enormous energy: *90 trillion joules*! This is equivalent to the energy released by burning a million gallons of gasoline or exploding 25,000 tons (25 kilotons) of dynamite,[18] enough to destroy an entire city! And that's all from one gram of matter. The Sun *does* convert mass into energy, but the Sun doesn't just convert one gram of mass into energy … it converts *4 million tons* of mass into energy—every second! It's as if the Sun is exploding 2 billion hydrogen bombs every second. Except that the Sun's nuclear reactions are stable, steady, and constant, not like the violent destruction of an H-bomb (these nuclear reactions are also a safe distance away from Earth, 93 million miles).

WRAP-UP

So, now you know how the Sun shines. It is not on fire, burning wood or coal as people once thought. Its method of generating energy (nuclear reactions at its core) is not at all obvious and could only be discovered after we humans figured out how atoms really worked and started making some nuclear reactions of our own, and learning from them. Personally, I find it amazing that the Sun "found" a way to generate energy using nuclear fusion, especially given how hard humans struggle to do the same. Of course, the Sun is not conscious; it didn't have to *try* to make this reaction happen. Gravity pulls together the Sun's massive body so that hydrogen atoms fuse into helium in the very dense core. This energy flows out to the surface of the Sun, where the magnetic fields wind their way through sunspots, and then it streams out into space. The very same process also powers other stars, as we discuss in Chapters 6 and 7.

What a blessing it is for all of us on Earth that the Sun figured out how to generate energy this way. I guess you could say that in spite of my scientific understanding—or actually because of it—I am just as much in awe of the Sun as Akhenaten, the Egyptian pharaoh who wrote a hymn to his Sun god, or any of our ancient ancestors who worshipped other solar deities.

---

18 "High explosives," such as dynamite and TNT, use *chemical* reactions to release large energy. But nuclear reactions release much more energy. A small nuclear bomb, for example, releases about as much energy as 25,000 *tons* of TNT. In fact kilotons of TNT is a unit used to measure nuclear explosions. More powerful H-bombs, using fusion, can release many *megatons* of TNT equivalent—a thousand times more.

REFLECTION QUESTIONS

1. To get a feel for the Sun's enormous energy output, consider its power: 380,000,000,000,000,000,000,000,000 watts, or in scientific notation, 3.8×10^{26} W. Compare this to the power output of all energy sources used by humans on Earth, estimated at 18,000,000,000 watts, or 1.8×10^{10} W. How many *times more* energy does the Sun produce than humans use?

2. Nuclear reactions power the Sun and other stars. We humans have used nuclear reactions to create powerful weapons and to generate large amounts of energy. Do you think we should build more *fission* reactors, which are proven to work, but which sometimes melt down and contaminate the environment? (They also produce considerable toxic waste, which must be stored.) Or should we invest more in *fusion* reactors? They don't have a meltdown risk and don't generate much radioactive waste, but haven't been proven yet. Or should we avoid both types of nuclear reactor? (One advantage that both types have is that they don't produce carbon dioxide pollution, which causes climate change; see Chapter 13.)

BIBLIOGRAPHY

Auroras
You can check if there is activity on the Sun or auroras in the forecast at http://spaceweather.com

There are also a number of sites with excellent photos and videos of auroras:

A video called *South Pole | Night in Antarctica* was filmed at an astronomy research station in Antarctica, where they search for light from the Big Bang. It shows the Aurora Australis, or Southern Lights: https://www.youtube.com/watch?time_continue=16&v=t57DPnH06V0&feature=emb_logo

NASA Sites
NASA has a large amount of free videos, images, links, and documents about the Sun at https://www.nasa.gov/sun

One of my favorite NASA videos is *Fiery Looping Rain on the Sun*:
https://www.youtube.com/watch?v=HFT7ATLQQx8

CREDITS
Fig. 5.1: Copyright © by Neoclassicism Enthusiast (CC BY-SA 4.0) at https://commons.wikimedia.org/wiki/File:Relief_depicting_Akhenaton_and_Nefertiti_with_three_of_their_daughters_under_the_rays_of_Aton_01_(cropped).jpg.
Fig. 5.2: Copyright © by Geoff Elston (CC BY 4.0) at https://commons.wikimedia.org/wiki/File:Sun_white.jpg.
Fig. 5.3a: Copyright © by Luc Viatour (CC BY-SA 3.0) at https://commons.wikimedia.org/wiki/File:Solar_eclips_1999_5.jpg.

THE STARS

We are all in the gutter. But some of us are looking at the stars.

—Oscar Wilde

Close your eyes and think of an animal, perhaps your favorite animal. If I could read your mind, I could guess your animal. But no ... I don't know how to do that. However, I can guess one thing about your animal: its number of eyes. My guess is your animal has **two** eyes. Was I right? That wasn't hard to guess; most animals have two eyes. But *why* is that? Why not just one eye, like the mythical Cyclops? Why not three? Well, animals need to survive. That means knowing where predators are so they can avoid being eaten and knowing where prey is so they can eat. Having one eye would tell an animal *what* is out there, but having two eyes tells the animal *how far away* that predator or prey is. The method animals use (and "animals" includes you!) to measure the **distance** to some object is the same one that astronomers use to measure the distance to *stars*.

In this chapter, we'll see how you can find the **distance** to something if you view it from two different perspectives, as we do with our two eyes. Knowing the distance to *stars* is the first step in understanding them. The next step is to find out how powerful they are. In other words, "How much energy does that star release?" This is called the star's **luminosity**. When we combine these two key pieces of information (using a graph to help us visualize), we can then find out almost everything there is to know about a star: how old it is, how long it will live, and even how it will die. The science of astronomy thus allows us to predict the future for stars, including the Sun. Stars are so important to astronomy that it was *named* for them (remember that *astro-* means star). We will use this chapter and the next two chapters to explore stars; how we measure their distance, luminosity and age (Chapter 6), how they generate energy, and change (Chapter 7), and how they end their lives (Chapter 8). But let's begin by thinking about how valuable it is to have two eyes.

SECTION 1. We Measure Stars' Distances Using Two Points of View

To see the value of having two eyes, try this little experiment at home.

DO TRY THIS AT HOME: SEE PARALLAX YOURSELF

Look around you and find some object on the wall. Next, hold up one finger, *at arm's length*, and close your left eye. Line up your finger with the object on the wall. **Now, switch eyes.** Close your right eye and open your left eye. Did you see your finger jump? That jump is called **parallax**. Of course, your finger didn't actually move. What changed is your *perspective*. When we view things from a different point of view, we get a different perspective, and understand them better. Let's try to *measure* this parallax as an **angle**. Roughly how many degrees did your finger jump? Don't be afraid to make rough guesses. For example, you know that it jumped much less than 90 degrees, right? That would be all the way to the side. I'm sure the jump was also much smaller than half of this angle: 45 degrees. When I try the experiment, I estimate a little less than 10 degrees.

Now, let's redo this experiment, using the same object on the wall. This time, **decrease the distance** to your finger. In other words, hold it closer. Line it up with the same object with your left eye closed, and then switch eyes while looking at your finger. What's different? Was the parallax jump more or less? Write down your observation here:

The simple experiment of blinking our eyes back and forth reveals the **parallax angle**; that is, the angle that your finger "jumps" by when your perspective changes from right eye to left eye. But it also shows that if your finger is **closer**, then it jumps by a larger angle. Conversely, if the *distance* to your finger is *large*, then its *parallax is small*. When one thing goes up while another goes down, we say that these two things are **inversely proportional** to each other. Parallax angle is inversely proportional to the distance to your finger. Now, look at the objects in the room around you. Because you have two eyes and can observe objects from two perspectives, you can estimate the distance to all these objects. This is *why* you have two eyes: they let you measure distances to things by looking at them with both eyes at the same time. Your brain does the distance calculation instinctively. As it turns out, you've been calculating distances using parallax all your life, using your two eyes.

The reason for doing this finger experiment is that, believe it or not, astronomers use the *same method* to find the distance to a star. No, we don't stare up at stars and blink our eyes, but we do look at a star from two different viewpoints. The farther apart these points are, the better our perspective will be. Can you think of a way to observe the same star from two different places that are far apart? If you thought of using two widely separated observatories, that's a great idea! They could be thousands of kilometers apart because the Earth's diameter is about 13,000 kilometers. But to find the distances to stars, we'll need to make our measurements from two points over 100 *million* km apart. We could send someone on a spaceship to do this, but there's an easier way. You *just sit there* for six months. Earth will *carry you* to the opposite side of the solar system, a distance 2 Astronomical Units[1] away.

Parallax means observing from two different viewpoints, such as your left eye and your right eye. Astronomers don't observe fingers in space, we observe stars, and our two vantage points are on either side of Earth's orbit. To complete this analogy, we need the background objects. Remember that you lined your finger up with something much farther away, on the wall. Astronomers just use stars that are very far away as background objects to measure the parallax "jump" of a nearer star. This jump tells us how far away the star is.

To find a star's distance, which we will call "d," we first measure its parallax, which we'll call "P." Remember, parallax is the **angle** of the jump, a few degrees in the case of your finger. But astronomers measure much smaller angles for stars; their parallaxes are much less than 1 degree. So, we divide degrees into smaller **units**: each degree is chopped into 60 minutes of arc, and each of these minutes is subdivided into 60 seconds of arc, or **arc seconds**. This, of course, is the same way we divide an hour into 60 minutes, then 60 seconds.[2] And just as there are 60 × 60 = 3,600 seconds in an hour, **there are 3,600 arc seconds in a degree**. We need these tiny units of angle because stars are so far away—light-years away, in fact. But when using parallax to compute a star's distance, astronomers use a unit that's larger than a light-year, called a **parsec**. One parsec is 3.25 light-years. So if you think of a light-year as a foot, then a parsec would be a yard (or more precisely, a meter: 1 meter = 3.28 feet).

With these two units, we can relate a star's distance (d, measured in parsecs) to its parallax angle (*p*, measured in arc seconds):

$$d = \frac{1}{p}.$$

This equation makes it easier to see that distance is inversely proportional to parallax. If *p* is a large number, then 1 divided by *p* will be a small number. That's what happened when your finger was close;

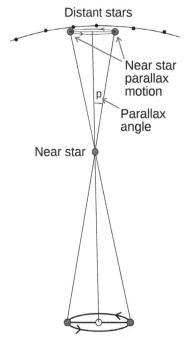

Distant stars

Near star parallax motion

Parallax angle

Near star

Earth's motion around Sun

FIGURE 6.1   Parallax tells us the distance to a star. We observe the nearby star from Earth on two different nights, separated by about six months. Each observation gives us a different perspective as Earth orbits the Sun. The star seems to "jump" compared to fainter background stars by some angle, called the parallax angle (*p*).

---

1   Remember that 1 AU is the average distance from the Earth to the Sun. It's the radius of Earth's orbit. Since diameter is twice radius, you are a distance of 2 AU away from your starting point after six months. So, if you want to go on a space journey of hundreds of millions of miles, just sit here on spaceship Earth.

2   By the way, this system of counting 60 numbers at a time goes back thousands of years. It was first used by the Babylonians, in modern-day Iran and Iraq. For a summary, see https://en.wikipedia.org/wiki/Babylonian_mathematics

its distance (d) was small, but the parallax angle that it jumped by when you switched eyes (p) was large. Let's see some examples of **stellar parallax**.

Sirius, a bright star near Orion, has a parallax of 0.4 arc seconds. As Earth orbits the Sun, we notice that Sirius seems to "jump" back and forth by this angle compared to very distant stars. On the other hand, the North Star, Polaris, doesn't jump much: its parallax is just 0.008 arc seconds. Can you tell which star is closer? When answering a question like this, it is helpful to get out your finger and blink your eyes, as we did before. Polaris has a *smaller* parallax jump, just like when your finger is held *far* away. Therefore, Polaris is farther away than Sirius. Can you calculate how far away Polaris is? Yes, you can. Just use the equation above, with parallax, $p = 0.008$. Try it on a calculator now. Did you get $1/0.008 = 125$? This means that Polaris is 125 **parsecs** away.

Measuring distance is the first step to truly understanding a star. It is so important, in fact, that astronomers have developed several different ways to measure distance, which we will discuss later in the book, besides parallax. When you know the distance to something (a star, a galaxy, a car on a road, or a mountain on the horizon) then you can judge how *large* using its angular size. And as we'll see in the next chapter, you can also figure out how *powerful* it is.

SECTION 2. The Power of Stars

Speaking of the North Star (Polaris), did you get a chance to see it yet in the night sky? (See Chapter 1 for how to find it.) If so, then you noticed that this star, which is so important for navigation, is not actually very bright. So, you'll probably be surprised when I tell you that this faint star is in fact 1,300 times more **powerful** than our Sun. For us, the Sun is the **brightest** star and the most important one. But that's just because it is so close to us, only 1 AU away. The next nearest star, Proxima Centauri, is a quarter million times farther away, and the other stars are farther still. Polaris, as we calculated above, is 125 **parsecs** away, which is about 400 **light-years** distant. This is what makes the North Star look so dim. What's up with "power?"

COMMON MISCONCEPTION

Misconception: Stars are gone during the day

Fact: We usually don't think about looking up at the stars during the daytime. Many people just presume the stars go out when the Sun comes up, or that they are not there. But they *are* there … I know because I have seen stars during the day! When I observed a total solar eclipse in 2017, I saw stars "come out" around noontime because it was so dark. I also saw planets. The Sun is so bright that it lights up the whole sky, not just where it is. This makes it very hard to see stars and planets. But not impossible. If you know where to look, you can actually see the brightest planets, Venus and Jupiter, during the daytime.

The word *power* has many common uses: there are power structures in society, the power company provides electricity, and in math we say "*x* to the second power" to mean *x* squared (x^2). Astronomically, power just means one thing: **energy per time**. In the metric system, energy is measured in **joules** and time in **seconds**. So **power** is measured in joules per second (J/s), just like speed is measured in kilometers per second (km/s, or miles per hour if you prefer). If you've ever bought a light bulb, then you are familiar with wattage. For a given type of light bulb, a 40-watt bulb produces more light than a 20-watt bulb. Wattage is just power: one watt equals one joule per second (1 W = 1 J/s). The Sun is like a giant light bulb. Its nuclear reactions produce a power of:

$$L_{Sun} = 380{,}000{,}000{,}000{,}000{,}000{,}000{,}000{,}000{,}000 \text{ Watts} = 3.8 \times 10^{26} \text{ W}.$$

In case you are wondering how to even pronounce that huge number, it would be: "380 *septillion* watts," or "380 yottawatts." It's a whopping 10 trillion times more than the entire energy use of everyone on Earth. But don't bother with that huge number. We will simplify things by using a different unit, L_{Sun}.

"L" stands for **luminosity**. That's the astronomy term for wattage. A star's luminosity is how much energy it produces every second. Since one watt is far too small a unit to measure stars' luminosity in, we instead measure it using units of solar luminosity, or L_{Sun}. For example, here is the luminosity (L) of a few stars:

To read the second line above, say, "The luminosity of Sirius is *25 solar luminosities*." This means that Sirius emits *25 times more* light, heat, and energy than the Sun. Other stars are even more luminous, like Polaris. There is a star in the southern skies called Eta Carinae, whose luminosity is 5 million L_{Sun}! In *five seconds*, this star can emit as much light as our Sun does in *an entire year*.

TABLE 6.1

Star	Luminisity (L)
Sun	1.0 L_{Sun}
Sirius	25 L_{Sun}
Polaris	1,300 L_{Sun}
Proxima	0.002 L_{Sun}

The energy production of a star is called its Luminosity. Astronomers use the Sun's energy output (Lsun) to measure luminosity. Some stars, like Polaris, can generate more than a thousand times the energy of the Sun, while others, like Proxima, produce much less.

In addition to luminosity, there's another way to measure a star's light output. The old-school method is called **magnitudes**. Over 2,000 years ago, ancient astronomers classified stars into simple categories. The *brightest* were called stars of first magnitude. Next brightest were second magnitude stars, etc., on down to 5th magnitude for the faintest ones. It was a bit like they were giving these stars some kind of award: first place for brightest, second place, etc. Surprisingly, even today, we still measure stars using **magnitudes** (which we call "mags" for short and represent with the symbol **m**). But we've extended the scale to include numbers beyond the original range: 6th, 7th, 8th, and higher magnitude stars are all **fainter** than 5th mag stars, and magnitudes less than one are used for the brightest (e.g., m = 0 or m = –1). We also use decimals to record magnitudes that are not whole numbers (e.g., m = 2.5). Take a look at the magnitudes of the stars on Figure 6.2. Which stars have the highest magnitudes? Which have the lowest?

I grew up in California, so *earthquakes* have always been part of my life. Earthquakes are measured with magnitudes also, but with a higher number indicating a bigger quake. Here's the thing: if you've ever experienced a magnitude 6 earthquake, you know that it is **much** more powerful than a mag 5 or 4 quake. That's because both earthquake magnitudes and star magnitudes are not *linear*. They are called logarithmic scales, which means that the magnitude numbers we deal with only change a little, while the thing they measure (light in the case of stars) can vary a lot.[3] This is exactly *why* the magnitude system is still used. It allows us to describe a huge range of phenomena—from the very brightest star to the faintest distant galaxy—all with just a few numbers.

The magnitude scale was developed back before telescopes or cameras existed. It is based on the response of the human eye (which, by the way, is an amazing light-detecting device, if you think about it). Your eyes can help you see on the darkest moonless night and also in the brightest sunlight. If you've ever tried photography under these conditions, you know how hard it is to accomplish. Using their eyes, ancient astronomers created a system in which a magnitude 1 star is *100 times brighter* than a magnitude 6 star. Every *difference* in magnitude of 5 corresponds to a *factor* of 100 in brightness. Table 6.2 has some examples. To get a better feel for magnitudes, let's try a guessing game. Without peeking below, can you guess which object in the sky has the *lowest* magnitude? Remember how the numbers on the magnitude scale work: large magnitudes are for fainter objects. What's your guess?

TABLE 6.2   HOW BRIGHT IS THAT STAR?

There are two ways to answer that question: magnitude and luminosity. This table shows how they are related. Imagine there are two stars. The first has magnitude M_1 and luminosity L_1. The second has magnitude M_2 and luminosity L_2. As you can see from the table, one star can be many times more luminous, but their magnitudes will only differ by a small and manageable number. Here's a specific example: if the first star's magnitude is 6 and the second star's is 1, then the **magnitude difference** is $M_2 - M_1 = 5$. So the *second* star is 100 times more luminous (brighter) than the first. (The **luminosity ratio** is 100.)

Magnitude Difference ($M_2 - M_1$)	Luminosity Ratio (L_1/L_2)
1	2.5
2	6.3
3	15.8
4	39.8
5	100.0
6	251.2
7	631.0
8	1584.9
9	3981.1
10	10000.0
15	1000000.0
20	100000000.0

---

3   Mathematically, a magnitude is proportional to the *logarithm* of a star's light output. The logarithm (log) tells you about the power to which a number is raised. For example, $\log(10) = 1$ and $\log(100) = 2$ because $100 = 10^2$. Even a large number like 1,000,000 has a logarithm of only 6.

The **Sun** has the lowest magnitude of anything in the sky because it is the brightest thing in the sky. Its magnitude is about –27. The next brightest object is the Moon, which comes in around –13. The brightest star (Sirius) and the brightest planet (Venus) also have negative magnitudes. The other stars that make up your favorite constellations have higher magnitudes, ranging up to about 6th mag for the fainter stars you typically see. But if you live in a big city, it is worse; you'll only see stars brighter than about 4.5.

Magnitudes are useful in comparing how bright one star appears compared to another. But there's a problem: a truly powerful star might *appear* dim if it is far away from us. Or a nearby star, which would look quite bright, might trick us into thinking it was more powerful than it is. Magnitudes, as we've discussed them so far, just tell us how bright a star *appears*. This is why they are called **apparent magnitudes**. Since they don't account for a star's distance, apparent magnitudes don't give you a fair comparison. It's a bit like asking "Who is tallest?" when some people are standing on different steps of a staircase. To solve this problem, astronomers define a second type of magnitude that equally compares all stars. A star's **absolute magnitude** actually tells you how much light it emits. To define it, we imagine that all stars have been brought to the same distance away from Earth, 10 parsecs. (This would be like putting people all on the same step before measuring their height.)

We can easily measure a star's *apparent* magnitude just by looking at it and comparing it to other stars. To get its *absolute* magnitude, we'll need to measure its distance. Perhaps we can use the parallax method to find its distance. With this known distance, we calculate what its magnitude *would be* if it were at a distance of 10 parsecs. That's the absolute magnitude. Absolute magnitudes are directly related to a star's true energy output, its luminosity, L. So, they tell us about a star's true, intrinsic properties.

By the way, in case you are curious: to calculate how bright or dim a star would be at a distance of 10 parsecs, astronomers use a principle called the Inverse Square Law. We need not bother with the calculation

TABLE 6.3   APPARENT MAGNITUDES OF SOME ASTRONOMICAL OBJECTS

Object	Apparent Magnitude
Sun	–27
Full Moon	–13
Venus	–5
Jupiter	–3
Mercury	–2
Sirius (brightest star)	–1
Vega	0
Polaris (North Star)	2
Faintest stars visible in cities	5–6
Faintest stars visible in dark skies	7
Proxima Centauri (Nearest star)	11
Pluto	14
Faint distant galaxy	30

here, but the principle is interesting. As you get farther from a source of light, its brightness decreases—a lot. You can see this at home, for example, by reading a book on a couch, a short distance away from a lamp. If you switch positions to the other side of the couch so you are three times farther away from the lamp, the amount of light you get will not be three times less, but nine times less. That's because 9 is 3 squared: $9 = 3^2$. This fact arises because light from your lamp, or light from a star, shines out into a large sphere and is diluted across the whole surface area of that sphere. This area is proportional to the square of the distance from the center of the sphere. As usual, *inverse* means the two quantities are inversely related; when distance to a star increases, the strength of its light decreases. Table 6.4 summarizes three different ways we measure a star's light output.

TABLE 6.4   WAYS TO MEASURE HOW POWERFUL STARS ARE

Quantity	Meaning	Symbol	Units of Measure
Luminosity	Energy output per second	L	Joules per second (J/s) or Watts
Apparent Magnitude	How bright a star looks	m	magnitudes (mags)
Absolute Magnitude	How bright a star really is	M	magnitudes (mags)

Luminosity is the star's true energy output. It is directly related to the absolute magnitude. On the other hand, apparent magnitude accounts for how faint a star *appears* because of how far away it is.

The connection between apparent and absolute magnitudes is **distance**. We need a star's distance to calculate its absolute magnitude and learn its true properties. However, there is a flip side to this. If we can somehow figure out a star's absolute magnitude (and sometimes we can), then we can calculate its distance. We'll discuss this strategy later on.

SECTION 3. Spectral Types: The Diversity of Stars

People come in all types. Some astrologers say there are 12 types of people, one for each sign of the zodiac, and that your personality is determined by the month of your birth. Chinese astrologers, on the other hand, recognize 12 different types of person, but these are determined by the *year* of your birth. Another popular system, based loosely on psychology, distinguishes 16 personality types. Or maybe there are no types: perhaps everybody is their own "type." Humans are complicated. Luckily, stars are not so complex. There is great diversity among the stars, but fortunately we can classify nearly all stars into just seven physically meaningful types. Here's the story of the women who discovered this.

In the early 20th century, the field of **spectroscopy** was new. An ambitious project at Harvard University was trying to get a spectrum of every star in the sky brighter than 9th magnitude. That's over 300,000 stars ... a lot of data. The project required a lot of math calculations, so they used computers. But back then, "computers" meant *people* who did computations by hand! The director of the project, Edward Pickering, mostly hired women to do the extensive mathematical calculations needed. Why women? While he must have known they were good at math, he admitted the real reason: they came cheap.

Women were paid much less than men, so he could hire more of them. They worked six days a week and were paid about 25 cents per hour (Sobel 2016). Even though under US law these women could not vote, several of them made remarkable contributions to the field of astronomy.

One of these remarkable women was Annie Jump Cannon. Born in 1863, she learned about astronomy from her mother. In her youth, there was an epidemic of a disease called scarlet fever (which is related to strep throat). Cannon survived the illness but was left almost completely deaf (Druyan & Soter 2014). Still, she studied physics and astronomy and graduated from Wellesley College as valedictorian. While still in her twenties, Cannon lost her mother but continued her career at Radcliffe (Harvard) University in Boston. There she was hired by Pickering to classify stars into different categories according to the stars' spectra. She would look at the absorption lines in the spectrum of a star and place it in one of several **spectral types**. She was very good at this and ended up classifying over 350,000 spectra in her career, more than anyone alive. While these types were originally simply called "Type A," "Type B," etc., Cannon realized there was a better way to organize them. She found that

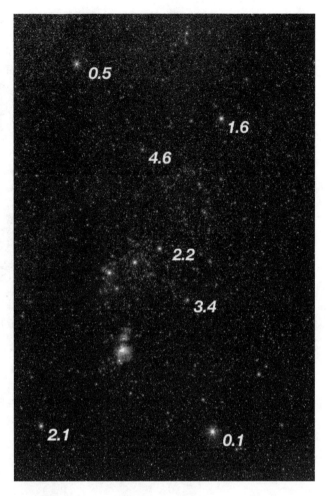

FIGURE 6.2   Magnitudes of stars in the constellation Orion. What do you notice about the magnitudes of the brightest stars compared to the faintest?

most stars fell into just seven types and that the spectral lines changed in strength continuously if the spectral types were organized differently: start with Type O, then go through types B, A, F, G, K, and finally end with type M.

Cannon later teamed up with Cecilia Payne (whom we discussed in the last chapter) to show that this sequence of spectral types actually records the **temperature** of the star from hottest to coldest. Years later, the international astronomy community accepted this system as the best for classifying stars, and it is still used to this day. When an astronomer shares a discovery about a new star, often the first question is: "What is its spectral type?" Living in a world that provided few opportunities for women and fewer for people with disabilities, Annie Jump Cannon overcame both challenges to become one of the most influential astronomers of the 20th century.

The spectral type system worked out by Cannon and Payne is so important that astronomers have been memorizing it for almost a century. You need to know that when the seven spectral types are arranged in this order, O, B, A, F, G, K, M, they represent a sequence from the hottest to the coldest stars. One very

FIGURE 6.3   Annie Jump Cannon was one of several women hired at Harvard University to do math calculations and to obtain and analyze spectra of stars. In her long career, she analyzed over 350,000 stellar spectra.

old way to remember this is to take the first letters of the sentence: "**O**h, **B**e **A** **F**ine **G**irl/Guy, **K**iss **M**e!"[4] But people are constantly coming up with better mnemonics for spectral types. Here are a few that my students came up with.

On **B**reak **A**fter **F**inals: **G**ood, **K**ey **M**oment

On **B**oats **A**nd **F**erries, **G**ood **K**nots **M**atter

Only **B**oys **A**ccepting **F**eminism **G**et **K**issed **M**eaningfully

Occupy **B**anks **A**nd **F**inancial **G**iants, **K**eeping **M**oney

Octavius **B**ecame **A**ugustus, **F**ighting **G**allantly, **K**illing **M**any

Can you come up with one that's easy for *you* to remember? The key point is that the *order* of spectral types tells you *how hot* a star is. "O-type" stars are the hottest, "M-type" the coolest. Since the Sun is a "G-type" star, you can tell that it is hotter than K- and M-types.

Break time! Up to this point in the book, I've shared with you a huge amount of information on how astronomers understand stars. Let's pause for a moment to relax and reflect on what you've learned. In Chapter 4, we saw a way to find the temperature of a star using the rough shape of its spectrum (Wien's law). In this chapter, we got a little more specific and defined seven spectral types (O, B, A, F, G,

---

4   The choice of Girl or Guy (or both) is up to you. ...

K, and M), each with a different temperature. We saw in Chapter 3 how telescopes enable us to measure very faint amounts of light from distant stars. In this chapter, we showed one of the ways to measure just how far away those stars really are (parallax) and how we can use their distance to determine how much energy they give off (their luminosity). In the next section, we'll see how we can use a visual, too, to translate this wealth of information into a deep understanding of stars—what they are, how they live, and how they die.

SECTION 4. The HR Diagram

Modern life can be an information overload. Have you ever done an internet search that returned thousands and thousands of results? You don't have time to view every one, so you can refine the search by adding search terms for the specific thing you are interested in. Astronomers face the same problem. In the early 20th century, astronomers at Harvard compiled a catalog of over 300,000 stars, each with a spectral type and a magnitude. Other catalogs focused on different types of measurements. Some projects recorded how much infrared light stars produce. The 2MASS Catalog, for example, gives infrared magnitudes for over 300 million objects! The GAIA spacecraft was launched in 2013 to measure the parallax of over 1 *billion* stars.[5] Its mission will continue until 2024 or beyond. Having all this information is great, but it can be overwhelming. Most of us can't make sense of a huge list of numbers.

One way to better organize information is to make a graph. Human eyes are good at pattern recognition,[6] and if these numbers are correlated to each other, then a pattern will emerge in the graph. Astronomers have found that some interesting patterns emerge when we make a graph that compares a star's luminosity to its temperature. Usually the hottest stars are graphed on the left and the cooler stars on the right. In other words, the x-axis of the graph measures temperature, but the temperature decreases as you go from left to right. The y-axis of the graph is luminosity, with the most luminous stars on top and the dimmest ones on the bottom. Such graphs were first produced by the American astronomer Henry Norris Russell and Danish astronomer Ejnar Hertzsprung. We refer to them as Hertzsprung-Russell diagrams, or more simply **H-R diagrams**. Astronomers consider them the most useful tool for figuring out information about a star. It's not too hard to make an H-R diagram, like Figure 6.4, of your own. You just need the temperatures and luminosities of a few stars.

To read a graph like this one, first check out the labels on the x-axis and the y-axis. Looking up and down on the y-axis, you can see that stars range from a very low luminosity of $10^{-4} L_{Sun}$ (that's 10,000 times lower than the Sun's energy output, 0.0001 L_{Sun}) to extremely high, $10^6 L_{Sun}$ (1,000,000 L_{Sun}, or 1 million times the Sun's energy output). Reading left to right on the x-axis, we see that stars can range from very hot (40,000 K) to very cool (3,000 K, which is still hotter than an oven, but is considered cold for a star). Looking now at where the stars fall on the graph, the first thing you notice is that most fall on a diagonal line from the top left (hot, bright stars) to the lower right (cool, dim stars). This line is called the main sequence. The Sun is one of the stars on the main sequence. Stars are clustered along that line for an important reason: they all

---

5   In fact, GAIA measures not just distances to stars (using parallax) but also their brightness (apparent magnitude) and motion, making use of the Doppler effect. For details, check https://sci.esa.int/web/gaia/

6   That's why we see constellations when we look at random patterns of stars.

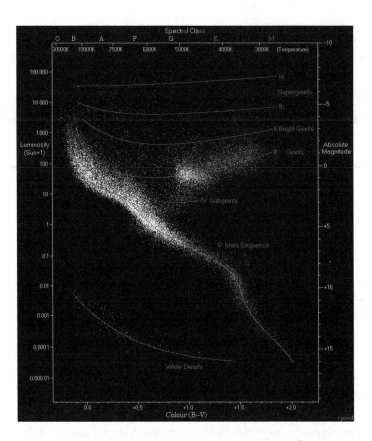

FIGURE 6.4   The Hertzsprung-Russell diagram is the astronomer's way of understanding stars. Each star appears as a dot on the diagram positioned based on its luminosity, graphed on the y-axis from bottom to top, and its temperature, graphed on the x-axis, graphed from right to left, and shown on the top of the graph along with spectral type. Most stars can be found along the Main Sequence, but some giant stars are extremely bright and found near the top of the graph. There are also very dim stars called white dwarfs. In the next two chapters, we will see that as stars age, they leave the Main Sequence, becoming giants, white dwarfs, and in some cases, exploding. (On the right panel is an equivalent measure of luminosity, absolute magnitude, and on the lower axis is a magnitude-related measure of temperature, B-V, with which we will not concern ourselves.)

get their energy from the same source, nuclear fusion of hydrogen. It turns out that stars fusing hydrogen all have the same relationship between their temperatures and luminosity (energy output).

But not all stars are on the main sequence. The points on the graph that are above and to the right of the Main Sequence represent stars that are much more luminous, but also cooler in temperature. In fact, you've seen many of these stars. They shine brightly in our sky and are seen in constellations like Orion and Scorpius. Cooler in temperature, their light output is more red than blue. They are called **red giants** because they are truly enormous in size. Some have diameters 100 times larger than the Sun. And there are even larger stars called **supergiants** that are 1,000 times larger than the Sun. If we had one of these stars in our solar system instead of the Sun, it would swallow up Mercury, Venus, and Earth! A supergiant could even swallow Mars and possibly Jupiter. Now, I have some scary news for you: we *are* going to have a red giant in our solar system. The Sun will turn into one ... eventually.

There's one more type of star we haven't mentioned, but you probably saw it on the graph. The stars below the main sequence and to the left are both hotter and much less luminous. You've never seen one with your eyes because they are too faint. They are faint because they are small in size. In fact, they are named for their size, and called "dwarfs."[7] Stars in the lower left part of the H-R diagram are called **white dwarfs**. They have reached the end of their lives and are no longer generating energy the way normal stars do.

So, if you can place a star on the H-R diagram, you can learn a lot about it. You can even determine its fate; that is, how long it will live and how it will die. Stars on the main sequence are young or middle-aged, healthy stars. They all are generating energy the same way the Sun does, through fusion of hydrogen. Red giant stars *were* on the main sequence, but they have aged and have now run out of hydrogen fuel, which has caused them to swell up to enormous size. White dwarfs are even older. They are all that is left when a star dies and loses its outer layers. In fact, as we will discuss in the next chapter, they used to be the core of a normal star that has now died. So, while I can't read minds or predict the fate of people, I can predict the fate of a star. I can tell you where it is in its life by first measuring its temperature and luminosity, then graphing it on the H-R diagram.

SECTION 5. Binary Stars

If you look carefully at the second star in the handle of the Big Dipper (Figure 1.1), you will notice that it is actually *two* stars, called Alcor and Mizar. As it turns out, stars are often found in pairs. Sometimes two stars just appear close on the sky due to our perspective; this is called a **double star**. But when the two stars actually orbit each other, they are called **binary stars**. Astronomers love binary stars because they allow us to measure the mass of the star. Here's how.

In Chapter 2, we discussed how planets orbit the Sun following Kepler's laws and how Newton proved these laws using gravity. But what if a planet was as massive as the Sun it orbited? In that case, the two objects would *orbit each other*. Both would move in response to the gravity of the other. That's what happens in a binary star system. Kepler found that planets in our solar system orbit according to his third law, $P^2 = a^3$. Newton came up with a slightly different version of this law that can be used for other star systems:

$$P^2 = \frac{a^3}{(M_{TOT})}$$

---

7   In science, the term "dwarf" has been applied to anything that is smaller than others of its kind. It is used to describe plants, animals, planets, galaxies, and human beings of shorter stature. The biological condition called "dwarfism" can have various causes, including some related to growth hormones. Historically, humans with dwarfism, or little people, have had to overcome discrimination and prejudice to be accepted into normal roles in society (as we saw in Chapter 2, Tycho used a little person as a court jester.) Dwarfs also appear in mythology, folklore, and in the fantasy genre, where they are often endowed with superhuman strength, and skills in mining and metallurgy.

where, as before, P is the orbital period of two binary stars around each other, and a is their semi-major axis, the distance between them.[8] The new quantity, M_{TOT}, represents the *total mass* of both stars. To "weigh" a star in a binary system, astronomers measure P and a and calculate the total mass of the two stars. They then use the fact that the less massive star will move around the most, to deduce the individual masses. If both stars are moving the same amount, then they have the same mass. But if one hardly moves at all, then it is much more massive. This is the case in our solar system, in fact. Our Sun actually moves in response to the gravity of the planets, especially giant Jupiter. However, it doesn't move much; even Jupiter is 1,000 times less massive than the Sun.

In this chapter, we've seen how we can learn about the stars. We can measure their distance using parallax and determine their light output (using either luminosity or the magnitude system). And now we see that astronomers have a trick for measuring the **mass** of stars, as long as they are moving in orbit around another star. I describe this whole process with one simple phrase: **motion measures mass**. Later, we will see that this strategy helps us discover planets outside our solar system, measure the mass of a black hole at the center of our galaxy, and discover mysterious dark matter throughout the universe.

WRAP-UP

We think of stars at night and the Sun during the day. But as we saw, the stars *are* there during the day. Here on Earth, the Sun easily outshines the stars, but many of them actually put out more light than the Sun. Stars *appear* dim because of their great distance from us, which we can measure using the parallax effect, as Earth swings from place to place in its orbit. Indeed, stars have all the same properties as the Sun (luminosity, temperature, and mass) because the Sun *is* a star. We can understand our own star, the Sun, by comparing it to other stars. The H-R diagram lets us see how the Sun fits in with the family of stars. It is a healthy, middle-aged star, using fusion to generate energy, like other stars on the main sequence part of the H-R diagram. The Sun's mass is in the middle of the range of other stars. As we'll see in the next chapter, this is an extremely important fact because stars with too much mass will explode!

REFLECTION QUESTIONS

1. In which part of the H-R diagram can most stars be found? What can you say about stars that *don't* fall in this part of the diagram? (We will study these stars in the next chapter.)

2. How can observations of a visual binary give us information about the masses of its stars? Why *can't* we measure the mass of single stars?

---

8   Just to clarify, the P in Kepler's Third Law (period) has nothing to do with the "p" (parallax angle) we discussed in Section 1.

BIBLIOGRAPHY

Druyan, Ann, and Steven Soter. *"Sisters of the Sun"* (Episode 8), *Cosmos: A Spacetime Odyssey,* 2014. Hosted by Neil deGrasse Tyson. (For more information on Annie Jump Cannon and her colleagues.)

Sobel, Dava. *The Glass Universe: How the Ladies of the Harvard Observatory Took the Measure of the Stars.* New York: Viking, 2016. (This book details the lives of the women "computers" at Harvard.)

You can find interviews with Dava Sobel here:

https://www.theatlantic.com/science/archive/2016/12/the-women-computers-who-measured-the-stars/509231/

https://www.sciencefriday.com/segments/the-female-astronomers-who-captured-the-stars/

Parallax Measurement:
A unique parallax measurement was accomplished by NASA's *New Horizon* spacecraft after it passed by Pluto:

https://www.nasa.gov/feature/nasa-s-new-horizons-conducts-the-first-interstellar-parallax-experiment

CREDITS

7

HOW STARS LIVE

Pressure. Pushing down on you, pushing down on me.

—"Under Pressure," Freddie Mercury and Queen and David Bowie

D o you ever feel like you are "under pressure"? Most of us do at times. There are responsibilities, deadlines, etc., that impact our lives. In science, the term ***pressure*** refers to a **force** that is distributed over an **area**. For example, the air in our atmosphere exerts a pressure of 14.7 pounds of force on every square inch of Earth's surface, so we say that atmospheric pressure is 14.7 pounds per square inch,[1] or psi. Scuba divers experience even higher pressure when they go underwater. In fact, the lowest part of the ocean has a pressure of almost 16,000 psi. But that's nothing compared to the pressure inside the Sun: 3.8 *trillion* psi. Talk about being under pressure. In this chapter, we'll see that while pressure can make human life difficult, it is essential for making a star like the Sun work. It is the force that fights back against the force of gravity. Without pressure, a star would collapse on itself. As stars live out their lives, they need to have some source of pressure throughout their lives. They are always under pressure.

---

1   In the metric system, pressure is a measure in newtons of force per square meter. One newton per square meter ($1 \ N/m^2$) is called a *pascal* of pressure. Atmospheric pressure is 101,325 pascals, or 101 kilopascals.

SECTION 1. Stars Form in Large Nebulae ... Somehow

When we study star clusters using the H-R diagram, we find that some of them are very old, while others are quite young. The young ones must have formed recently. But how do stars form? Do they just come from empty space? That doesn't make sense. The answer lies in the fact that space is not empty. There is matter out in space *between the stars*. We use the word **interstellar** to mean "between the stars," and we call this matter the **interstellar medium**. It is made of gas and dust and can be found in large clouds in space. The general name for such a cloud is a **nebula**, which comes from a Latin word meaning fog.[2] You probably have observed one of these nebulae even if you didn't realize it. No doubt you've seen Orion's belt, three bright stars in the winter constellation Orion. Just below the belt, you'll notice three dimmer stars in a downward line, which are thought of as Orion's dagger hanging from his belt (Figure 7.1a). But the middle star is not a star. Take a look. With keen vision, you'll see that it is actually a foggy cloud in space, **Orion Nebula**. You don't need a telescope to make this observation, which means ancient people could see it too. As far as I know, the only ones to record it were the ancient Maya, who regarded this glowing area as a traditional incense fire (Carrasco 2001).

Looking through powerful modern telescopes, we see this region as a giant cloud (Figure 7.1b), some 24 light-years across, containing enough gas and dust to make 2,000 Suns. And, in fact, the nebula is making stars, some more massive than the Sun, some less. It is an example of a star-forming region, or "stellar nursery," and there are many of them known throughout our home galaxy, the Milky Way. But just *how* a large cloud turns into stars is not fully known. Gravity must play a role, pulling gas closer together. But there is more to it than that because all gas has some **pressure**, which can resist the pull of gravity. Pressure is defined as force divided by area. If you've ever inflated a bike or car tire, you may have had to check the pressure, which is measured in pounds per square inch.[3] If tire pressure is too low, gravity will pull the vehicle's wheels down to the ground.

Pressure depends on heat, so for stars to form, part of a nebula must lose its heat, decreasing its pressure, so that gravity can take over, pulling the gas together. But whenever something comes together, it starts spinning faster and faster than ever before. If you think of an ice skater bringing their hands in, you'll have a good example—they speed up dramatically. And when something rotates faster, it tends to flatten out. This makes me think of people I've seen making pizza. First, they get a round ball of dough, then throw it in the air while spinning it. The spherical blob soon turns flat. Five billion years ago, something like this happened when the Sun formed.

We don't exactly know how our Sun (or any other star) formed, but it likely went something like this: 5 billion years ago, part of a large cloud of gas and dust cooled down enough to shrink under the force of gravity. As it shrank in size, it flattened out to form a disk. But matter kept falling toward its center. This matter would eventually form a star—the Sun. We call such matter a **protostar** (*proto-* means "before" or "early," as in a prototype of a new invention). The disk, however, did not fall to the center but kept spinning. Out of this disk the planets formed. This is why they all are in the same plane, the ecliptic plane. As gravity pulls the protostar into a tighter ball, this just makes the gravity force stronger. The collapse continues, and the process accelerates. At this point, you might even wonder what can stop this collapse.

---

2   If you speak Spanish, you'll recognize the connection to *niebla*, "fog."

3   Or newtons per square meter, in the metric system. This unit is also called a pascal.

(a)   (b)

FIGURE 7.1   The Orion Nebula can be seen in winter with the naked eye (a). It is the fuzzy spot below Orion's belt. When viewed with the Hubble Space Telescope (b), the nebula is revealed as a large star-forming region.

The answer is fusion. As this ball of gas gets smaller, its **density** increases. The distance between the atoms of gas eventually shrinks so much that the nucleus of one atom can touch the nucleus of another and react. These nuclear reactions, as we discussed in Chapter 5, generate enormous heat. Heat creates pressure, so the inside of this ball of gas can now push back out, against the force of gravity pulling in. A star is born!

Of course, when we say "born," we're not talking about birth in the usual sense. Stars are not alive, as a biologist would quickly point out. They don't reproduce sexually as animals do, including humans. Instead of saying stars are born, the formal term is ***star formation***. Even still, it is almost *as if* stars are "alive": they consume fuel (hydrogen) and need to produce energy (through fusion) in order to stay alive (that is, avoid collapsing). Also like living beings, their lives come to an end. Stars can die in different ways. For example, the most massive stars explode. We'll continue to use these terms (metaphorically), because it's a fun way to describe what happens to stars. We'll also use the term ***stellar evolution*** to describe what happens to a star over the course of its life, even though biologists use the term evolution quite differently.[4]

While this rough picture represents how we think stars like the Sun are born, there is still much we don't know about star formation. For example, a majority of stars (but not the Sun) are accompanied by another star in a binary (or even triple or quadruple) system. Exactly how these systems form is still

---

4   In biology, a whole population, or species, **evolves**. In astronomy, we say a single star evolves.

being investigated. There seem to be differences in the way high-mass stars form compared to lower-mass stars. One nebula may have a different chemical composition from others, and this could also have an effect on how stars form. Astronomers are actively studying star-forming regions to try to learn more.

SECTION 2. A Star's Fate Depends on Its Mass

While we don't know exactly *how* star formation proceeds, we do know *what* it produces. We can take a survey of stars to find out their demographics, so to speak. We find that there are very *few* massive **O-type** stars. On the other hand, stars like the Sun, which is a **G type,** are much more common, but these are not as numerous as the low-mass **M-type** main sequence stars. For every massive bright O-type star, there are thousands of these small low-mass M dwarfs. This situation, where there are many of the small things and few of the big things, is common in nature. Think about how many ants there are compared to elephants.

But what if something less massive than an M-star forms? It *is* possible for a gas cloud to condense into a dense ball that is not massive enough to start nuclear fusion. Such objects are not stars; they are called **brown dwarfs**. Because they cannot sustain nuclear fusion, some people also call them "failed stars." Brown dwarfs are more massive than planets and less massive than stars. They are very faint and eluded astronomers for decades. As part of the research I did to earn my PhD, I helped discover some of the first few brown dwarfs. Now, thousands of them have been discovered.

All true stars are powered by fusion. As soon as nuclear fusion begins, the protostar becomes a true star. This new source of energy will support the star for millions or even billions of years. This balance between gravity pulling in and pressure pushing out is called **hydrostatic equilibrium**.[5] A similar balance can be seen in a hot-air balloon: fuel is burned to create heat, which lifts the balloon up, defying gravity. If the balloon's pilot is skilled she or he can keep the balloon at the same height, exactly balancing the forces. But not forever—eventually, fuel will run out, the balloon will come down, and gravity will win. The same principle applies to stars.

For a star, the fuel is hydrogen. It is being converted to helium, producing energy, in the center of every normal star during the main part of its life. When we graphed such stars on the H-R diagram, they all fell on the main sequence. How long will the fuel last? That depends on how much of it there is and on how quickly it is being used up. We can compare this to cars. Some large cars, such as SUVs, burn gasoline at a very large rate. Even though their gas tanks are larger, drivers find the vehicles running low on gas often. Smaller cars and electric hybrids consume their fuel much more slowly and only rarely run out.

Stars can be divided into three categories, according to their mass—how much total matter there is inside them (M_{Star}). Each different category of star has a different destiny. Remember that for stars, we measure mass not in kilograms or pounds, but in terms of the Sun's mass (1.00 M_{Sun}). Lightweight stars are less massive than the Sun. The lowest mass category includes stars with mass less than half (50 percent) the mass of the Sun ($M_{Star} < 0.50 \, M_{Sun}$). The next category includes the Sun and all other stars

---

5 *Hydro-* means fluid, like water (hydrogen is an element in water). But it also applies to gases, like those that make up stars. *Static-* means stationary, so the star is not contracting or expanding. Equilibrium refers to a state of physical balance.

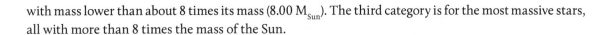

with mass lower than about 8 times its mass (8.00 M_{Sun}). The third category is for the most massive stars, all with more than 8 times the mass of the Sun.

Three Categories of Stars

Lightweight stars: $M_{Star} < 0.50\ M_{Sun}$

Middleweight stars: $0.50\ M_{Sun} < M_{Star} < 8\ M_{Sun}$

Heavyweight stars: $8\ M_{Sun} < M_{Star}$

The lightweight category of stars is similar to very efficient cars. These stars hardly ever run out of fuel. In fact, they *never* run out of fuel! At least not yet. They are so efficient that so far, in the 13.8-billion-year history of the universe, not one of them has ever run out of fuel. This means that we don't really know what happens when they run out of fuel because we've never seen it happen.

The reason the lowest-mass stars live so long is that they have low luminosity. While that makes them dim and hard to see, it also means that they produce energy at a much slower rate and consume their hydrogen fuel at a lower rate than other stars. Another advantage they have is that they are fully convective. When discussing the Sun, we mentioned that convection occurs in the Sun's outer layer. But low-mass stars have convection even down to their cores. This has the effect of mixing the star well, which brings extra hydrogen fuel to the core where it can react. For these reasons, low-mass stars can live for even 100 billion years.

SECTION 3. Sun-like Live for Billions of Years Becoming Red Giants, Then White Dwarfs

Middleweight stars have more than 0.5 M_{Sun} in mass but less than 8 M_{Sun}. Since the Sun's mass is 1.00 M_{Sun}, it is in this category. So, our discussion of the fate of middleweight stars is of great interest to us here on Earth. It concerns the fate of *our* star, the Sun. We can briefly summarize the Sun's fate like this: it is 5 billion years old now. It will continue its life for another 5 billion years, then swell up to become a **red giant**, and finally end its life as a **white dwarf**. Let's take a look at the details and see what's up with the fate of our own Sun.

Like other stars, the Sun is remarkably stable. As you know, it uses nuclear fusion to convert hydrogen into helium. But since the helium has less mass, there is some mass lost in the process. Of course, this mass becomes energy, with the exact amount of energy given by $E = mc^2$. Even though the Sun converts about 4 billion tons of matter into energy per second, this represents only a tiny fraction of the Sun's total mass. But there are a lot of seconds in a year, not to mention a million years—or a billion years. Eventually, the hydrogen in the Sun's core starts to run out. Starting from the moment of the Sun's birth, we estimate that it will take the Sun 10 billion years to use up all of its hydrogen fuel supply. Since the Sun is about 5 billion years old now, we can say that it's in the middle of its life. This means that 5 billion years from now, it will begin to die. Here's how we think that will happen.

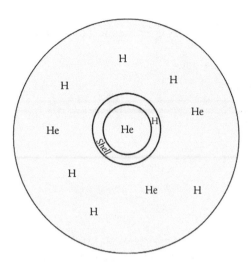

FIGURE 7.2   Shell fusion. Nuclear fusion happens in the core (center) of a star, converting hydrogen (H) into helium (He). After a star like the Sun has done this for 10 billion years, the core is full of helium. So, while fusion can't happen in the core, it can happen in a *shell* surrounding the core because that area is hot enough and still contains some hydrogen.

To imagine the fate of the Sun, first think about how important **pressure** is to a star. Without it, gravity would pull down the top layers of the star toward the center in a gravitational collapse. For 10 billion years, the Sun can avoid this fate by generating energy and heat in its core. Like a hot-air balloon, it can burn its fuel, generate heat and pressure, and stay aloft. But after the hydrogen is gone, pressure in the core decreases and gravity takes over. The core shrinks. This may sound bad, but it gives the Sun a second chance at life. Some of the matter above the core is still rich in hydrogen. It moves inward to the point where nuclear fusion again happens. While the core doesn't have any hydrogen to burn, this surrounding layer, called a shell, does. The name for this is *shell fusion*, but I like to call it "Plan B." It's what the Sun will do in 5 billion years to stay alive.

Shell fusion works for a time. The energy generated in this shell creates pressure to hold off collapse. But the pressure is so large that the layers above the shell get pushed out, and the star expands in size. The star's surface also cools down and its color changes; it becomes a large red star called a **red giant.** Because of their huge size, red giants give off much more light than they ever did before. With a different temperature and luminosity (cooler, but brighter), a red giant's location on the H-R diagram is in the upper right, as we discussed before. The star has now left the main sequence. It is beginning to die.

Plan B does not work forever. Eventually the *shell* also runs out of hydrogen. This element, which has sustained the star as its only fuel source, will never be used again. Without a way to generate heat, the core of the star begins to collapse and the pressure becomes intense. Pressure is force over area, so every atom inside the star feels more force. The helium (He) atoms that make up the core start moving so fast that the nucleus of one helium atom can collide with the nucleus of another and react. In fact, a third He nucleus can come along and combine with the first two. Helium has 2 protons in its nucleus,[6] so if three helium atoms come together, we'll have 6 protons total. Take a quick look at a periodic table (you can find them online). Look up which element has 6 protons. Remember that the atomic number that appears for each element is just the number of protons. Did you see that element #6 is C? C is for carbon. When Plan B stops working, a star switches over to Plan C—fusing helium into carbon.

This new way of generating energy is harder to get going than hydrogen fusion, but at this point the star has no choice. It needs a new source of energy to survive; that is, to avoid collapsing under the force of gravity. This new plan has consequences, however. The star was already a huge red giant when helium fusion began, and now it gets huger. In fact, it expands so much that its outer layers are lost to space—they

---

6   This is why helium fusion requires a hotter temperature. When two helium nuclei collide, there are four protons repelling each other, not two in the case of hydrogen fusion. The repelling force is stronger, so the He nuclei require more force to react.

just drift away. We know this can happen because we have seen this happening with other stars. Their outer layers, starting off in a spherical shape, drift out and become giant clouds of gas, nebulae. When they were first discovered, these round-shaped gas clouds were mistaken for planets. They're not planets, but we still call them **planetary nebulae**.[7] In fact, you've already seen one. Turn back to the first page of Chapter 4. The "mystery object" I showed there is, in fact, a planetary nebula.[8]

The outer layers of a sunlike star drift out into space to become a planetary nebula. But something is left behind—the core of the star, where fusion had been converting helium into carbon. After the outer layers are lost, this dense core, made mostly of carbon, is left behind. It is called a **white dwarf**. The core of a star is very small, and white dwarfs are tiny. In fact, they are about the size of the Earth, which is 100 times smaller than the Sun. That's why white dwarfs give off so little light and thus are found in the lower part of the H-R diagram. They are on the left side of the diagram because they are so hot, heat that is left over from when the star was undergoing nuclear fusion. White dwarfs are stable; there are no further steps in the evolution of a middleweight star.

So, that is the fate of our Sun. It will continue to shine for another 5 billion years, then swell up into a red giant. At this point it will have swallowed Mercury and Venus and scorched the Earth. After some time, its outer layers will be lost, possibly forming a lovely planetary nebula. If you visited our solar system more than 5 billion years in the future, you'd see a white dwarf at the center, and perhaps you'd also spot the gas giant planets like Jupiter and Saturn. It may be sad to think of our Sun ending its life this way. I prefer to say that the Sun will have a quiet retirement. This contrasts strongly with the way some other stars will end their lives—in violent explosions, as we will see in the next chapter.

SECTION 4. Cepheid Variable Stars
Let Us Measure Distance

Before we discuss the violent deaths of stars (in the next chapter), I'd like to mention a special class of stars that astronomers just love. We love them not because of their colors or brightness, but because they help us to learn more about the universe. While other scientists use tools like microscopes, sometimes astronomers use the stars themselves as a tool. But not any star. There is a special type of star that can tell you how far away it is, if you know how to read its signals. The star is called a Cepheid, and its properties were discovered over a hundred years ago by a woman named Henrietta Leavitt.

Leavitt worked at Harvard University in the same department as other pioneering woman astronomers such as Annie Jump Cannon and Cecilia Payne, whom we discussed earlier. Like the other women in that department, she was paid very poorly, about 30 cents per hour! Initially hired to do math, she later studied stars in a nearby galaxy called the Large Magellanic Cloud.[9] (For an image of this galaxy,

---

7 A planetary nebula is made by just one star, so it is much less massive than the gas clouds we talked about in the first section of this chapter; these gas clouds can form thousands of stars.

8 There are many lovely planetary nebulae, including the Ring Nebula and the Cat's Eye Nebula. To see images of these, search online or use the Search feature at NASA's Astronomy Picture of the Day, https://apod.nasa.gov/apod/

9 The Large Magellanic Cloud (LMC) consists of millions of stars and is a small satellite galaxy of our own galaxy, the Milky Way. The LMC is easily visible in the southern hemisphere. People from Europe were unaware of it until explorers,

FIGURE 7.3   Henrietta Leavitt working at Harvard University in the early 1900s. Her discovery that Cepheid stars can be used to measure distance has been used ever since.

see Chapter 11.) Of interest to her were **variable stars**, stars whose luminosity changes. There are many types of variable star. Some change their brightness quickly, others remain the same for years, only to suddenly flare up. Leavitt studied a type called **Cepheid variable stars**[10] (pronounced SEF-ee-id). The brightness of these stars changes constantly, getting brighter and dimmer than some average value. This is because the stars actually pulsate; they get larger and smaller. They are a bit like a beating heart.

What's odd about Cepheids is that the *time* it takes to do this, called the star's **period**, is *different* for each star. After studying thousands of stars, Leavitt made a striking discovery: the long-period Cepheid stars (which took weeks to change brightness) were all much brighter than the short-period ones (which just took a few days to change brightness). All these stars were the same distance away because they were all in the Large Magellanic Cloud. This meant that the only explanation for the difference was each that star's period (the time it took to vary) depended on its absolute magnitude and thus its luminosity (its true energy output). The reason this discovery is of great importance is that it allows us to measure the star's distance. We just compare its apparent magnitude (how bright it looks) to its absolute magnitude (how bright it really is). If a star looks much fainter than it should, it's far away. If it looks too bright, it's close. We just need to measure a Cepheid star's period, and we can determine its luminosity and distance.

Stars like Cepheids, whose true energy output (luminosity) can be known in advance, are called **standard candles**. Like a candle, they give off light, but always the same amount. As I mentioned, we astronomers love them because we can learn so much from them. In the next chapter, we'll see that there are other standard candles, including an exploding star. They all allow us to measure the distance to a star or to the galaxy the star lives in. Previously, we discussed parallax as a way to measure a star's distance. But that method is limited. Remember that the parallax angle gets smaller the farther away a star is. Most stars are so far away that their parallax is too small to measure. When Henrietta Leavitt made her discovery, astronomers were having trouble measuring the distance to stars just 20 light-years away. Thanks to her

including Ferdinand Magellan, sailed south and saw it. But indigenous people in South America, Africa, and Australia knew about it for thousands of years. So, perhaps we should instead call it by one of its original names. What do you think?
10   They are named for the constellation Cepheus, where the first of this type of star was found.

discovery, they now had a new method to measure stars' distances, called the **period-luminosity relation**. You can tell how useful her discovery was by the fact that other astronomers immediately started using it, as we will see in Chapter 10 on galaxies. Over 100 years later, these Cepheid stars are still considered important tools that help astronomers better understand the universe.[11]

WRAP-UP

One of the problems with astronomy is that nothing ever happens—or rather, things normally happen quite slowly. We can't directly witness the birth of a star. But we *can* study nebulae with newly formed stars in them. We can't wait for a medium-mass main sequence star to evolve into a white dwarf; that would take billions of years. But we can study many stars in different stages of evolution. This would be like studying humans by interviewing many people of different ages. You could deduce how long each stage lasts. When we collect stars on the H-R diagram, we learn that most of a star's life is spent on the main sequence; that stars become giants for a short time; and that they remain as white dwarfs for a very long time. The H-R diagram also has a region where Cepheid variables are found. These special stars allow us to measure the distance to a star when we can't measure the parallax. So, by observing enough "snapshots" of individual stars at different stages of life, we can figure out how stars live. In fact, there are a few times when something very sudden, and quite violent, happens to a star: they explode. In the next chapter, we'll see how and why this happens.

REFLECTION QUESTIONS

1. In your own words, discuss **hydrostatic equilibrium**. It can be described as an equally matched battle between *which* two things? (This battle will play out when stars die, as we will see in the next two chapters.)

2. In 5 billion years, the Sun, a G-type star, will die, and whoever is alive on Earth will need to seek out a new home. This would *not* be true if we lived around an M-type star, which can live an amazing 100 billion years. Try telling this to one of your friends. Explain why M stars last much longer than the Sun. Do you wish you lived on a planet that orbited an M star?

BIBLIOGRAPHY

Carrasco, David, ed. *The Oxford Encyclopedia of Mesoamerican Cultures: The Civilizations of Mexico and Central America*. Oxford: Oxford University Press, 2001.

---

11   The study of Cepheid stars has many facets that we don't have time to go into. Eventually, astronomers realized that there are two types of Cepheid. Both are useful, but we need to distinguish which is which because they have different period-luminosity relations. There is even another type of variable star, an RR Lyrae star, that can also be used for distance measurement.

CREDITS

Fig. 7.1a: Source: https://commons.wikimedia.org/wiki/File:Orion_composite1.jpg.

Fig. 7.1b: Source: https://commons.wikimedia.org/wiki/File:Orion_Nebula_-_Hubble_2006_mosaic_18000.jpg.

Fig. 7.3: Source: https://commons.wikimedia.org/wiki/File:Leavitt_henrietta_b1.jpg.

8

HOW STARS DIE

We are made of star-stuff.

—Carl Sagan

L ooking to the skies, we tune in to cycles like the seasons or the phases of the Moon. The Earth itself has cycles. Water molecules in the ocean, heated by sunlight, evaporate into clouds that make rain that falls on the land. Rivers return this water to the sea. Our food is grown in the Earth, but the atoms in the food we eat eventually are returned to the Earth. Skilled farmers know how to convert decomposing waste matter into compost to enrich the soil with nutrients that go into the next generation of plants. Here's a freaky fact for you: every meal you eat contains atoms that were once in another human![1] Don't worry, it's perfectly healthy. Atoms are being recycled all the time. In the cosmos, a different type of recycling is happening to atoms, taking millions of years. As we'll see, these atoms that make up our bodies were once inside other stars, long ago and far away.

In the last chapter, we saw that the Sun (a medium-mass star) will have a quiet retirement as a white dwarf. This is in contrast to more massive stars, all of which will end their lives in a violent explosion we call a **supernova**, the most powerful thing in the universe. But before we discuss those, we'll cover

---

1   That's because the number of atoms in a meal (at least 6×10^{23}) is so large that some of them must come from waste produced by humans or who died and decomposed, returning their atoms to the ecosystem. To be fair, most of the atoms you eat were *not* previously in a person because humans make up a tiny portion of all living matter, just 0.01 percent (Bar-on et al. 2018).

the one way that a sunlike star *can* go out with a bang. This explosion is also called a supernova, but it happens quite differently.

SECTION 1. White Dwarfs Are Incredibly Dense

When discussing the H-R diagram, we pointed out white dwarfs in the lower left corner of the graph. This means they have very low luminosity but hot temperatures. We can now see the reason they are so hot: they are the leftover cores of larger stars. While they no longer are the site of nuclear reactions, they are still quite hot; a white dwarf might have a temperature of 30,000 Kelvins, or five times hotter than the Sun's surface. White dwarfs are common. We know of at least four of them in the very small part of our galaxy closest to us, called the Solar Neighborhood,[2] and hundreds more beyond. As the final step in the life of a medium mass star, they may seem a little dull.

But white dwarfs are bizarre and fascinating. When astronomers discovered the first one, they nearly freaked out. It was unlike anything else seen in space, so small, yet so massive.[3] For nearly 20 years, they had seen the bright star Sirius tugged back and forth by the gravity of *something*. To pull a star like Sirius around, this something had to have a huge mass. So, when they finally got a picture of one in 1862, they were amazed at how small it looked. Figure 8.1 shows a modern telescopic view of the Sirius star system. In the center is Sirius, familiar since ancient times as the bright star you see off to the left of Orion's belt. The small dot is called Sirius B, and it orbits Sirius every 50 years. More precisely, the two stars orbit each other as they fly through space together in what we call a **binary star system**.

So, how can Sirius B have so much mass if it is so small? The answer can be found in its density. **Density** refers to the amount of mass found in a given volume. Different objects you are familiar with have different densities. For example, a full water bottle you could hold in your hand weighs more than a whole trash bag full of feathers because water has a higher density. Here on Earth, the most dense material most of us see is **lead**. This heavy metal has a density 11 times larger than water.[4] While a teaspoon of water weighs 5 grams, a teaspoon of lead weighs 55 grams. But if you scooped up a teaspoon out of a white dwarf, you wouldn't be able to lift it—it would weigh 5 tons!!! The white dwarf Sirius B is so dense that it packs a mass equal to that of our Sun into a volume only as big as the Earth (which is tiny!).

Scientists were also baffled because white dwarfs no longer have nuclear fusion, which, in normal stars, provides the pressure that prevents the star from collapsing (Chapter 7). How does a white dwarf even exist? The structure of white dwarfs was a mystery until the 1930s, when the new theories of **quantum physics** were applied to astronomy. (These theories, discovered in the early 20th century, allowed humans to understand atoms for the first time.) White dwarfs were first understood by an immigrant to the

---

2   This definition of Solar Neighborhood includes all stars less than 5 parsecs (16.3 light-years) away. See https://en.wikipedia.org/wiki/List_of_nearest_stars_and_brown_dwarfs

3   Note that massive means having great mass, not large in size.

4   Density is measured as mass per volume with units like kilograms per cubic meter (kg/m^3) or grams per cubic centimeter. The density of water is 1 g/cm^3.

FIGURE 8.1   The bright star Sirius (just to the left of Orion) has a small, faint companion called Sirius B, seen to the lower left in this image by the Hubble Space Telescope. In spite of its small size, Sirius B has a mass about as large as the Sun's. This very dense star was the first white dwarf to be discovered.

United States whom his friends called "Chandra." **Subrahmanyan Chandrasekhar**[5] left India at age 20 to study at Cambridge University in England, where he earned a PhD. Chandra found that the cores of stars could become so dense that the electrons in their atoms would almost touch each other. This strange state of matter is called *degeneracy*. But the new quantum theory said that electrons couldn't touch.[6] Instead, they would push back, creating a force called **electron degeneracy pressure**. Chandrasekhar's work explained why white dwarfs exist and how they could be so small. But his work also led to another conclusion, that under certain circumstances, a white dwarf can explode!

SECTION 2. A White Dwarf in a Binary System Can Explode

Chandra's extensive mathematical calculations revealed a curious fact about white dwarfs: above a certain mass, they can't exist! If a white dwarf gained mass until it reached this point, then it would explode. The extra mass would cause extra gravity, which would put increased pressure in the white dwarf until its support mechanism (electron degeneracy pressure) was overwhelmed. This would trigger a runaway

---

5   He lived from 1910 to 1995. His family name comes from Sanskrit words meaning Moon (*Chandra*) and flower (*sekhar*, pronounced "say-car").

6   This idea, called the Pauli exclusion principle, also governs the way electrons fit into orbitals in atoms. You may have seen p-orbitals or s-orbitals in a chemistry class.

nuclear reaction that could cause the star to detonate like an enormous bomb. But what could cause a star's mass to change?

Luckily, not much. The only way to add mass to a star is from *another* star. If two stars orbit each other in a **binary star system**, then matter can transfer from one star to another. Chandrasekhar found that if matter falls on a white dwarf this way until its mass gets to 1.4 times the mass of the Sun (1.4 M_{Sun}), then the white dwarf will explode. Thus, 1.4 M_{Sun} is the highest mass any white dwarf can have and is called the **Chandrasekhar limit**. Our *Sun* will become a white dwarf, but it won't explode. It is a single star, not part of a binary system. Even Sirius A and B, which is a binary system, probably won't explode, because the two stars are so far apart from one another that not much matter would transfer between them. But when such an explosion does occur, watch out: it is one of the most powerful events in the whole universe and is called a **supernova**.

Chandra's discoveries had a profound influence on our understanding of how stars die. This type of explosion (involving a white dwarf that gains too much mass) is now called a **Type Ia supernova**. As we will see in the next section, stars can also explode in other ways. We will also see later that Type Ia supernovae, when understood fully, can be powerful tools for measuring the size—and indeed fate—of the entire universe. Chandra's accomplishments are all the more remarkable when we consider that he faced strong opposition to his new ideas but not based on their scientific merits. As an immigrant from India, his ideas were dismissed by one of the top scientists in England in what now appears to have been a clear case of racial bias. As we discussed in Chapter 2, the problems of society are also the problems faced by scientists. The field of astronomy is fortunate that Chandra was able to persevere. He moved to the United States and became a distinguished professor at the University of Chicago. In 1983, he was awarded the Nobel Prize in Physics, and in 1999, NASA named a space telescope for him.[7] His calculation that the maximum mass for a white dwarf is 1.4 M_{Sun} has stood the test of time; after almost a century, over 30,000 white dwarfs have been studied, and none has been found with a greater mass (Farihi 2021).

FIGURE 8.2   Indian-American astronomer Subrahmanyan Chandrasekhar (1910–1990), or "Chandra." He applied the modern theory of quantum physics to astronomy and showed how white dwarfs can exist with mass of 1.4 MSun or less (the "Chandrasekhar Limit"). He also showed that white dwarfs sometimes explode. He won the Nobel Prize in Physics in 1995.

---

7   See https://www.chandra.harvard.edu for some of the discoveries made by this telescope.

SECTION 3. All Massive Stars Explode

While a few white dwarfs that happen to be in binary systems will explode, most will not. The fate of medium-mass stars like the Sun is just to end their lives as hot, white dwarfs forever cooling down in the darkness of space. The same cannot be said about the most massive stars. If a star is eight times the mass of the Sun or more, then it will end its life in a violent explosion called a **Type II supernova**. Unlike the Type I supernovae discussed above, which completely destroy the white dwarf, a Type II supernova leaves some matter behind. This matter can take one of two forms: it will either be an extremely dense ball called a **neutron star**, or it will collapse completely into a **black hole**. Yes, the death of massive stars is violent and bizarre. Let's see how these strange stellar corpses come about.

Stars with mass greater than eight times the Sun's ($M_{Star} > 8\ M_{Sun}$) support themselves the same way as less massive stars, they fuse hydrogen into helium converting mass into energy. Like the Sun, they eventually run out of hydrogen in their cores, but much more quickly. The reason is that they generate more energy than the Sun. You can see this from their position on the H-R diagram: they occupy the high-luminosity part of the main sequence during their normal lifespan. That energy comes from mass in their cores, which gets depleted much faster than in the Sun. The next time you look up at the bright stars in Orion, such as Mintaka (in Orion's belt, spectral Type B1) or Bellatrix (the right shoulder, spectral Type B2), take pity. These stars don't have long to live—just a mere 10 million years or less. While the Sun will be doing fine 1 billion years from now, these stars will be dead in 1 percent of that time.

In a few million years, for example, the core of Bellatrix will be all helium. It will then do the same thing the Sun will do when it gets to this stage, fuse hydrogen **in a shell** around the core. This also causes the star to swell up, becoming a **red supergiant**. Such a star is even larger than a red giant. A supergiant in our solar system would swallow not just the Earth, but Mars and Jupiter as well! You have seen a red supergiant called Betelgeuse in the upper left of Orion. Perhaps you can even notice its red color with your eyes. This star is so large that you could fit 400 million Suns inside its huge volume! Its **mass** is about 12 times larger than the Sun's mass—enough to give it an entirely different fate than the Sun.

FIGURE 8.3   The core of a massive star that is about to explode. (The star itself is many times larger than its core.) Running out of fuel, the star fuses a different element in each layer, with the hottest layers closest to the center. Hydrogen (H), helium (He), carbon (C), neon (N), oxygen (O), and silicon (Si) all produce energy by fusion. But iron (Fe) can't. When iron builds up on the core of a massive star, it will soon explode as a supernova.

More mass means more pressure in the core of the star, which means more nuclear reactions. The Sun will be able to fuse helium into carbon when it needs to, but massive stars keep going beyond carbon. They can also create elements like nitrogen, oxygen, neon, magnesium, and even silicon. Heavier elements like silicon require more pressure to fuse, so they can be made only in the hottest part of the core of the star, the very center. In fact, if we sliced open the core of the star, it would look a bit like a sliced onion, with many different layers, each fusing a different element (see Figure 8.3). Now, if creating heavier elements generates energy and keeps a star alive, you might expect that high-mass stars like Bellatrix would create all the elements on the periodic table. But they can't. It turns out that elements heavier than iron do not help. They don't generate energy if made because the nucleus of the iron atom has the lowest energy of any element. Once a star creates iron in its core, it is about to die.

Astronomers are still working to figure out exactly how this happens, but the overall picture is clear ... and explosive. Without nuclear fusion to provide heat and pressure, the core of the star cannot hold up the layers above. Everything falls to the center as gravity takes over, crushing the star's atoms and creating a bizarre new reaction. The protons at the centers of the atoms combine with electrons to form neutrons. You've probably never heard of this reaction, because it almost never happens.[8] We can write this reaction this way:

$$p^+ + e^- \rightarrow n + \nu.$$

In words, this reaction means a proton (p^+) and an electron (e^-) combine to form a neutron (n) and one more particle, a **neutrino**, represented by the Greek letter *nu* (ν). We mentioned neutrinos before. They are very light particles emitted by some of the Sun's nuclear reactions. While *light* from the Sun has a huge impact, neutrinos don't; they easily pass through almost everything. But a collapsing star is so dense that these neutrinos *do* impact it—they accelerate the explosion that is about to happen. At this time, the core of the star is made of *pure neutrons* and forms an outrageously dense nugget that will become what we call a **neutron star**. The infalling layers above hit this nugget at great speed and literally bounce off it! Accelerated by energy from newly produced neutrinos, these layers are blasted out into space. This entire process takes a matter of seconds, and the energy that is suddenly released is more than all the energy our Sun produces in millions of years! Soon, a **shock wave** from this exploding supernova will expand out into space, devastating anything in its path. This type of explosion is called a **Type II supernova**. Because it is caused by the collapse of the core of the star, it is also called a **core-collapse supernova**.

Supernova explosions are the most powerful things in the universe. For a brief time, one exploding star might produce as much energy as all the stars in a galaxy combined. Because they are so bright, we can see them from very far away. In fact, supernovae can be used as a tool (much like Cepheid variable stars) to measure distances across the whole universe. Recently, supernovae of Type Ia were used to make a remarkable discovery about how the universe is expanding. Just to clarify, we've discussed two types of supernova: A Type Ia supernova is a white dwarf in a binary star system that explodes after accumulating too much mass from the other star. A Type II supernova, as we just discussed, happens after a massive star runs out of nuclear fuel. It's how every high-mass star ends its life.

---

8   In fact, the opposite reaction is more likely: $n \rightarrow p^+ + e^-$ (neutron becomes proton and electron) because the higher-mass neutron can easily decay into a lower-mass proton.

DO TRY THIS AT HOME: MAKE YOUR OWN SUPERNOVA

To see how a supernova unfolds, you can conduct a simple fun experiment at home if you happen to have some sports equipment. Get a fully inflated basketball or soccer ball and another smaller ball, like a tennis ball or racquetball. Stand up on a solid floor, e.g., in a garage or on a sidewalk (not a carpet), and hold both balls in front of you at arm's length with the smaller ball on top. Make sure they are touching and that the small ball is centered. Now, release both balls at the same time and let them fall to the floor. Did the smaller ball make a high bounce? :) The basketball represents the core of a collapsing star that is about to explode. The tennis ball represents the star's outer layers that are falling down on top of it. In both the star and the balls, it is gravity that provides the action. While at first everything was falling downward (or toward the center of the star), in the end the outer layers are blasted away into space after bouncing off the hard core. This core is left behind after the explosion and will become a neutron star.

All massive stars ($M_{Star} > 8 \, M_{Sun}$) will explode as a core-collapse supernova (Type II). *After* the explosion, as we discussed, an extremely dense nugget of pure neutrons will be left behind, a **neutron star**. However, there is another possibility. Sometimes, the mass left behind will be too great to form a neutron star. In that case, the matter remaining collapses completely and forms a **black hole**. Both scenarios will be discussed in the next chapter.

SECTION 4. Observing Supernovae

While supernova explosions are easy to see because they are so bright, they are also hard to *observe* because they are very rare. In a typical galaxy, there might only be one or two supernovae in a *century*,

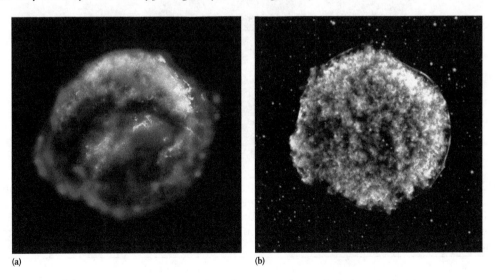

(a)   (b)

FIGURE 8.4   Luckily, past astronomers sometimes kept a good record of where in the sky an event occurred. We can now observe those regions with advanced technology. Image a) shows what we see today in the location where Kepler saw a supernova in 1604, and image b) shows our modern view of Tycho's supernova (1574). These images were made using X-rays and visible and infrared light gathered by NASA's space observatories.

or maybe none. Our own galaxy, the Milky Way, has over 100 billion stars. But for the last 400 years, we have not observed a single supernova in our galaxy. One strategy is to look to the past for evidence.

As you recall from Chapter 2, Tycho Brahe was a keen observer whose measurements of planets were used by Johannes Kepler to formulate the laws of planetary motion. In the year 1572, Tycho observed a "new star" in the sky shining brighter than any other star or planet. He wrote about it using the Latin words for new star, *nova stella*. This is where we get the word *nova*, meaning a new star that appears in the sky, and *supernova*, an extremely bright new star. Not long afterward, another new star was seen by people around the world. As with Tycho's supernova, its location was accurately recorded, by Kepler. When we look to those locations today, we find that they were each the scene of a tremendous explosion. What remains behind after a supernova explosion is called a **supernova remnant**. Figure 8.5 shows these two supernovae remnants and others recorded throughout history.

Kepler and Tycho weren't the only ones to record a supernova for posterity. The earliest such record we currently have comes from ancient China. In the year 185, Chinese astronomers observed what they called a "guest star," which appeared for a time and then faded away. Another guest star was observed by Chinese astronomers in 1054, who carefully noted its position. This supernova was seen elsewhere in the world, including, quite possibly, by Native Americans living in Chaco Canyon, New Mexico. The Ancestral Puebloans who lived there were clearly accomplished astronomers; they created large buildings aligned with astronomical events. Sometime around 1054, they left a pictograph (a painting on rock) showing a crescent Moon, a very bright star pattern, and a human hand. Modern astronomers have determined that a supernova exploded on July 4th, 1054, when the Moon was in crescent phase. It was so bright, it could be seen by day. There are also clear records of this event from Japan and Iraq, but none from Europe.

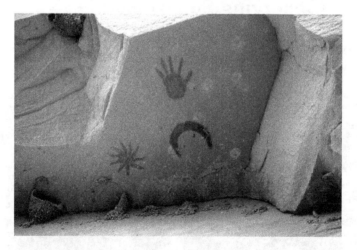

FIGURE 8.5   A pictograph now found in Chaco Culture National Historical Park in New Mexico appears to depict the supernova of 1054 CE, which was also seen elsewhere on Earth on July 4th near a crescent Moon. The Ancestral Puebloans, an ancient Native American culture that lived in this location at that time, were exceptional astronomers. They oriented buildings and constructed artistic monuments to track solar and lunar cycles.

While supernovae have been observed throughout human history, none has been seen to explode in our galaxy since 1604, before the telescope was invented. Lacking detailed observations of nearby supernovae, astronomers have turned to computers to simulate what must happen when they explode.

They use what we know about nuclear reactions and thermodynamics to predict how quickly a massive star will explode and how much energy it will give off. But these theories must be checked by making a observations. Astronomers would love to be able to observe a supernova in our galaxy with modern equipment. It might happen soon because we are overdue for another supernova. One day, you might be observing your favorite constellation and find that there is one extra star that isn't normally there. If this happens, call your local astronomer immediately—you may have just witnessed the first supernova in the Milky Way Galaxy in 400 years!

SECTION 5. Stellar Recycling

Here on Earth, we see cycles of life and death. Some plants die in the winter, but then their seeds grow in the spring. Animals reproduce and their young survive after they die. Most life forms depend on the death of the life forms, whether plant or animal, to survive. Indeed, the atoms in our bodies were once in the bodies of other plants, animals, and yes, other people, going far back through history. Life recycles life. Something similar happens to stars, as they live, die, and as new stars are born.

Stars survive by nuclear fusion. They fuse lighter elements into heavier ones, and this produces the energy they need. The heaviest element the Sun will ever create is carbon, or perhaps oxygen. But more massive stars, as we have seen, can create elements as heavy as iron. But there are many other heavier elements, some of which are part of our ordinary lives. Silver is in jewelry and electronics, gold is in wedding rings. Iodine is used as an antiseptic and also helps the thyroid gland in our bodies. Lead is very dense and used when heavy weights are needed. All these heavy elements are made by exploding stars!

When a high-mass star goes supernova, the explosion sends the elements it has made out into space in an expanding shock wave. This debris will form a supernova remnant, but with time, that remnant will disperse and mix with other matter in the interstellar medium. Eventually, it may become part of a star-forming nebula. When new stars form in this area, they will be enriched with the elements created by the star that died. We can say that the elements created by this star were recycled into another star, and perhaps into that new star's planets. As we saw in the last chapter, medium-mass stars will become red giants, then lose their outer layers to space, which may form a planetary nebula. These layers will contain some of the elements forged by the star during its lifetime. So, they, too, will be returned to the interstellar medium.

This process has been going on for billions of years. The early universe only contained the lightest elements, hydrogen and helium (and a small amount of lithium). These are not enough to form life as we know it. Life in the universe had to wait until elements were produced. Aluminum, magnesium, and silicon are needed to make up the rocks of a planet like Earth. Oxygen and nitrogen for the atmosphere. Carbon for the many complex organic molecules life requires. All these were made in stars, then returned to the interstellar medium, where they lingered for millions of years. Eventually, they formed new stars and new planetary systems, one of which was our solar system. When the Sun and planets of our solar system formed, the matter that made them up was already enriched with heavy elements by the death of previous stars. So, if you are wearing a gold ring on your finger or a silver earring in your ear, then you are wearing a supernova! And every one of the carbon atoms in our bodies was made in a star. As the astronomer Carl Sagan said, "We are made of star-stuff."

WRAP-UP

This is the chapter in my book when things got weird. First, I told you that white dwarfs are more dense than anything on Earth and that this density is maintained by a bizarre quantum physics effect, electron degeneracy. Then, I went on to say that these dense stars can actually explode if too much mass gets dumped on them. At least, that's what Chandrasekhar worked out in the mid-20th century. This type of explosion (a Type Ia supernova) does happen. We have now seen hundreds of them explode—so many, in fact, that we can use the bright light from these explosions to map out the most distant parts of the universe. And these aren't the only type of explosions we've witnessed. Numerous Type II supernovae have also been observed, after very massive stars ($M > 8\ M_{Sun}$) have violently ended their lives. We can also find the remains of both types of explosion in the form of supernova remnants. Some of these look like explosions that just went off, while the older ones are wispy nebulas drifting through space, enriching the interstellar medium with elements created by the supernova. Perhaps one day these elements will be incorporated into another star, or one of its planets, or even into an organism living on that planet.

REFLECTION QUESTIONS

1. What is the Chandrasekhar limit? What happens if a white dwarf's mass becomes larger than the Chandrasekhar limit, and how might this happen?

2. Take a moment and look around yourself. Make a note all of the things around you made of elements you might know: gold and silver in jewelry perhaps, iron in steel, silicon in glass, etc. Also, consider the elements in your own body: calcium in teeth and iron in blood cells, for example. What comes to mind when your reflect on the idea that these items were once present in another star?

BIBLIOGRAPHY

Daley, Jason. "Humans Make Up Just 1/10,000 of Earth's Biomass," *Smithsonian Magazine,* 2018. https://www.smithsonianmag.com/smart-news/humans-make-110000th-earths-biomass-180969141/

Bar-On, Yinon, Rob Phillips, and Ron Milo. "The biomass distribution on Earth," *Publications of the National Academy of Sciences.* 2018. https://doi.org/10.1073/pnas.1711842115

Farihi, Jay. Private communication with the author, 2021.

Chandrasekhar:
For more on the life of Chandrasekhar, see:

Wali, Kameshwar. "Chandrasekhar vs. Eddington—An Unanticipated Confrontation." *Physics Today* 35, no. 10 (1982): 33–40. https://doi.org/10.1063/1.2914790

Weart, Spencer. "Oral Histories Interview." American Institute of Physics (1977). https://www.aip.org/history-programs/niels-bohr-library/oral-histories/4551-1

CREDITS

Fig. 8.1: Copyright © by NASA (CC BY 3.0) at https://commons.wikimedia.org/wiki/File:Sirius_A_and_B_Hubble_photo.jpg.

Fig. 8.2: Source: https://commons.wikimedia.org/wiki/File:Subrahmanyan_Chandrasekhar.gif.

Fig. 8.3: Copyright © by R.H. Hall (CC BY-SA 3.0) at https://commons.wikimedia.org/wiki/File:Evolved_star_fusion_shells.svg.

Fig. 8.4a: Source: https://commons.wikimedia.org/wiki/File:Keplers_supernova.jpg.

Fig. 8.4b: Source: https://www.nasa.gov/image-feature/the-tycho-supernova-death-of-a-star.

Fig. 8.5: Copyright © by Alex Marentas (CC BY-SA 2.0) at https://commons.wikimedia.org/wiki/File:Anasazi_Supernova_Petrographs.jpg.

NEUTRON STARS AND BLACK HOLES

9

H ave you heard of black holes? Many people think they are mysterious and sinister. Quite simply, black holes are one of *two* things that can happen to a very massive star. As we saw in the last chapter, all massive stars will explode. During this supernova, electrons and protons are pushed together to form **neutrons**. While the outer layers of the star explode away, the center of the star remains as an incredibly dense ball called a **neutron star**. But if the matter left behind is *too* massive, then our modern theories of physics predict that it cannot exist as a neutron star. Instead, it will completely collapse to a point of infinite density called a black hole. But theories must be tested; science is based on observation, not speculation. Black holes and neutron stars would not be considered real unless they had been observed.

SECTION 1. Solving an Extraterrestrial Mystery

White dwarfs, as we discussed in the last chapter, are corpses. They are what is left after a medium-mass star (such as the Sun) dies. They are very dense, packing the mass of the Sun into the volume of the Earth. But that's nothing compared to the density of neutron stars, which pack a mass larger than the Sun into a tiny ball, about the size of a city. While a teaspoon of white dwarf matter weighs as much as a school

FIGURE 9.1   Jocelyn Bell (Burnell) in 1967, the year she discovered the first neutron stars. A radio telescope she built detected mysterious pulses of radio waves coming from an object in space later called a pulsar.

bus, a teaspoon of *neutron star* matter would weigh 100 million tons! That's as much as 2,000 cruise ships! Such bizarre objects seem almost unbelievable. Do they really exist? The answer to that question came from a graduate student in England doing her PhD research in the 1960s.

In 1967, Jocelyn Bell[1] was a graduate student at Cambridge University in England. For her PhD[2] research project, she built a radio telescope array that could detect faint radio waves coming from space. After pouring over mountains of data from this new device, she made a striking discovery. From deep space, she picked up a radio signal that kept repeating, a sort of "beep ... beep ... beep" appearing as radio waves. Immediately, attention turned to one possible explanation: could it be a signal from extraterrestrial beings trying to communicate with us? After all, no known natural phenomenon could produce such a regularly repeating signal—one blip every 1.33 seconds. Extensive study showed that this was a natural phenomenon but one that had never been observed before, a pulsating source of radio waves, called a **pulsar**. Jocelyn Bell had discovered the first known neutron star.

As we described in the last chapter, a Type II supernova happens when the core of a massive star collapses and becomes a neutron star. The collapse causes the slowly rotating star to rotate much more quickly, much like an ice skater who brings their arms in and speeds up. Since neutron stars are so small, this effect causes them to rotate at amazing speeds. Earth's rotation rate is one rotation per day. Can you imagine if, instead, we rotated once *per second*, like the neutron star discovered by Bell? There would be a new sunrise every second, followed by a sunset half a second later!! Remember that neutron stars are packing enormous mass, several times the mass of the Sun and a million times the mass of the Earth. And that pulsar isn't even the fastest one we know. There are some pulsars that rotate hundreds of times per second—as fast as a blender! But why do they make pulses of radio waves?

The second effect caused by the core collapse that produced the neutron star is that the star's magnetic field becomes incredibly strong. It was once spread out over a region larger than the Sun, but now it is concentrated into a region as small as a city (perhaps 10 kilometers or 6 miles across). Previously, we saw that charged particles from the Sun (the *solar wind*) are pushed by Earth's magnetic field to the poles of Earth, where they create the Northern Lights. Similarly, the intense magnetic fields of a neutron star will push particles around as the neutron star rotates. The particles, mostly protons and electrons, then give off light, specifically a beam of radio waves that lines up with the

1   Born in 1943 in Northern Ireland, she changed her name to Jocelyn Bell Burnell after she married.

2   To earn a PhD, or doctor of philosophy degree, a college student, who already has an undergraduate degree, completes years of graduate classes, then must do original research and discover something never known before.

magnetic field of the neutron star. The pulsating effect is caused by the fact that a neutron star's magnetic field is not perfectly aligned with its rotation axis. (This is also true for the Earth; the Magnetic North Pole is not the same as its geographic North Pole, around which Earth rotates.) As the neutron star rotates, it sends out a beam of radio waves in the same way that a lighthouse sends out a beam of light from a lamp that rotates around every few seconds. Indeed, this is called the lighthouse model for neutron stars.

The importance of Jocelyn Bell's discovery was soon recognized with a Nobel Prize in Physics ... but it was her male supervisor who was credited (and got the money), not her. Because she made the actual discovery, this has long been regarded as a case of sexism. Nonetheless, she has had a long and successful career in astronomy, occupying leadership roles as the manager of the James Clerk Maxwell Telescope and president of the Royal Astronomical Society. In 2018, she won a $3 million prize[3] for her pulsar discovery many years before. She donated all the money to serve the needs of underrepresented students in science.

SECTION 2. Black Holes Are Dead Stars

As we mentioned, neutron stars are like white dwarfs, only much more dense. There is another way in which they are similar, apart from being stellar corpses. They both have a maximum mass. In the case of white dwarfs, this is the Chandrasekhar limit, $1.4\ M_{Sun}$. A white dwarf with more than 1.4 solar masses cannot exist; it will explode as a Type Ia supernova. Similarly, studies of nuclear physics[4] show that a neutron star cannot have a mass larger than about 3 solar masses ($3\ M_{Sun}$). A neutron star with a large mass cannot support itself against the force of gravity. Instead, it will completely collapse. There is no known force that can prevent gravity from pulling all its matter closer and closer together, until it reaches a single tiny point of enormous density. This strange phenomenon is called a **black hole**.

You may have heard of black holes before. They appear in science fiction and sometimes in news stories. You may have wondered, "What's up with black holes?" They sound mysterious, and indeed they are. But fundamentally, a black hole is just a dead star or another type of stellar corpse, as I call them. The *most massive* stars die as black holes. As you know, all stars above $8\ M_{Sun}$ explode as a Type II supernova. This explosion blasts most of their mass into space. If what is left behind has a mass less than $3\ M_{Sun}$, then it can exist as a neutron star. But if the remaining mass is larger, it *must* collapse completely into a black hole. The smaller it gets, the more intense the gravity. The mystery of black holes comes from this gravity. It is so intense that nothing can escape its pull, not even light. That is why black holes are black—they even pull *light* back into them. If that sounds bizarre to you, it is with good reason: the physics of black holes is unlike the physics of our ordinary life because the conditions in and near black holes are so different. Indeed, at the beginning of the 20th century, none of the existing theories of physics could explain such a strange object.

---

3   The Breakthrough Prize for Fundamental Physics (https://breakthroughprize.org/Laureates/1/L3830).

4   Studies conducted by Robert Oppenheimer and colleagues. Neutron stars are held up by neutron degeneracy pressure in much the same way electrons are held up by electron degeneracy pressure. Oppenheimer went on to lead the Manhattan Project, the United States' top secret program to build an atomic bomb. He later spoke out against nuclear weapons.

COMMON MISCONCEPTION

Black holes often appear in science fiction and have a reputation for swallowing up everything. This is not accurate. While the gravitational forces are intense near a black hole, that is just because black holes have a lot of mass in a small place. The amount of gravity they exert is proportional to the amount of mass they have. But the strength of the gravity force becomes much weaker the farther away you are from the massive object, so their influence is limited.

But black holes *can* swallow up stars and other things that get too close. What is "too close"? The **event horizon** (Section 3) of a black hole is its point of no return. Anything crossing into this invisible sphere *will* be pulled into the black hole. But even outside the event horizon things can get risky. If a star is near a supermassive black hole, for example, then the "close" side of the star will feel a stronger pull than its "far" side. These so-called *tidal* forces can tear a star apart![1] In that case, some of the star will probably fall into the black hole. As it falls, it may pick up speed and crash onto a disk of matter surrounding the black hole, producing a bright flash of light (Section 4). These bursts can be observed by astronomers and used to understand more about black holes.

Not a misconception: Black holes allow future **time travel**, in principle. A black hole curves space and distorts time, as predicted by Einstein's theory of general relativity. What this means is that time elapses more slowly for someone near a black hole. If you could safely fly a spaceship around a black hole (staying just above the event horizon), then when you returned, you would find all your friends had died, for you would be hundreds, or perhaps thousands, of years in the future! However, black holes do not allow you to go backward in time. That would violate causality. (See discussion below on wormholes.)

---

1   The Moon and the Sun exert similar (but much weaker) forces on Earth, causing the ocean to have tides.

SECTION 3. Einstein to the Rescue

During every star's life, there is a battle between gravity, pulling in, and pressure, pushing out. When a star completely collapses into a black hole, we can say that gravity has won. All the remaining mass that once made up the star collapses down to a point from which not even light can escape. To see why light can't escape, consider a simpler case: if you want a rocket to escape the Earth, say, to go to the Moon, it must be launched with a certain speed, called the escape velocity. For Earth, the escape velocity is 12 km/s. This means that if you threw a baseball straight up from Earth at 12 km/s, it wouldn't come down! Escape velocity depends on the size and mass of the planet. Jupiter's escape velocity is much higher because it is more massive. If you were an astronaut standing on a small asteroid, watch out! Even an easy jump up would cause you to escape—you'd fly away.

Stars have escape velocities too; larger for more massive stars. For a black hole, the mass is so great that the speed required for escape is the speed of light! That is why, at least within some distance from the center of a black hole, *not even light* can escape. This distance, called the Schwarzschild radius, marks the point of no return. Because no physical object, such as a rocket ship, can go as fast as the speed of light (or faster), this distance is the closest anyone or anything can get to a black hole. Cross that line, called the **event horizon**, and you will be sucked into the black hole forever.

But how do we know all this, and do black holes even really exist? We will cover observations of black holes in the next section. The theory that allowed us to understand black holes is called the theory of relativity, and it was developed by Albert Einstein, starting around 1905. Einstein first realized that space and time are relative—they are perceived differently by different observers.[5] This led to a conclusion that we have already discussed, that mass and energy are equivalent, expressed in the equation $E = mc^2$. The conversion of mass to energy via nuclear fusion is essential to the Sun's energy production. But Einstein didn't stop there. He went on to consider gravity, and concluded that the 300-year-old theory of gravity developed by Isaac Newton was wrong! Instead of being a force acting at a distance, Einstein said gravity consists of the bending of space. Space can be curved by the presence of a large mass, such as the Sun. So, by the year 1919, there were two very different theories to explain gravity that scientists were using. But only one of them was right. What's great about science is that a revolutionary new idea can overthrow ideas that have been around for centuries, if it can be confirmed by observations. We saw the same thing happen when Copernicus proposed that the Earth orbited the Sun. Observations eventually supported his idea and disproved the geocentric model that had been used for centuries.

Einstein's theory predicted that light from a distant star would bend as it passed near our Sun. The only way to check was to observe a star that appeared near the Sun in the sky. But when the Sun is up in the sky, we can't see stars—the Sun is too bright. But there is one time when it is possible to see stars while the Sun is in the sky—a total solar eclipse. Photographs taken during a total solar eclipse in 1919 proved Einstein's relativity theory was right. The space around the Sun (or anything else with mass) is *curved* by the **mass** of the Sun. Scientists, who had been using Newton's theory of gravity for 300 years, realized they were wrong and abandoned that theory relatively quickly.[6] Sometimes I wonder what would happen if humans would just as quickly abandon old, outdated ideas regarding social issues (such as race and gender) that no longer make sense.

> *In science it often happens that scientists say, "You know that's a really good argument; my position is mistaken," and then they actually change their minds and you never hear that old view from them again. They really do it. It doesn't happen as often as it should, because scientists are human and change is sometimes painful. But it happens every day. I cannot recall the last time something like that happened in politics or religion.*
>
> —Carl Sagan (1987)

In any case, if the mass of the Sun can *curve space* and deflect starlight, then *more* massive bodies, such as neutron stars and black holes, can do the same, only more so. Black holes bend light *so much* that it changes direction and falls back onto the black hole. So, all light within a certain distance of the center of the black hole is trapped. Matter and light can approach this event horizon, but if something goes in, it will not come out. Even approaching it would be dangerous. The powerful gravitational forces there would rip apart most types of matter. Einstein's theory thus makes predictions about how black holes will behave. But it cannot tell us if they really exist. For that we need observations.

---

5   But not everything is relative. For example, two observers moving toward each other will both agree on their speed of approach. More profoundly, all observers experience the same laws of nature.

6   Newton's theory of gravity is still frequently used as an approximation for situations where the gravity is not extreme, such as on the surface of Earth.

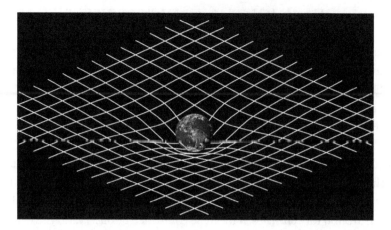

FIGURE 9.2   According to Einstein's theory of gravity, space and time (represented by the grid of lines) are **_curved_** by the presence of any mass, even the Earth. This theory was confirmed in 1919 when the curvature of space, caused by the Sun, was measured during a solar eclipse. A black hole has much **_more_** mass and curves space much more than the Sun, producing some bizarre effects.

SECTION 4. Black Holes Have Been Detected and Imaged

The idea of observing a black hole might seem preposterous at first. After all, they give off no light—that's why they are black. However, there are several ways in which we can detect the presence of a black hole, and now, even take a picture of them. We can detect the effects a black hole has on objects near it; then we can detect the *presence* of a black hole, even if we don't see it. Remember that a black hole was once a normal (but large) star. If that star was in a binary system, the other star that was in the system will still be orbiting the black hole.[7] As we saw in Chapter 6, a binary star system can allow us to measure the mass of both stars, making use of Kepler's Third Law. Even if we don't see a black hole, we can tell that *something* is there, causing a star that we do see to orbit. If that something has a large enough mass, then the only thing it could be is a black hole. This is the case for **Cygnus X-1**, the first black hole to be discovered.

Astronomers measuring the spectrum of a star in the constellation Cygnus (the Swan) noticed that the star was moving in a circular orbit around some small unseen object. They calculated that this mystery object must have a mass at least 15 times larger than the Sun's mass ($M = 15\ M_{Sun}$). Therefore, it could not be a white dwarf or a neutron star because their maximum masses are 1.4 and about $3\ M_{Sun}$, respectively. Also, Cygnus X-1 was observed to emit X-rays. This is exactly what we would expect if it were a black hole. That is because a black hole in a binary system would strip matter away from the second star. This gas would then fall toward the black hole, spiraling around it to form a disk of

---

7   Assuming it survives the supernova explosion that created the black hole, which seems likely, as long as it was a big enough star.

matter that will eventually fall onto and merge with the black hole. We say that this matter will *accrete* onto the black hole. This **accretion disk** will become very hot because matter is falling onto it with great speed and energy. According to Wien's law (Chapter 4), a *very hot* object will glow with light of *very short* wavelength. X-rays are the type of light with the shortest waves, so it is not surprising that black holes are accompanied by X-rays. In addition to Cygnus X-1, several black holes have now been discovered in a similar manner. Just to be clear, these X-rays don't come from the black hole itself, but from matter just outside the event horizon that is about to fall into the black hole, but which has not yet crossed this point of no return.

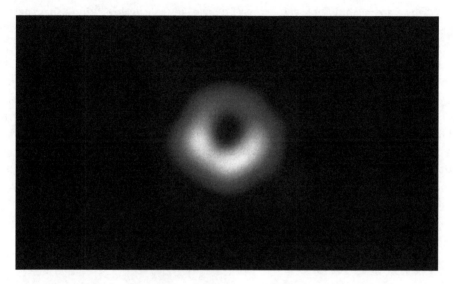

FIGURE 9.3   The first image of a black hole was made in 2019 by the Event Horizon Telescope project, which combined light from many telescopes with extremely high precision, not possible before. This supermassive black hole is located in the elliptical galaxy Messier 87 (M87) but is similar in size to the one located in our own galaxy, the Milky Way.

In recent years, new techniques have allowed black holes to be discovered in other ways. As we will discuss in the next chapter, astronomers have discovered that a black hole exists at the center of our galaxy and have measured its mass. They did this by observing stars that orbit the black hole for many years. More recently, astronomers have teamed up to produce the first image of a black hole, this one in another galaxy. We will discuss these extremely large black holes later, but for now we focus on **stellar black holes**—that is, black holes that simply formed as a result of the death of a star. To summarize, here are the key points.

- All massive stars explode as supernovae, and the *most massive* of these form black holes after the explosion. (Those that leave behind less than 3 M_{Sun} can form neutron stars.)

- The physics of black holes is bizarre, but can be understood using Einstein's theory of general relativity.

- Black holes are real! Many have now been discovered. Observations of stars that orbit the black hole and X-rays from its accretion disk confirm their existence.

DO TRY THIS AT HOME: MAKE YOUR OWN WORMHOLE

To see how space can be curved, get out a piece of paper and marker pen. Draw five horizontal and five vertical lines, making a grid like the x- and y-axes of graph paper. On opposite corners of this grid, label two locations, A and B. Lay the paper flat on a table (representing flat space), and measure the distance between A and B. For a typical piece of paper, they might be 30 centimeters apart or perhaps 13 inches. But Einstein's theory of gravity (general relativity) says that space will *curve* if massive objects (like black holes) are present. So, imagine there is a black hole nearby. Pick up your piece of paper and curve it so that points A and B are much closer together; make them nearly touch. Now, using a sharp pen or pencil, poke a hole in the paper that punctures points A and B. Try poking your finger through the hole and sticking it out, like a little worm.

Theoretically, wormholes are consistent with Einstein's theory. If they existed, they would allow a spaceship to travel a great distance in a short time—that's why they are often included in science fiction stories. However, there are some reasons to think that they do not exist. Unlike black holes, astronomers have never found evidence for a wormhole. Also, since they seem to allow travel faster than the speed of light, they would allow a light beam to arrive at its destination *before it left*! Such a nonsensical situation is called a violation of **causality** because effects come *after* causes. So, while you are not likely to ever travel through a wormhole, at least you know what they are if you hear about them in a science fiction story.

WRAP-UP: STARS

For five chapters (starting with the Sun), we have discussed stars and how they live and die. We studied the Sun, our closest and most important star, in detail, and saw that it lives (generates energy) by nuclear fusion, converting hydrogen into helium. Other stars do the same, but the more massive stars can also generate energy by fusing heavy elements, like carbon, neon and silicon, whereas the heaviest element the Sun will ever fuse is helium. The Sun may be our most important star now (since Earth gets its energy from sunlight), but other stars that lived long ago are also essential to life. The elements they cooked up in their cores became part of our Sun (which we called stellar recycling) and part of the Earth. These elements include silicon in our rocks, oxygen in our air, and iron in our blood. The huge stellar explosions called supernovae helped to blast these elements into space, thus enriching the interstellar medium. So, when it came time for Earth to form, our planet was fortunately endowed with the elements necessary for life. These explosions also leave behind two very strange corpses. The first, neutron stars, rotated rapidly and sometimes sent fast pulses of radio waves to us, created by their magnetic fields. We call them pulsars. The second, black holes, have collapsed entirely. Their gravity is so intense that it curves space and time around them, producing bizarre effects.

It is now time to move on. We will now consider much larger structures made up of stars—billions of them—called **galaxies**. Our Sun and the rest of the solar system are in one such galaxy, called the Milky Way. But we will be able to use what we have learned about stars and about light and matter as we study galaxies. For example, the goal of figuring out how far away things are is important in all parts of astronomy. When humans first realized *how far* galaxies are from us, their minds were blown, and we

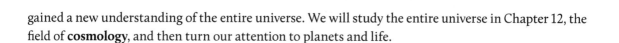

gained a new understanding of the entire universe. We will study the entire universe in Chapter 12, the field of **cosmology**, and then turn our attention to planets and life.

REFLECTION QUESTIONS

1. In what ways are neutron stars similar to white dwarfs, and in what ways are they different? Consider the mass of the original star and whether or not a supernova must take place.

2. If your friend asked you about black holes, what would you say? They sound bizarre and are often seen in movies, so people think they are fictional. What evidence would you give that black holes are real?

BIBLIOGRAPHY

Sagan, Carl. Keynote address to Committee for the Scientific Investigation of Claims of the Paranormal. *Skeptical Inquirer*, Vol. 12, No. 1 (1987). https://skepticalinquirer.org/1987/10/the-burden-of-skepticism/

10

THE MILKY WAY

Our galaxy itself contains a hundred billion stars;

It's a hundred thousand light-years side to side;

It bulges in the middle, sixteen thousand light-years thick

But out by us it's just three thousand light-years wide.

—Monty Python, "The Galaxy Song"

Your great-grandparents saw it. So did all their ancestors. Your grandparents might have seen it. Perhaps your parents saw it, if they lived far away from big cities. And if you are lucky, perhaps you have even seen it too. But most people alive today on Earth have not seen it. We are talking about the **Milky Way**, a glow of light in the night sky that looks like a cloud. To those of us who live in cities, it is only visible when we get out of town and go to a dark sky location, in the mountains perhaps. When there, you will see a band of light stretching through the sky, like a long irregular cloud. It is a stripe of light whose edges are jagged and whose center is, in fact, dark. Looking in the summertime, you would see that this stripe bulges out, to become much wider as it passes through the constellation Sagittarius. Earlier generations of humans—our ancestors—pondered what it could be.

SECTION 1. The Lore of the Milky Way

Before electric lights were common, everyone on Earth saw the Milky Way in the sky regularly. As with the constellations, ancient peoples from all parts of the Earth came up with stories and

FIGURE 10.1 You can see the Milky Way in dark sky locations.

myths to help them understand what they saw. Here are a few examples. The Khoisan people, who live in the Kalahari Desert of southern Africa, traditionally regarded the Milky Way as embers from a fire, tossed into the sky by a girl. In Irish mythology, it was regarded as a reflection of the sacred river Boyne and called Way of the White Cow. Egyptians also thought about cows and regarded the Milky Way as milk from a cow, connected to the sky goddess Hathor. Ancient Greeks thought of it as human milk from the mother goddess Hera.[1] In India, the Milky Way was associated with the sacred river Ganges, and also with a dolphin, swimming through the sky. Aboriginal people in one part of Australia see a large, elongated emu, outlined by the Milky Way. By viewing the sky in these ways, people were able to connect what they were seeing in the sky with things that were important to their own lives.

SECTION 2. What Is the Milky Way?

A scientific understanding of this Milky Way came slowly. However, at least one ancient scholar, Democritus (who lived around 460–370 BCE), hit upon an idea that would later be confirmed by observation. He proposed that the "river of light" people saw in the sky was really just made up of thousands of stars. (This wasn't his only excellent idea; he also proposed that all matter was made up of small particles he called *atoms*.) It is remarkable to me that a few creative thinkers proposed modern scientific ideas way back then, when most people understood the world around them via mythology. In fact, there have been many scientific minds in different times and in different places. Mediaeval Persian astronomers al-Biruni[2] and al-Tusi[3] also wrote that the Milky Way must be made of stars.

These early ideas were proven correct in the 1600s. When Galileo pointed his homemade telescope to the Milky Way, he found that instead of being a blob of milk, it was actually made up of thousands and thousands of stars. To us on Earth, the Milky Way appears like a cloud. And that's a good analogy, because a cloud is, in fact, made up of many droplets of water. If you've ever seen fog lit up to reveal millions of droplets, then you can imagine each of them as a star and visualize the millions—actually billions—of

---

1   The words *galaxy* (from Greek) and *Via Lactia* (from Latin) refer to the Milky Way. There are many related words in English: lactation (production of milk for breastfeeding) and lactose (a sugar found in milk).

2   Abū Rayhān al-Bīrūnī (973–1048) was a scholar who made contributions in many fields, including math, physics, astronomy, and history. He spoke six languages.

3   Naṣīr al-Dīn al-Ṭūsī (1201–1274) was an expert in astronomy, math, logic, and medicine. He wrote 150 books and invented an ingenious device that used circles to produce a straight line. Like al-Biruni, he was a product of an era that historians call the Islamic Golden Age. Later scholars of the European Renaissance read and were inspired by works from this era, as well as classics from more ancient times.

stars in the Milky Way. After Galileo, a number of astronomers used more powerful telescopes to map out this huge arrangement of stars that surrounds the Sun. Some of these observations were made by a unique team of observers, a brother and a sister.

William Herschel (1738–1822) and his sister **Caroline** (1750–1848) carried out a huge number of observations using telescopes they made at his estate in England. Discoveries made there included the planet Uranus (the first planet to be found since ancient times), several comets, and faint nebulae. They often worked together, but Caroline also worked on her own and discovered several comets, after which she was paid a salary by the king to do research. This makes Caroline Herschel the first known *professional* female astronomer in history. While for centuries it was common to dismiss research work done by women, thankfully, Caroline's work was recognized in her lifetime with several awards.

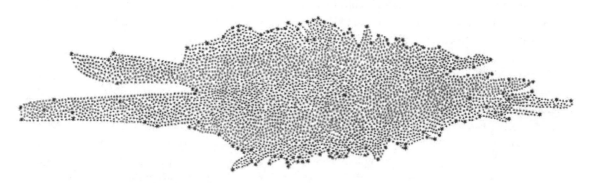

FIGURE 10.2   Early map of the Milky Way by William Herschel.

After many nights spent counting stars in different directions, William Herschel published a book that showed his idea of the shape of the Milky Way (Figure 10.2). But there was a problem with this map and other studies at that time. While these astronomers painstakingly observed and actually *counted* millions of stars, they were making a mistake. They didn't realize that gas and dust between the stars (the interstellar medium) was obscuring their view and giving them a distorted notion of our place in the universe. Most of their maps showed our *solar system at the center* of the Milky Way.

The breakthrough came in 1917, when American astronomer Harlow Shapley came up with a better strategy than just counting stars. He turned his attention to **globular clusters.** These are large groups of up to a million stars, held by gravity into the shape of a sphere (or globe; hence *globular*). Over 100 of globular clusters are known, but most congregate around the part of the Milky Way that bulges out. Shapley figured that the globular clusters should congregate around the true center of the Milky Way Galaxy. If he could measure the distances to each globular cluster, he could locate the true center of our galaxy. He would

FIGURE 10.3   A globular cluster, seen up close using the Hubble Space Telescope. There are dozens of these clusters known. Harlow Shapley used them to find the center of the Milky Way.

then know whether or not other astronomers were correct when they concluded that *we* were at the center of the Milky Way.

DO TRY THIS AT HOME: SEE THE MILKY WAY

Plan a trip to a dark sky location. Be sure to avoid the full Moon. In fact, the best time to go would be within a few days of the new Moon, when the Moon is a thin crescent. Look for a location where you can camp or stay the night. Depending on how big a city you live in, you may need to drive for an hour or two. Spring and summer are good times to look in the northern hemisphere. You'll want to wait until it is very dark, at least one hour after sunset. Also, give your eyes time to adjust. They are more accustomed to bright indoor lighting. But after about 20 minutes, they become very sensitive. Pick a location that gives you a wide view of the sky and isn't blocked by trees or buildings. If you have a blanket, you can lie down in a large meadow. (You'll probably want to take warm clothes or maybe even a warm drink in a thermos.) You can invite friends and have a star party, or perhaps enjoy the beauty of the night sky on your own. As the sky darkens and your eyes adjust, you'll see many things. First, you'll notice just how *many* stars are now visible—much more than you can see in the city. You may see satellites within an hour or so of sunset. They can be distinguished from planes because they don't blink. In time, your vision will become aware of a huge band of light stretching through the sky. That is the Milky Way. You can reflect on seeing something that thousands of generations of our ancestors saw, but which most people on Earth can't see now due to light pollution. In the far south, you should be able to see the bulge of the Milky Way, which contains its center. There are even a few globular clusters in this area that you just might be able to spot, especially if you have binoculars.

If you want an extra challenge, try to visualize all those stars as an enormous disk, a bit like a pancake with a thick center. And now imagine that your star, the Sun, is one of those many stars in the disk. It is challenging to visualize, but if you even try, you will get a better sense of your place in the universe.

To find the distance to the globular clusters, Shapley used the distance measuring method that was discovered by Henrietta Leavitt, Cepheid variable stars. Recall that while these stars change in brightness, they are reliable indicators of **distance**. Using Cepheids and related stars, Shapley was able to determine the distance to a few globular clusters. He also used some approximations to get the distances of others. Eventually, he was able to map out the location of enough globular clusters to figure out where the center of the Milky Way was. Shapley's result was revolutionary. We are not at the center of the Milky Way after all! The center is located about 27,000 light-years away from us (or 8,200 parsecs.) Astronomers had fallen into the false belief that *we* are at the center of everything—and not for the first time. Recall that ancient astronomers thought that the Earth, where we humans live, was the center of the solar system and thus the center of the known universe. It wasn't until Galileo made observations of Venus with a telescope that this geocentric idea was disproved. Harlow Shapley displaced the Sun (and our solar system) from the center of the Milky Way galaxy in the same way that Copernicus displaced the Earth from the center when he advanced his heliocentric idea. Shapley thus applied what we now call **the Copernican principle**, which can be stated "We do not occupy a special place."

Nowadays, we have a much better understanding of the Milky Way. It is not a random blob of stars, but in fact is a majestic **spiral galaxy**. The *spiral* name comes from the **spiral arms**, large arcs where more stars can be found than the places in between them. Our Sun is in one of the smaller spiral arms. All of the stars in these arms, and indeed the entire galaxy, are swirling around the Galactic Center, about 27,000 light-years away. The Sun takes all the planets with it on a journey, orbiting the galaxy once every 240 million years or so. These lovely spiral arms cannot be seen if we view the Milky Way *edge-on*. That's because it is really a very thin disk, like a frisbee or a pancake. From above you would see the spiral pattern, but we actually live *inside* the Milky Way, so its details are hard to make out. For example, if you found yourself in a new city, it would be hard to get your bearings, unless you had a view of the city from above (like a map). From the inside, it has been difficult to map out the Milky Way, especially because the disk of the Milky Way (which we are in) has a lot of obscuring gas and dust. But astronomers have pieced together a picture, using longer waves of light that aren't obscured by the dust as much, such as infrared and radio waves. We are also guided by images of *other* galaxies, which we can see more clearly than our own. (More on them in the next chapter.) The images in Figure 10.5 show our best guess as to what the Milky Way looks like.

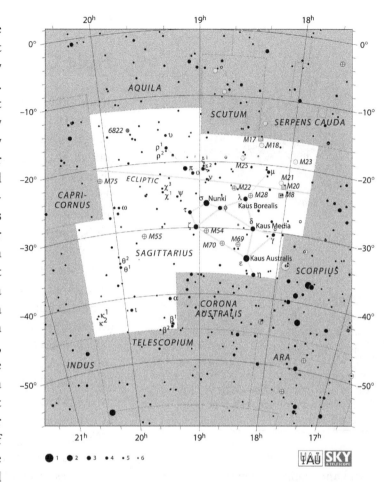

FIGURE 10.4   The constellation Sagittarius has several globular clusters (marked with a circle and + symbol, such as *M55*). Harlow Shapley measured their distances and found the location of the center of our Milky Way Galaxy. The galaxy is not centered on our Sun, but on a point some 27,000 light-years away (8,200 parsecs, or 8.2 kpc)!

The overall structure of the Milky Way consists of a **disk** that is about 100,000 light-years across. So, light from a star on the edge of this disk would take 100,000 years to make it all the way across. If you wanted to travel to different parts of the Milky Way (like some of my favorite science fiction characters do), you'd have to be very patient. Spaceships can't move as fast as light, so it would take centuries for you to get from here to there.[4] Above and below the disk is a region we call the **halo** of the galaxy. This is where the globular clusters are found. They congregate around the center of the galaxy, which we will consider next.

---

4   Most science fiction stories create a way to get around this problem to make their stories more interesting, such as employing hyperspace or wormholes, which both allow faster-than-light travel. But no such technologies are known, and fundamental principles of the theory of relativity prevent spaceships from accelerating up to the speed of light or beyond.

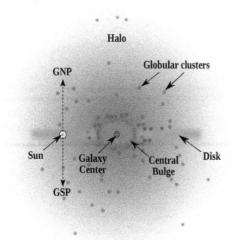

FIGURE 10.5   Diagram of the Milky Way Galaxy, seen edge-on. By finding the location of the globular clusters, astronomer Harlow Shapley was able to find the center of the Milky Way. Most stars are found in the disk, while globular clusters are in the halo. (The dotted lines indicate the Galactic North and South Poles, as seen from our position orbiting the Sun.)

SECTION 3. The Black Hole Center of the Galaxy

Just looking at the Milky Way on a dark night, you can tell that one part of it is special. While most of it looks like a strip of light in the sky, one part *bulges* out, so we call it the bulge of the Milky Way. Since Shapley found the center of the Milky Way within this bulge, astronomers have explored this region in much more detail. One such astronomer is Andrea Ghez, a professor at the University of California–Los Angeles. I first took an interest in Dr. Ghez's work when I was a student of hers there. She was an inspiration to me, and she kindly offered to be a member of my dissertation committee and review my PhD research project.

Here's how Dr. Ghez and her team work. To even see "into" the center of the Milky Way, they use infrared light, which is less obscured by the intervening dust. Infrared images reveal several stars that appear to be moving around a massive central object that gives off no light. To get the most detailed view of these stars possible, she used the largest telescope in the world and equipped it with an advanced **adaptive optics** system. This system fires a laser into the air, creating an artificial star in the sky that can be observed at the same time. This star is used to correct for changes in Earth's atmosphere. (These changes are what make stars twinkle when we look at them.) After observing in this way for many *years*, Dr. Ghez and her colleagues made a striking discovery. The stars nearest the center of our galaxy must be orbiting a **supermassive black hole**! By "supermassive," we mean that it has a mass of about 4 million times the Sun's mass. This is clearly no ordinary black hole, produced by the death of one star. This black hole is so large that it can swallow entire stars and has done so thousands of times. She was able to draw this conclusion by mapping the orbits of stars around the black hole (see Figure 10.6). Each star orbits in an ellipse, just as planets orbit the Sun in ellipses. Each orbit provides a measurement of the black hole's mass, according to Newton's Law of Gravity. For making this fascinating discovery, Andrea Ghez won the Nobel Prize in Physics in 2020.

So what does it mean that there's a black hole at the center of our galaxy? Does this mean that all the stars in the Milky Way, including the Sun, will be sucked into it? No. As we discussed in the last chapter, stars and planets can safely orbit a black hole as long as they are far away from its edge, or **event horizon**. At a distance of 27,000 light-years, we are safe. What it means is that somehow, probably when our galaxy first formed, an enormous amount of mass was pulled together by gravity into a single spot. Exactly how this happened is not obvious. But we can find clues to the origin of our galaxy by studying its youngest and oldest stars.

SECTION 4. Young Stars, Old Stars, and the Origin of the Milky Way

Perhaps you can see the constellation Orion tonight. (It is easily visible from November through March.) Previously, in this book we discussed the Orion Nebula, which you can see with your naked eye. It is home to some of the youngest stars in the whole galaxy. They are only a few million years old. In the same part of the sky, moving to the right and using Orion's belt as a pointer, you should be able to see the red star Aldebaran in the constellation Taurus. Going farther right, you'll encounter the Pleiades. You'll see a small cluster of stars that looks a bit like a tiny Little Dipper. In some myths, these stars were called the Seven Sisters. Studying this region with telescopes, we have found that it consists of thousands of stars, all of them relatively young. The Pleiades is one example of an **open cluster**, of which there are thousands in the Milky Way. Open clusters differ from globular clusters: they have fewer stars and are more irregularly shaped, not spheres like globular clusters. But the most important distinction is that open clusters are very *young*, while globular clusters are very *old*.

How do we know this? When stars are graphed on the H-R diagram, the most prominent part is the main sequence. But the top part of the main sequence (high-mass stars) is missing for globular clusters. Recall that a high-mass star does not live long and will explode as a supernova. So, as a group of stars ages, it loses its high-mass stars *first*.

Open clusters contain some of the youngest stars in the galaxy. You can think of them roughly as the next evolutionary step after star-forming regions like the Orion Nebula (Chapter 7, Figure 7.1). But in an open cluster, most of the matter has already formed into stars; there is little gas and dust left. In Figure 10.6, you can see a famous open cluster, the Pleiades. You can see the Pleiades cluster on a winter night—it is just to the right of Orion's belt. Open clusters are found in the disk of the galaxy and not in the halo. This tells us something. Stars are made of gas and dust, and most of the gas and dust in the galaxy is found in the disk, not in the halo.

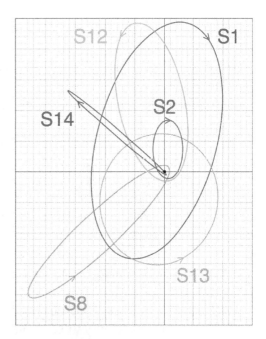

FIGURE 10.6   Stars orbiting the supermassive black hole at the center of the Milky Way. Each ellipse shows the measured orbit of a star (named S1, S2, etc.). All stars appear to be orbiting a central point, so there must be something massive there. But there is no light coming from that point. By measuring the period and semimajor axes of these ellipses, astronomers showed that this point (called Sagittarius A*) has a black hole more than 4,000,000 times more massive than the Sun.

FIGURE 10.7   The Pleiades open cluster.

The spiral arms of a galaxy are where new stars are formed. These new stars light up the surrounding gas, which shines out with a blue glow.

Globular clusters also have a story to tell. Since they are the oldest things in the galaxy, they reveal to us what the galaxy was like a long time ago. Each globular cluster is a sphere of stars, but the 100-plus globular clusters in our galaxy, found mostly in a halo, are themselves arranged in a sphere centered on the bulge. Since the globular clusters were the first things to form in our galaxy, this implies that the Milky Way was originally a sphere. The disk shape came later. These facts allow us to put together a rough picture of the history of our Milky Way galaxy, starting with its formation billions of years ago.

Some 10 billion years ago (or more), an enormous sphere of gas began to contract. But before it got much smaller, individual pockets of gas condensed into the stars that now make up the globular clusters. If you took a picture at this time, the whole Milky Way would look like a sphere. The rest of the gas (which didn't form globular clusters) may have been rotating just a little. But as gravity pulled it together, this rotation sped up. A rotating object tends to flatten into a disk. In Chapter 7, we saw that a similar process is thought to explain the origin of our solar system. (In that case, the disk that surrounded the forming Sun provided the raw materials from which the planets were formed.) While the globular clusters stayed in their spherical arrangement, all stars that formed later would be found in the disk. This includes the Sun. The disk of the Milky Way still contains plenty of gas from which new stars are being made. The effects of gravity and rotation, working together, formed the spiral arms.

WRAP-UP

Discoveries in astronomy come in two kinds. Sometimes a researcher, like Jocelyn Bell in the last chapter, finds something, like pulsars, that is entirely new and unexpected by most people. But sometimes our discoveries allow us to understand something we've known about for a long time. That's what we saw happening in this chapter with the Milky Way. Even though ancient people knew about it from prehistoric times, nobody could tell that the Milky Way was made of stars until Galileo looked at it with a telescope. Observations by the Herschels and by Shapley revealed that we live inside a huge galaxy, made of over 100 billion stars, one of which is our beloved Sun. We are fortunate to live at a time when humans can understand that we are not at the center of our galaxy, but are orbiting the center every 240 million years. And that the center of the Milky Way contains a supermassive black hole, which we can measure (as Andrea Ghez did) by observing the stars trapped by its enormous gravity. As fascinating and peculiar as the Milky Way may seem, with its supermassive black hole, its old globular clusters and young open clusters, we now know that there are other galaxies out there much like our own Milky Way. In fact, there are billions of them!

REFLECTION QUESTIONS

1. The Sun orbits the center of our galaxy. And at the very center is a **supermassive black hole**. So, just for fun, try confronting your friends with this true statement: "Did you know you are orbiting

a black hole right now?" How do they react? If they start to freak out, you can reassure them that every other star orbits the center of the Milky Way, and that even though this black hole is 4 million times more massive than the Sun, we are orbiting at a safe distance and aren't affected by it.

2. In the next two chapters, we will consider other galaxies and the universe as a whole. One idea we'll consider is the center of the universe. What if someone asked you, "Is the Milky Way at the center of the universe?" Based on what you have learned in this chapter (and in Chapter 2 on the geocentric and heliocentric models), try taking a guess as to whether or not the galaxy you happen to live in is at the center of the universe. What arguments would you use in support of your guess?

BIBLIOGRAPHY

Krupp, Ed. *Beyond the Blue Horizon*. Oxford: Oxford University Press, 1992.

Ridpath, Ian. *Star Tales, Revised and Expanded Edition*. Cambridge: Lutterworth Press, 2016. See also http://www.ianridpath.com/startales/milkyway.html

11

GALAXIES

I'm sorry I know so little. I'm sorry we all know so little.
But that's kind of the fun, isn't it?

—Vera Rubin

Looking up on a dark night, you can see about 6,000 stars. With even a small telescope, you can see many more—millions. ALL these stars are part of the Milky Way Galaxy, even those that are not in the "milky" part of the sky. By the 1920s, people began to understand that all these stars, and our Sun, formed a giant disk with a bulge in the center, joined by globular clusters above and below the disk. As we saw in the last chapter, Harlow Shapley's observations proved that our solar system was NOT at the center of this disk. Indeed, we now know that the center of the Milky Way has a supermassive black hole. Back in the early 1900s, people generally thought that the stars of the Milky Way were all there was, that our galaxy was the entire universe. But there was one thing they couldn't explain.

SECTION 1. Discovering Other Galaxies

As early as 1800, observations from large new telescopes (such as the one at Birr Castle, Ireland—the largest in the world at the time) revealed elegant swirling objects in space (See Figure 11.1) They were called **spiral nebulae**, but nobody knew exactly what they were. Some people thought they were solar systems in formation. If this plausible guess were true, then each of them could be expected to consist of just *one* star (and perhaps some planets). Other researchers called them "island universes" and said they

FIGURE 11.1 Drawing made in 1845 by William Parsons of a spiral nebula after looking through the Leviathan Telescope in Ireland. This is the first drawing made by humans of a spiral galaxy.

consisted of billions of stars, that each one was as large as our own Milky Way. The question was debated hotly. In 1920, two astronomers publicly debated the issue, Harlow Shapley (who found the center of the Milky Way) and Heber Curtis. If these mysterious objects really contained billions of stars, they must be very far away because they don't look very large in the sky. To solve the mystery, we need to know *how far away* the spiral nebulae really are.

The largest spiral nebula is Andromeda[1] (see Figure 11.2). The reason astronomers didn't know the distance to the Andromeda Nebula is that their favorite technique for measuring distance, **parallax**, didn't work. It is so far away that its stars do not appear to move *at all* as Earth orbits the Sun. But there is another way to measure distance. American astronomer Edwin Hubble realized that he could use Cepheid variable stars to measure distances. The technique had just been discovered a few years before by Henrietta Levitt (see Chapter 7). So Hubble carefully observed the Andromeda Nebula night after night. Finally, when he found one of its stars changed in brightness, he got so excited he wrote "VAR!" on the photographic plate—short for "variable star." Subsequent observations of Cepheids and other variable stars that could also serve as a standard candle showed that the Andromeda Nebula was, in fact, **2.5 million** light-years away. Since our own Milky Way galaxy is only 1,000,000 light-years across, then Andromeda *must* be outside of the Milky Way. It is indeed an island universe consisting of billions of stars. Today, we call it the Andromeda Galaxy and regard it as a sister galaxy to our own Milky Way. In fact, the Milky Way might be the little sister, since Andromeda actually appears to have more stars.

FIGURE 11.2 The Andromeda Galaxy is the closest galaxy to our own Milky Way and can be seen with the naked eye. It is larger than the Milky Way, and has about 1 trillion stars!

Hubble's discovery of the huge distance to Andromeda radically changed human understanding of our place in the universe. No longer could we claim that *our* system of stars, the Milky Way, was the entire universe. There were other galaxies out there as well. Most of them appeared smaller in angular size than Andromeda, which meant that they were farther away. The mind-blowing enormous size of the universe became clear to humans for the first time. Andromeda is 2.5 million light-years away, but other galaxies are *hundreds of millions* of light-years away; some are even *billions* of light-years away.

---

1   This spiral nebula is now called the Andromeda Galaxy because it is located in the constellation Andromeda.

DO TRY THIS AT HOME: FIND ANDROMEDA

"On a clear day, you can see forever." So goes an old song. But how far *can* you see? Think of the farthest away thing you've ever seen. While you might first think of seeing a ship on the horizon, clearly looking up in the sky lets you see farther. You've seen the Moon, which is almost a quarter million miles away.[1] We can also say that the Moon is 1 light second away, since light takes about a second to get here from there. The Sun is 8 light *minutes* away. But the stars are much farther—they are light-*years* away. In fact, there is one that's about 3,000 light-years away that can be seen with your naked eye. But what if I told you that you can see something that's over **2 million light-years away**, without using a telescope? The **Andromeda Galaxy** contains over a hundred billion stars and can be seen with your naked eye. You can see it in late summer and fall, but you'll need a dark sky location, not a large city.

First, turn toward the northern part of the sky and try to find Cassiopeia. This constellation looks like a *3* or a *W*, depending on how it is oriented. The pointy tips of the *W* look a bit like two *V*'s or arrows. The brighter of these *V*'s points to the Andromeda Galaxy. It is about three times the distance between two of the stars in Cassiopeia. You're looking for a faint, fuzzy patch of light that is rather wide.

Once you see it, you can congratulate yourself: this is the farthest distance you'll ever look without using a telescope. Isn't it amazing that our eyes are sensitive enough to see something that is 2.4 million light-years away? To put it another way, those waves of light from the Andromeda Galaxy have been traveling through space (at the speed of light) for 2 million years, and only now they enter your eye and strike your retina to allow your brain to see them. That's quite a journey for them.

Computer programs and cell phone apps can help you find Andromeda and other celestial objects. A few of the more popular ones are Stellarium, TheSky, and StarryNight for computers and StarWalk, SolarWalk, and Sky-Safari for cell phones. Search online for "planetarium software" or "stargazing apps."

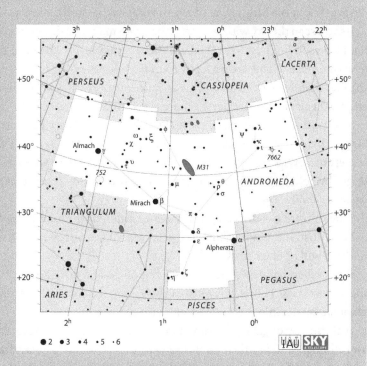

FIGURE 11.3 The constellation Andromeda, showing the location of the Andromeda Galaxy.

---

1 More precisely, the Moon is 239,000 miles, or 384,000 kilometers, away. Amazingly, some old cars have actually driven this distance. If someone has a car with this many miles on its odometer, you can tell them, "You could have driven to the Moon!"

SECTION 2. There are Three Types of Galaxy: Spiral, Elliptical and Irregular

If you have a telescope, you can see many more galaxies besides just Andromeda. Many of the galaxies you would spot would be similar to Andromeda and the Milky Way, spiral galaxies. This type of galaxy always has long, curved structures called **spiral arms**, which make them look like pinwheels and a bit like the images of hurricanes we get from satellites. The spiral arms are simply dense portions of the galaxy, where more stars and gas can be found. All the stars in a spiral galaxy rotate in a disk around the center of that galaxy. However, the spiral arms do not rotate with them; stars move in and out of spiral arms. There are even different types of spiral galaxies. Some have their arms tightly wound, others loosely.

When we view a spiral galaxy, we see its disk from a certain point of view. Some appear face-on, meaning that their swirling spiral arms are in full view. Yet others will be tilted so that all we see is a thin strip of light, much like when we look at the Milky Way in our own skies. They are similar because we must always look at the Milky Way edge-on. We have no choice because we are inside of it.

As you scan the sky with your telescope, you may see a different type of galaxy—one that is round, not flat like a spiral. These are called **elliptical galaxies**. Their overall shape is a bit like a rounded football (or a rugby ball). Some are perfectly round, while others are more stretched out. Their name comes from the fact that if you draw an outline around one of them, it will often look like an ellipse. Unlike spirals, elliptical galaxies are not flat; they are three-dimensional objects.

There aren't quite as many ellipticals as spirals, but they each are just as big. In fact, many are much bigger than most spiral galaxies, including the Milky Way. They typically contain many older stars, sometimes over 1 trillion (1,000,000,000,000) stars! There are even ellipticals that seem to have grown larger by colliding with other galaxies and swallowing them, a process that goes by the creepy name *galactic cannibalism*.

One thing that makes elliptical galaxies different from spirals is that ellipticals don't have very much gas and dust. If you see an elliptical galaxy in your telescope, you'll mostly be looking at stars, and most of them will be older stars.

Remember that new stars are made out of gas and dust. So ellipticals don't have the raw materials to make new stars. This is why most of their stars are old. In this sense, an elliptical galaxy is similar to a globular cluster in our galaxy, except with many more stars.

A third type of galaxy is even more rare than ellipticals. **Irregular galaxies** are smaller than spirals and ellipticals, and as their name implies, don't have any regular shape. In fact, you are already familiar with two irregulars, the Large and Small Magellanic Clouds. These two irregular galaxies are the closest galaxies to the Milky Way. As we discussed before, the Large Magellanic Cloud (LMC) was studied by Henrietta Leavitt, who discovered that Cepheid variable stars can be used as distance indicators (see Chapter 7). The LMC was also the scene of a supernova explosion in 1987.

FIGURE 11.4   Examples of the three types of galaxies. NGC 6814 is a spiral galaxy (a), while M87 (b) is an elliptical galaxy (whose central black hole has recently been imaged). The Large Magellanic Cloud (c), which we discussed in Chapter 7, is an example of an irregular.

SECTION 3. Mapping The Universe:
Clusters and Superclusters of Galaxies

In order to map out the universe, as described in the last section, astronomers need to measure the distances to galaxies near and far. As mentioned, we will typically use units of megaparsecs (Mpc) to measure distances to galaxies. But the measurement strategy cannot rely on parallax, which we used for the nearest stars. Instead, we rely on a standard candle. As discussed in Chapter 7, this term refers to anything whose true luminosity we already know. We can determine the distance to a standard candle by checking how bright or dim it looks. Since we know how bright it *should* look, if it looks dim, that means it is far away. Edwin Hubble used a standard candle, Cepheid variable stars, to measure the distance to the nearby Andromeda Galaxy. But other galaxies are too far away for Cepheids to be seen. We need something brighter: a supernova.

Recall from Chapter 8 that when a white dwarf's mass increases (because matter is being dumped on it by a companion star), it can explode. This Type Ia supernova is so bright, it can be seen all the way across the universe. These explosions all have the same brightness because they always occur when the white dwarf's mass reaches 1.4 M_{Sun}. Therefore, they are good standard candles. Astronomers *love* it when a star in another galaxy explodes. It lets them figure out the distance to this galaxy. If the explosion looks very dim, then the galaxy is far away. If it looks bright, it is closer. This type of stellar explosion, a Type Ia supernova, is now used regularly to find distances to galaxies and to map out the universe.

The Large Magellanic Cloud and the Small Magellanic Cloud are the closest galaxies to our Milky Way. In fact, they are so close that they are gravitationally bound to our galaxy. That means that they orbit around it, slowly, over millions of years. Indeed, the LMC has left a stream of stars connecting it to the Milky Way like a bridge. Oh, and by the way, when I say the LMC is close to us, I mean that it is only about 160,000 light-years away. This might sound like a huge distance, but remember that the Milky Way itself is about 100,000 light-years across. If you think of the Milky Way as a dinner plate, the LMC might be a piece of food on your fork, hovering up above the plate, that you are about to eat. The Small Magellanic Cloud is farther, about 200,000 light-years away. The Andromeda Galaxy would then be another dinner plate in the far corner of the room.

Still, these numbers *are* getting somewhat large and awkward. We need a different unit with which to measure distance. Do you remember **parsecs**? We used them to measure the distances between stars. One parsec is 3.25 light-years. To measure the distance between *galaxies*, we use a much larger unit, the **kiloparsec**. Just as a kilometer is 1,000 meters and a kilogram is 1,000 grams, a kiloparsec (or **kpc** for short) is 1,000 parsecs. The Large Magellanic Cloud is just about 50 kpc away.

TABLE 11.1   DISTANCE-MEASURING UNITS

Unit	Definition	Used to Measure	Comments
kilometer (km)	1,000 meters	distances on Earth	about half a mile (1 km = 0.6 miles)
astronomical unit (AU)	distance from Earth to Sun	planets in our solar system	1 AU = 150,000,000 km
light-year (l.y.)	distance light travels in one year	distance between stars	Nearest other star is 4 light-years away
parsec (pc)	3.25 light-years	distances between stars	a star whose distance is 1 parsec has a parallax of 1 arc second
kiloparsec (kpc)	1,000 parsecs	distance to closest galaxies	Nearest galaxy is 777 kpc away
megaparsec (Mpc)	1 million parsecs (1,000,000 pc)	galaxies across the entire universe!	Farthest known galaxy is 9,800 Mpc away

The LMC and SMC are small, irregular galaxies. The closest full-sized galaxy to the Milky Way is Andromeda. Its distance to us (first measured by Edwin Hubble) is about 2,500,000 light-years. We can simplify this by using better units. In terms of kiloparsecs, Andromeda is 770 kpc away. But, other galaxies are farther away than Andromeda. In fact, we usually measure their distances using **megaparsecs**. A megaparsec (Mpc) is 1 million parsecs.

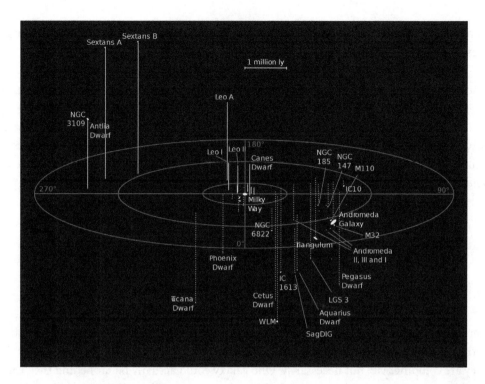

FIGURE 11.5 The Local Group of galaxies contains over 50 galaxies, of which 30 are shown here. Most are small and faint, but three of them: The Milky Way, Andromeda, and the Triangulum Galaxy (M33) contain hundreds of billions of stars.

Taken together, the Milky Way, Andromeda, the LMC, and the SMC comprise a group of galaxies called the **Local Group**. There is one other large galaxy in this group called the Triangulum Galaxy, or M33, and several small irregular galaxies, for a total of perhaps 80 galaxies, most of them small. The Local Group is an example of a **galaxy cluster**. Many galaxies are found together with other galaxies in such clusters.[2] Our Local Group is much smaller than a typical galaxy cluster. Some contain hundreds of galaxies, and others even contain thousands (see Figure 11.4). Remember that each large galaxy in such a cluster could contain 100 billion stars. The total number of stars in a galaxy cluster is mind-boggling!

As astronomers have mapped out the universe, they have discovered an even higher level of organization. Clusters of galaxies themselves seem to group together into *clusters of* clusters. These are called **superclusters**. The largest structures in the universe are irregular arrangements called *walls* and *filaments*. They are strung together in a loose cosmic web. What is peculiar about this arrangement is that the location of the matter (stars, gas, and dust in various galaxies) seems to mostly lie on the edges of enormous **voids** that contain almost nothing. Some people have compared this structure to a sponge you might find in your kitchen sink. The matter that makes up the sponge surrounds openings (holes or voids) that can soak up water. Just why do the largest structures in the universe look like this? That is

---

2   But some galaxies are all by themselves. NASA's Hubble Space Telescope photographed one such "void galaxy," called MCG+01-02-015. Its claim to fame is that it is the "loneliest galaxy in the universe!" (See https://www.nasa.gov/image-feature/goddard/hubble-views-a-lonely-galaxy for more details.)

a question we will consider in the next chapter. Going from smallest to largest, we can summarize the structures that stars can be found in:

star - star cluster - galaxy - galaxy cluster - supercluster - walls and voids - whole universe.

This hierarchy of organization tells us what the universe *looks* like. But a complete understanding includes what the universe is *doing*, or in other words, how galaxies are moving. Of course, spiral galaxies are rotating around their centers. The stars in elliptical galaxies *also* orbit the centers of those galaxies, though not in an organized pattern. But there is another, more wonderful way galaxies move.

SECTION 4. Galaxies Sometimes Collide, but the Universe Is Expanding

With over 100 billion galaxies in the known universe, you might not be surprised if I told you that galaxies sometimes collide. We sometimes see two galaxies right next to each other in the sky. But does this mean they are colliding? No, not necessarily. One galaxy could actually be far behind the other. But if the two galaxies are the *same distance* away from us, then they *must* be colliding, or at least interacting. Watching two galaxies collide is not like witnessing a car crash. These collisions take millions of years to play out. So, even if you watch for a decade or more, you won't see much happen! Instead, the best strategy is to make a **model** of the collision using a computer. In this model, you could simulate each galaxy as a collection of stars, each with a certain mass.[3] Each of these stars would exert gravity on the stars in the other galaxy, with the strongest gravity felt by those stars that are closest to each other. As time goes by, the two interacting galaxies will participate in a bizarre dance, flinging around each other while their bodies are badly distorted (Wheeler 2018). Since it is possible for galaxies to collide, you might be worried about our own home galaxy: will it suffer such a collision?

Before I share the frightening answer, first ask yourself this: how would we know if another galaxy was going to collide with ours? What could we observe? For example, how do you know if a car is on a collision course with you? When you step off the sidewalk to cross a street, you need to be on the lookout for the closest cars, as they are most likely to hit you. Next, you determine which of them are coming toward you and which are going away. Finally, you try to find the direction of motion for these cars. A car coming toward you might still pass harmlessly by if it is not coming *directly* at you.

It turns out that, yes, we in the Milky Way *are on a collision course* with the Andromeda Galaxy! How do we know? First, we measured the distance to Andromeda (about 2 million light-years), and found that it is the closest galaxy to us. Next, we used the **Doppler effect** to show that Andromeda is moving *toward* us. Its spectrum is blueshifted and not redshifted (see Chapter 4). The Doppler effect also lets

---

3   As a practical matter, it would be difficult to simulate all 100 billion stars in a galaxy, even with modern computers. So, researchers in this field (called computational astrophysics) usually create simplified models. You could model a galaxy with 100 points, each representing a billion stars, for example. Most sophisticated models have a larger number of points and also include the effects of gas, dust, and dark matter.

us measure Andromeda's speed and from this we can determine that the collision will take place about 3 billion years from now. So, are you frightened to know that your home galaxy will collide with another galaxy? Well, don't be. First of all, the collision won't happen for 3 billion years, based on the measured speed of Andromeda. Next, the collision might not be head-on, and even if it were, the Earth would be fine. In fact, the odds of a star from Andromeda hitting our Sun—or even entering our solar system—are very low. That's because stars are so small compared to the distances between them. To visualize this, imagine two people on opposite sides of a football or soccer field. If they both throw a grain of sand toward each other, what are the odds of the two sand grains colliding at midfield? As you can see, there's no need to worry about this impending galactic collision. Indeed, we on Earth have many more pressing problems to deal with before then!

The Andromeda Galaxy is moving toward us, but this is not the norm. In the early 20th century, astronomer Vesto Slipher made observations of galaxies at Lowell Observatory in Arizona. The spectra of all these galaxies showed a **redshift**. As you know, this means they are moving away from us; the Doppler effect is stretching the waves of light they emit to longer wavelength. Modern observations confirm Slipher's initial discovery. Galaxy after galaxy shows a redshift in its spectrum. This can only mean one thing: galaxies are moving **away** from us because the universe is **expanding**. In other words, the size of the universe is constantly increasing; the universe is growing larger every moment. In the next chapter, we will explore some of the fascinating implications of the expansion of the universe.

SECTION 5. Dark Matter

Astronomers have done a fantastic job of mapping and exploring the universe around us, finding galaxies, clusters of galaxies, and more. With our techniques to measure the enormous distances (in megaparsecs), you might just think that we've got everything worked out. But you'd be wrong. Now is the time that I have to confess that we astronomers are in the dark—literally—about most of the universe. In this book, I've been careful to share with you *how* we learned what we know about the universe. So, now I'll have to share *how* we know what we *don't* know!

It starts with someone who was a friend of mine. When I got out of college, I moved to Washington, DC, to do research. I had just finished my PhD at UCLA and started a postdoctoral research position at the Carnegie Institution.[4] One of the first people I met there was Vera Rubin, an astronomer, who invited me to join a lunch club she founded there many years before. Scientists of all different types would meet for lunch, cook for each other, and talk about their research, about politics, or whatever. Rubin was approaching retirement then, but she told me about the groundbreaking discovery she had made years before.

In the 1970s, she used spectroscopy to measure the speed of different parts of the Andromeda Galaxy. Spiral galaxies rotate around their centers, and people thought of them as roughly similar to a huge solar

---

4 If you want to become an astronomer, after you finish your bachelor's degree, you'll usually go on to earn a PhD (doctor of philosophy degree), which requires you to do original research. The next step is often a temporary research position called a postdoc (for postdoctoral). Some astronomers then try to become a professor at a university. But there are many other paths.

system. By measuring the speed, or velocity, of different parts of a rotating galaxy, we can figure out how it is rotating. If we make a graph of our results, this graph is called a **rotation curve**. There are actually several different ways something could be rotating. Here are some examples.

First Example: Take a simple merry-go-round that children play on. Which part of it rotates faster, the center or the edge? To answer this question, imagine the merry-go-round has upright metal bars and you accidentally put your head in front of one of them while standing next to the merry-go-round. If your head gets hit by one of the outer bars, it would hurt a lot more than if you leaned all the way in and got hit by one of the inner bars. The center of the merry-go-round hardly moves at all, but the outside moves quite fast. To make a rotation curve for a merry-go-round, we graph its speed (velocity, *v*) at different distances outward. Each of these different distances is the radius (*r*) of a larger and larger circle. A merry-go-round is a solid body. Like all solid bodies, its rotation curve is a straight line. The farther from the center (higher *r*), the faster (higher *v*). See Figure 11.6a.

Second Example: The solar system rotates, or at least its planets rotate around the Sun. Take a moment and make a guess for yourself. Which planet in the solar system do you think moves the fastest? Is it the outermost planet, Pluto?[5] Is it Jupiter, the largest planet? Could it be Earth? Do you have your guess? Okay. The fastest planet in the solar system is Mercury, the *closest* planet to the Sun. Ancient peoples noticed how fast Mercury moves, and some named the planet after a messenger god who had wings on his feet.

The reason Mercury moves fastest is that it feels the strongest gravity because it is closest to the Sun. You might say it has to be moving this fast to avoid falling into the Sun. Or you could recall Kepler's Second Law, which says that individual planets move fastest when they are closest to the Sun. All planets move slower the farther they are from the Sun, and Pluto moves slower than any of the planets in the solar system. The rotation curve for the solar system (Figure 11.6b) shows that planets close to the Sun

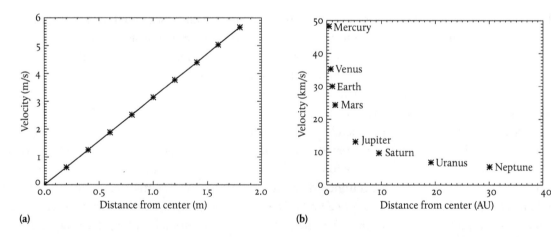

(a)   **(b)**

FIGURE 11.6 A rotation curve is a way to see how fast something is rotating. A merry-go-round is a solid body. The outer parts of it are rotating faster than the inside (a). The planets of our solar system also rotate, around the Sun. However, the fastest planet is the one closest to the Sun, Mercury (b). This is because the solar system, unlike a merry-go-round, is held together by gravity, which gets weaker with distance.

---

5   Oops, I almost forgot. Pluto is now considered a dwarf planet. If we don't consider Pluto as a planet, then the outermost planet is Neptune.

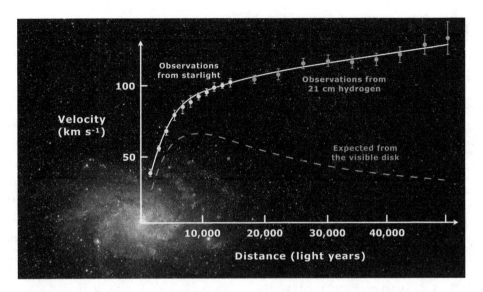

FIGURE 11.7   Rotation curve of a galaxy. The dots show the rotation speed of different parts of the galaxy. The outside is rotating faster, unlike the case for the solar system (Figure 11.6b) This implies that galaxies contain a huge amount of dark matter. Vera Rubin produced the rotation curve of a galaxy.

move faster than planets far from the Sun. This is quite different from the merry-go-round's rotation curve. That's because a merry-go-round is held together by steel, while the solar system is held together by the gravity of the Sun. Indeed, the graph looks the way it does because nearly all the mass in the solar system (about 99.9 percent) is in the Sun.

So, what would you expect the rotation curve of a whole galaxy to look like? In the 1970s, no one knew for sure, but most people suspected it would look something like the solar system's rotation curve, with the center of the galaxy moving fast and the outer parts moving slowly. This is where Vera Rubin comes in. To measure the rotation curve of the Andromeda Galaxy, she first measured light from the center of the galaxy, then a little farther out, then all the way out at the edges. For each of these measurements, she carefully pointed a telescope to the region of interest, let light pass into a spectrograph, and obtained a spectrum. Each spectrum shows absorption lines (see Chapter 4), which, when analyzed, can reveal that part of the galaxy's speed. This last step required Rubin to use the Doppler formula, as we discussed in Chapter 4. When she was done, she published the first rotation curve of the Andromeda Galaxy with her collaborator Kent Ford.

Her results were stunning. Andromeda did *not* rotate like the solar system; *nor* did it rotate like a merry-go-round. Instead, it rotated quickly near the central regions **and** quickly near the edge also! In fact, it appeared to be rotating so fast that it should fly apart! People found this odd and initially criticized her result. But it was confirmed by later observations of other galaxies as well. This new discovery showed that *something* was holding galaxies together. But what was it? It couldn't be the stars in the galaxy. We can easily see them and estimate their mass. They do *not* have enough mass to create the gravity required to hold a galaxy together. We can also see gas and dust in these galaxies, but there's not enough of it to explain why they hold together. There appears to be matter in galaxies that we cannot see but which has enough mass to hold the galaxy together via gravity. It is usually called **dark matter**, but I like to call it

FIGURE 11.8 Vera Rubin examines a slide with a spectrum of a galaxy.

invisible matter. ("Dark" things absorb light, but astronomical dark matter doesn't interact with light at all!) Rubin had thus discovered that galaxies must be filled with an unknown, unseen substance. If not, then they would fly apart. The amount of dark matter needed was stunning—nearly 10 times *more* dark matter exists than normal matter.

Vera Rubin's study of the rotation curve of Andromeda opened the way to the study of a whole new field, dark matter research. Astronomers have found dark matter in hundreds of galaxies, in clusters of galaxies, and even in our own Milky Way.[6] To this day, we still don't know what exactly dark matter is. It must be something that has mass but gives off no light. Black holes come to mind, or perhaps neutron stars. Both have large mass and give off no visible light. However, both of these come from stars, which we can see, and even count (roughly). The number of stars is too small for black holes or neutron stars to be part of dark matter. Brown dwarfs were once thought to make up a part of the dark matter, assuming that there were a huge number of them going undetected. However, we have now discovered enough brown dwarfs to know that they don't make up a large part of this mysterious dark matter. A better candidate, strange as it seems, is small invisible particles, like neutrinos. If there are enough of them, they could have enough mass to exert gravity on an entire galaxy and keep it from flying apart as it rotates rapidly.

The topic of dark matter is so important to modern astronomy that in 2019 the Nobel Prize in Physics was awarded to Jim Peebles for his research in dark matter. Vera Rubin could not have received the award that year because she died in 2016, but she could have received the award anytime during her life after making the discovery. Why didn't she get the Nobel Prize? It is not much of a stretch to imagine that sexism played a role here, as it did at other times in Rubin's career. For example, in the late 1940s, she was prohibited from studying astronomy at Princeton University because they didn't accept women.[7] Nevertheless, in 2021 a new, cutting-edge $500-million telescope was completed to discover and learn more about dark matter. Funding came mostly from government agencies in the United States. The US Congress voted to name the telescope in honor of Vera Rubin.[8]

In the decades since Rubin's discovery, more evidence for dark matter has come in from other methods. One of those is called **gravitational lensing**. The lenses you wear on your eyes (and the lenses *in* your eyes) bend light to focus it, but light can also be bent by gravity (as Einstein predicted in the early 1900s).

6 In fact, there were hints of dark matter before Rubin's discovery. Dutch astronomer Jacobus Kapteyn, who mapped the Milky Way, suggested that nearby stars were moving faster than could be explained by gravity from the mass of nearby stars. Also, Fritz Zwicky, a Swiss immigrant to the United States, noticed motions in the Coma Cluster of galaxies that could best be explained by the presence of unseen mass.

7 Twenty years later, the benefits of a Princeton education were *still* only available to men (Thomson-DeVeaux 2016).

8 https://www.vro.org

If light from a *far-off* galaxy first passes by a *close-by* galaxy with high mass, that light will bend because the mass of a galaxy *curves the space* that the light passes through. When we view this light from the right location, the light rays will be focused, as if we are using a magnifying glass. The light can also be distorted to produce two, three, or more images of the original galaxy. This is roughly similar to the way a curvy mirror distorts your image at a funhouse or carnival. Gravitational lensing depends on mass: the more the mass, the more the distortion. In fact, an entire **cluster of galaxies** can cause gravitational lensing. By studying these distortions, astronomers can measure the mass present in galaxies and clusters. What they find is that the amount of mass is much larger than what we see. Clusters of galaxies must also be full of dark matter, just like galaxies themselves. We now understand that 90 percent of the mass in the universe is dark.

These discoveries change our understanding of galaxies. Instead of simply thinking of them as beautiful swirling disks of stars or large elliptical balls, we now realize that every large galaxy is really a shining patch of light embedded in a much larger halo of dark matter. What we are seeing is only the tip of a massive, dark iceberg. A galaxy, embedded in dark matter, is like the visible tip of an iceberg that is mostly underwater. As our understanding of the universe grows, we realize there is so much we still don't know. That's fine with scientists like me. Our job is to discover new things that nobody knew about the universe, as Vera Rubin said in the quote that begins this chapter. If we already knew everything, then scientists would have nothing to do! We like to explore the unknown. In the next chapter, we will see how close astronomers have come to understanding the greatest unknown of all: the origin of the universe.

WRAP-UP

One of the interesting aspects of science is that the more we discover, the more we realize how limited and narrow-minded our previous thinking was. Humans first assumed that our Earth was at the center of the solar system, then assumed that our Sun was at the center of our galaxy. Both "self-centered" ideas were wrong. In this chapter, we broadened our view much more, recognizing that our galaxy, the Milky Way, is not special, but is one member of a group of galaxies, which is part of a cluster of hundreds of galaxies, which is part of a supercluster of thousands of galaxies. Some of these look like the Milky Way since they are spirals, but others are quite different, elliptical and irregular galaxies. We also realized we were making another mistake—neglecting the possibility that a large part of the universe might not give off any light at all. This possibility, that the vast majority of the matter in the universe is dark, was made an observed reality by the pioneering discoveries of Vera Rubin. In astronomy, it pays to be humble. You might just discover that the universe was more elaborate and wonderful than you previously thought possible.

REFLECTION QUESTIONS

1. Scientific discoveries often lead to other discoveries. Discuss how in 1924, Edwin Hubble found the distance to the Andromeda Galaxy by making use of the distance indicator discovered by Henrietta Leavitt in 1908.

2. If someone asked "What is dark matter?" What would you say? What evidence did Vera Rubin use in her discovery of dark matter? Can you make an analogy to help your friend understand how it is possible to detect something that can't be seen?

BIBLIOGRAPHY

Corbelli, E., and Salucci, P. "The Extended Rotation Curve and the Dark Matter Halo of M33." *Monthly Notices of the Royal Astronomical Society* 311, no. 2 (January 2000): 441–447. https://doi.org/10.1046/j.1365-8711.2000.03075.x

Thomson-DeVeaux, Amelia. "When Women Came to Princeton." *Princeton Alumni Weekly* (October 6, 2016). https://paw.princeton.edu/article/when-women-came-princeton

Wheeler, P. "New Simulation Shows What Happens When the Milky Way and Andromeda Galaxies Collide." *SciTechDaily* (February 20, 2018). https://scitechdaily.com/simulation-shows-what-happens-when-the-milky-way-and-andromeda-galaxies-collide/

Young, Kelly. "Andromeda galaxy hosts a trillion stars." *New Scientist*. (6 June 2006) https://www.newscientist.com/article/dn9282-andromeda-galaxy-hosts-a-trillion-stars/

CREDITS

COSMOLOGY

It is far better to grasp the universe as it really is than to persist in delusion, however satisfying and reassuring.

—Carl Sagan

This is it! We are now ready to explore the ultimate limits of human understanding. To delve as far into space as anyone ever has. In this book, we started with planets in our solar system, then explored our Sun, stars, our galaxy, other galaxies, and dark matter. We will now discuss **cosmology**—the study of the universe as a whole. The name of this field comes from *cosmos*, which means the whole universe.[1] We will study the origin of the universe, which has long been a topic of interest in religion and philosophy. You already know that when we look out in space, we look back in time. But how far back *can* we look? And what would you see? How old is the universe? Does it even *have* an age, or as some philosophers suggest, is it infinitely old? What is the farthest away thing humans have ever seen? You are about to find out. We'll also try to figure out how the universe will end. Will it continue to fly apart forever? Or will it ultimately collapse upon itself? It is amazing to me that we can actually address such profound age-old philosophical questions scientifically.

---

1   The meaning of *cosmos* has changed. In ancient mythology and philosophy, Cosmos (Κοσμοσ in Greek) represented the created universe and contrasted with Chaos (Χαοσ), a sort of disordered nothingness from which the universe began. *Cosmos* (1980) is also the name of a science program I saw on TV that inspired me to become an astronomer. It was hosted by Carl Sagan. More recently, Neil deGrasse Tyson remade the program into an intriguing TV series, *Cosmos: A Spacetime Odyssey* (2014). Both are well worth watching.

SECTION 1. The Universe Has No Edge or Center

Cosmology is the study of the universe. But what do we mean by *universe*? Astronomers use the word to mean *everything*—all matter, all energy, all space, and all time. If something exists, it is part of the universe. So, we can immediately say that there is no edge of the universe. There can't be a wall that separates things that are "inside" the universe from things that are "outside" it. Anything outside that wall would be considered part of the universe too. All the things you've ever thought about have an inside and an outside ... but not the universe. This shows that we need to expand our ways of thinking when we talk about the whole universe.

There *is* a sense in which we can speak of an edge to the universe, but it is not a physical barrier or wall. Since the universe is only 13.8 billion years old, light from galaxies more than 13.8 billion *light-years* away will not have had time to travel to us. Those galaxies exist, but we just don't see them because their light has not arrived yet. Perhaps one day in the future, we will see them appear! It is sometimes useful to speak of the **observable universe**, meaning everything we can see. The edge of the observable universe is called the **cosmic horizon**. We discuss the cosmic horizon (and a problem with it) later.

Space and time are part of the universe, and they are intertwined in Einstein's relativity theory. Indeed, as we saw when discussing black holes, space and time can bend and stretch, influenced by mass. The universe is expanding. We know this because the galaxies are moving away from us. But another way to describe this is to say that the space between the galaxies is *stretching out*. If you imagine a rubber balloon with dots painted on it, then you will notice that when you inflate the balloon, the dots will get farther and farther apart from each other. The dots represent galaxies; as the universe expands, each galaxy moves away from every other galaxy. Here in the Milky Way, we see other galaxies moving away from us. But other beings in far-off galaxies would see the same thing. For this reason, we cannot say that any one galaxy is at the center of the expanding universe. They all are! Indeed, the atoms and matter that make up every galaxy, including the Milky Way, including the matter inside your body, were all present at the beginning of the universe, in some form.

Usually, when there is an expansion, we can expect an answer to the question, "Where is the center of the expansion?" But not always, and not in this case. It might help to consider this question: "Which country is at the center of the Earth?" In ancient times, when people thought of the Earth as flat, some people considered their country the center of the world. But since we know the Earth is a sphere, we can now see that this question is meaningless. No country is at the center of Earth because all countries are on Earth's surface. As we understand the universe more deeply, we realize that some of the questions we might ask about it really don't make sense.

SECTION 2. The Expansion of the Universe Tells Us Its Age

Recall that Vesto Slipher had already measured redshifts for many of these galaxies, proving that they are moving away, and thus that the universe is expanding. If the universe is getting larger now, then it was smaller in the past. This leads to a profound conclusion: *the universe had a beginning.* If you play the movie of the universe backward, eventually everything in the universe gets closer and closer until it was all at one point. That moment is the **origin of the universe**.

After this discovery, Edwin Hubble measured the distance to many of these galaxies. He found a simple but remarkable pattern; the close galaxies (only a few Mpc from us) moved away from us slowly, while the most distant galaxies were flying away at a much higher speed. We can describe Hubble's discovery simply by saying "the farthest galaxies move fastest." It was a discovery with profound consequences because he measured the *rate of expansion* of the universe. Mathematically, Hubble found that a galaxy's velocity (v) is proportional to its distance (d). We can write this as a small equation that is now known as Hubble's Law:

$$v = H * d.$$

In this equation, "H" is a constant of proportionality. We now call it the Hubble constant. This constant measures *how fast* the universe is expanding, and it helps us answer one of the oldest questions ever—when did the universe begin? (Since we usually measure distance in megaparsecs and velocity in kilometers per second, the value of H is measured in wacky units, km/s/Mpc.)

To see the connection between the rate of expansion and the age of the universe (an amount of time), consider two cars that are traveling at different rates of speed. If you see them both arrive at your destination and you know they both traveled the same distance, then you'll know for sure that the faster car took less time to get there. This same logic can be applied to the universe. Since the universe is expanding now, it must have been smaller in the past. At some point in the past, all galaxies would have been at the same place. This represents the origin of the universe, and the time since then (call it t_u)is the **age of the universe**. Now, anything that's moving will cover a distance, *d*, in an amount of time that depends on its speed. For example, if you need to drive 120 miles and can go 60 miles per hour, how long will it take? To answer this simple question, you use an equation: $d = v * t$. Distance = velocity times time. If we are interested in the amount of time, then we can also write this equation as $t = d/v$. This is probably how you figured out that the time to travel 120 miles is 2 hours, because 2 hours = 120 miles divided by 60 miles per hour. Let's apply this same logic to the universe.

The time it has taken for a galaxy to get to its present location is the age of the universe, t_u. This relates to the galaxy's distance and speed (v) in the same way as with the car:

$$t_u = d/v.$$

But now we can use Hubble's Law ($v = H * d$) and substitute *v* into this equation, giving

$$t_u = d/(H * d)$$

$$t_u = 1/H.$$

This equation shows that the age of the universe (t_u) is *inversely proportional* to the Hubble constant (H). The larger H is the smaller the age of the universe is. This makes sense because H measures the *rate of expansion* of the universe. If something moves at a high rate (like a fast car), then it gets where it is going in a short time. But what exactly is the value of the Hubble constant, H?

Hubble's observations in the early 20th century provided a first estimate, but this turned out to be way off; they relied on distance estimates later realized to be faulty. The first scientifically solid measurement of the Hubble constant was made in the late 20th century by a team of 30 astronomers led by Wendy Freedman, who worked at the Carnegie Observatories in California. They measured Cepheid stars to get accurate distances to some 24 galaxies. They used the most famous telescope for this project, the Hubble Space Telescope, launched in space by NASA.[2] Freedman's team provided the first accurate measurement of the Hubble constant, about 70 km/s/Mpc. This measurement allowed humans for the first time to discover how old the universe is. We live in a universe that is about **14 billion years old**. To put things in perspective, our galaxy formed around 10 billion years ago; our solar system formed around 5 billion years ago; and humans began to evolve in Africa about 3 *million* years ago, which is only 0.02 percent of the age of the universe.

(a)

(b)

FIGURE 12.1   Wendy Freedman (a) led a team of astronomers using the Hubble Space Telescope (b) to measure the expansion of the universe.

Nowadays, since the Hubble constant has been measured so well, we can use it as a way to measure the distance to a galaxy far, far away. Edwin Hubble showed that a galaxy's velocity (v) is determined by its distance (d):

$$v = H_0\, d.$$

But this equation (Hubble's Law) can be solved for distance:

$$d = v/H_0.$$

Now that we know the Hubble constant (H_0), we just need to measure the galaxy's redshift and calculate its velocity. We can then calculate its distance using Hubble's Law.

At this point, it might seem like we astronomers have the universe figured out. After all, we can measure the distances to galaxies (in units of megaparsecs). Astronomers have used this method to conduct surveys of thousands of galaxies and map their locations. In fact, this is how the large-scale structures,

---

2   I think it's cool that a telescope named for Hubble was used to measure Hubble's constant!

such as walls and voids, were discovered. Thus, the discovery of the value of H_0 by Freedman and her team led to many other discoveries. This is an example of a general principle of science: once something is discovered, this information leads us to more discoveries. Another example was Henrietta Leavitt's discovery of Cepheid stars' important role in measuring cosmic distances. This led Shapley to measure the distances to the globular clusters and thus find our place in the Milky Way Galaxy. Leavitt's discovery also led to Hubble's measurement of the distance to the Andromeda Galaxy.

SECTION 3. The Universe Began Hot and Dense

Around 14 billion years ago, all matter in the universe was in the same place. It then blasted outward to create the expanding universe we observe today. This event, the origin of the universe, is called the **Big Bang** (for lack of a better name). The Big Bang theory is the scientific explanation of the origin of the universe. The first thing we can say about the Big Bang is that if all the matter in the universe was in the same place, then the **density** would be enormous. The Big Bang would also be incredibly hot because a huge amount of energy would have been confined to a small volume. If you want to think of the Big Bang as an explosion that started the universe, that's okay. However, there's one difference: every other explosion we can think of occurred in one place and blasted out into the surrounding area. This Big Bang didn't explode out into the universe: the Big Bang *was* the universe. That's why we can't point to any place in our current universe and say, "the Big Bang happened there." No. It happened everywhere.

As the universe expanded, it cooled down. When something cools down, its properties change. If you imagine steam from a boiling pot of water outdoors on a day when the temperature is below freezing, then you can contemplate several such **phase changes**. First, the steam will condense on some surface as liquid water. Then, this water will freeze solid into ice. Steam, water, and ice are three phases of the same substance (H_2O). Similarly, the universe begins hot and dense, then goes through phases as it expands. I'll now share with you some of what we know about the phases that led to the universe we see today. Frankly, it is amazing to me that we can understand what the universe was like so long ago. But as we'll see, the conditions back then were much simpler than those today, and we can make observations today that tell us what things were like back then. Still, the universe's very first moment remains a mystery.

Phase 0: The Mysterious Origin

The very first moment[3] of the universe was so hot and so dense that our current theories of physics cannot describe the situation. All theories must be tested by observations and experiments, and we do not have the ability to create such experiments. We just can't create temperatures that high in a lab. It is thought, however, that during this time, the four forces of nature (gravity, electricity, and the strong and weak nuclear forces) would have united and behaved as one force. This force would have acted on particles that are even more fundamental than the ones we know today. Not even protons could have existed at this time!

---

3   There is a technical definition of "first moment." It is called the Planck time and consists of a staggeringly small amount of time after the Big Bang but lasting only 10^{-44} seconds. That is, just about 0.00000000000000000000000000000000000000000001 seconds.

Another mystery is, "what caused the Big Bang?" We think of the Big Bang as the origin of space and time. If time *began* at the Big Bang, then *there was no before*. Still, some scientists are creating theories they hope could explain what caused the origin of the universe.

Phase 1: The First Matter

In the beginning of the universe, there was light. The universe was filled with photons of very high energy, such as X-rays and gamma rays. Since radiation is another word for light, we say the universe was **radiation dominated**. But as the universe expanded, it became cooler and cooler, allowing matter to form. As you know, mass can convert into energy; this is what's powering the Sun right now. But energy can also convert into matter. When we observe this process happening today, we always find that the matter is produced in pairs of particles, one positive, one negative; for example, an electron (e^-) and a positron (e^+). The positron is an example of **antimatter**, which we discussed in Chapter 5. Recall that when matter touches antimatter, they both are destroyed, producing energy. The strange thing about the early universe is that somehow it must have produced *slightly*[4] more matter than antimatter. The antimatter produced in the early universe would have destroyed an equal amount of normal matter. But somehow, when the dust settled, there was still some matter left. Scientists still can't explain this imbalance. But we're lucky it turned out that way. The normal matter left over from this colossal destruction is what became *us* and *everything we see today*!

I find this description of the early universe both bizarre and fascinating. And I'm amazed that there actually are ways to test these ideas. One strategy is to try to re-create the conditions present just after the Big Bang and study them. Since the temperatures were so high then, everything had very high energy. The best way to give particles high energy today is to accelerate them using powerful machines called **particle accelerators** (also called atom smashers). One such machine is the Large Hadron Collider (LHC) in Europe. Scientists using the LHC created a particle that had never been seen before, the so-called Higgs boson, for which they won the Nobel Prize in 2013. Discoveries like these help us understand the Big Bang. In any case, it didn't take long for the universe to cool enough to become **matter dominated**.

Phase 2: The First Elements

As you know, the different elements are distinguished from each other by what's in their nucleus. Carbon has 6 protons in its nucleus, while oxygen has 8. The nucleus is the most important part of the atom, so before the universe could even build atoms, nuclei had to be created first. The process of building, or synthesizing, a nucleus, is called **nucleosynthesis**. How did this happen? Well, for a short time early on, the entire universe was as hot as the inside of a star. As you have learned, stars use nuclear reactions to create new elements. That's what the whole universe did when it was about 10 seconds old. Starting with protons and neutrons, the universe gave us the elements hydrogen, helium, and lithium, as well as an isotope of hydrogen called deuterium. These are the first three elements on the periodic table, the lightest and simplest ones. But that's it. A few minutes later, the universe had cooled so much that nuclear reactions were now impossible and no new elements were made. All other elements, such as gold, silver, oxygen, and carbon, were created by stars and were not present at the origin of the universe.

---

4   By "slightly," I mean that there was only 0.000000001 percent more regular matter than antimatter. But that tiny difference proved crucial.

Phase 3: The First Atoms

An atom has a nucleus plus some number of electrons orbiting around that nucleus. But once the universe formed the first nuclei, it didn't form atoms right away. That's because it was too hot. The center of the Sun is also too hot to form atoms. Instead, the electrons that would normally cling to the nucleus of some atoms float freely in what we call a plasma state. We mentioned before that a plasma is high-energy gas in which the electrons are stripped away from the atoms. Heat is nothing more than fast motions of atoms. In a plasma, the atoms move so fast that when they collide, the electrons get bumped off. During this time, any *light* in the universe had a hard time getting anywhere. A photon of light would not travel far before it collided with an electron, which would easily scatter it. If you were there in the early universe, it would be like you were inside a thick fog. You wouldn't be able to see things even a few inches/centimeters away from you.

However, the universe was cooling down, which means that at some point, the temperature was low enough for electrons to join the nuclei and form the first atoms. Our best estimate is that this happened about 370,000 years after the Big Bang, forming the first atoms. If you were alive then, you would finally be able to see for the first time, as the "fog" of the early universe cleared. To be able to see means that light can travel great distances. If this part of the Big Bang theory is correct, then the light from this early time should stream freely through the universe and should even be around us today! After being produced by the hot afterglow of the Big Bang, this light would have traveled for about 13.8 billion years to reach us. During this time, the universe has expanded, so the light waves would be stretched out (redshifted) into the microwave part of the spectrum. This, then, is one of the best ways to *test* the Big Bang theory. If the theory is correct, we should see a **cosmic microwave background** coming from all parts of space.

The first direct evidence for this cosmic microwave background (CMB) came completely by accident. In the 1960s, two researchers, Robert Wilson and Arno Penzias, were developing a new communication technology at a lab in New Jersey. They set up a special antenna to collect microwave light waves. While testing it, they noticed a strange signal. Figuring it was a problem with their instrument, they looked inside and found a bird had made a nest in the antenna. After cleaning the nest out, the signal mysteriously remained! They pointed the telescope in different directions to see if the signal was coming from the Sun, for example, or from one of the planets. It is not. This signal is coming from *everywhere*! Eventually, they realized that they were actually observing the Big Bang. Or at least the moment 460,000 years after it when the CMB was formed. They later won the Nobel Prize for this discovery, which they made by accident!

The phases we just discussed represent our best current understanding of how the universe began, according to the Big Bang theory. Next, we'll review evidence for this theory and see that it has encountered some challenges.

SECTION 4. Challenges to the Big Bang Theory

Like any good theory, the Big Bang theory makes predictions that can be tested. Here are three of them:

1. The universe is expanding, starting from an initial "explosion";
2. The universe is filled with light called the cosmic microwave background, which is the afterglow of the Big Bang;
3. The universe should contain H, He, and Li, elements formed in the Big Bang in specific proportions.

All three of these predictions have been confirmed by observations. We discussed observations of the expanding universe and the CMB (predictions 1 and 2 above) before. But prediction number 3 of the Big Bang theory has also been confirmed. Using the most powerful telescopes in the world, astronomers have been able to find hydrogen, helium, and lithium in the most ancient galaxies and in proportions predicted by the theory. For example, the theory predicts that the Big Bang will produce about 75 percent hydrogen, 25 percent helium, and a much smaller fraction of lithium.[5] All these have been confirmed by observations.

But scientific theories are constantly challenged by new observations and new data. As time went on, astronomers found evidence that challenged their current understanding of the universe. One thing that seemed odd was the fact that the cosmic microwave background seemed to be perfectly smooth. The reason this is odd is that our universe today is *not* smooth. It has large lumps of stars, called galaxies, and it has clusters of galaxies separated by large voids. Since the CMB tells us what the universe was like just after its beginning, the question arose, "How did a smooth universe turn into the clumpy universe we have today?"

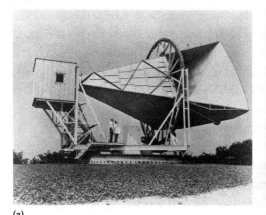

(a)   (b)

FIGURE 12.2   We can actually observe the Big Bang with these unusual telescopes, capable of detecting microwaves from space. In the 1960's, the Bell Labs Horn Antenna (a) was used to discover the Cosmic Microwave Background (CMB, light coming from the early universe.) To better view the CMB, space telescopes have been launched, including NASA missions like COBE, which discovered that the early universe was 'clumpy', and WMAP (b), which produced a detailed map of those 'clumps', shown in Fig. 12.3. Together with the European Space Agency's *Planck* spacecraft (which finished its mission in 2013), these projects help us humans understand how our universe began.

To answer this question, NASA launched a telescope in space in 1990. The Cosmic Background Explorer (COBE) satellite's purpose was just to study the CMB. This satellite had a special telescope designed to detect microwaves from deep space. Its first result was to measure the temperature of the universe. By detecting light of several different wavelengths, COBE found that the early universe is producing

---

5   These percentages come from what we know about nuclear reactions and how they depend on temperature. They represent the number of atoms of each element, divided by the total number of particles.

more light with a wavelength of 1.1 millimeters. Remember that in Chapter 4 we saw that such a peak wavelength (λ_{max}) can be used to measure the temperature of whatever is producing the light. Since this wavelength is rather large (about 2,000 times larger than the Sun's peak wave length), we would expect from Wien's law that the temperature would be that much smaller. The COBE satellite measured the current temperature of the universe to be 2.7 K. This means that the universe is just about 3 degrees above the lowest possible temperature.[6]

But the most important discovery COBE made was a map showing the amount of microwave light coming to us from every part of the sky. Unlike any previous measurement, this map showed that the cosmic microwave background was NOT smooth. As shown in Figure 12.3, there is a different amount of light coming from each part of the sky. Since the CMB comes from the early universe, this means that the early universe *was* clumpy after all, but the clumpiness was too subtle to have been seen by earlier, ground-based observations. Microwaves are partly absorbed by water vapor, so in this case it was crucial to conduct observations above Earth's atmosphere, in space where this wasn't a problem. The discovery of these fluctuations in the CMB allowed us to paint a new picture of the universe.

Not long after the Big Bang, we now can see that the universe had a lumpy look. Believe it or not, these lumps are thought to have begun as quantum fluctuation smaller than atoms. But they grew as the universe expanded. Gravity played an important role in bringing more and more mass together. After many years, the clumps had grown in size to become not just stars but galaxies and clusters of galaxies. This solved the mystery that prompted NASA to launch this satellite in the first place. The lumpy nature of our present universe has been there all along. Using computer simulations, cosmologists have been able to show that the patterns of an early clumpy universe can, given time, lead directly to the galaxies, clusters, and superclusters of galaxies we see today.

So, after years of observations, from the earliest telescopic views of other galaxies, to the spectroscopic observations showing the universe expanding, to space-based telescopes that can detect microwaves, we can finally tell a story that humans have been fascinated by for thousands of years—the story of what happened when the universe began. A hot, dense explosion of matter and energy expanded outward and cooled, consolidating into atoms, then stars, then galaxies and clusters. The afterglow of this intense moment (when the first atoms formed) is still visible today as the cosmic microwave background, and it contains clues to how all the large structures we see around us came to be. The ability to scientifically describe the origin of the universe is quite an accomplishment. However, there are still important parts of this story that scientists have not figured out. We don't know the physics of the earliest, hottest moment of the universe. We don't know what dark matter is and exactly what role it played in the formation of large structures in the universe.

So, research into the origin of the universe continues. Since the COBE satellite discovered that the CMB is not perfectly smooth, two more satellites have been launched to study the CMB in more detail. NASA launched the WMAP mission in 2001, and the European Space Agency launched the Planck satellite in 2009. And in 2022, NASA announced a new mission, SphereX, to study light from the early universe. The final section of this chapter will describe some recent cosmological discoveries.

---

6 Absolute zero, which is 0.0 K on the Kelvin scale (–273°C or –460°F).

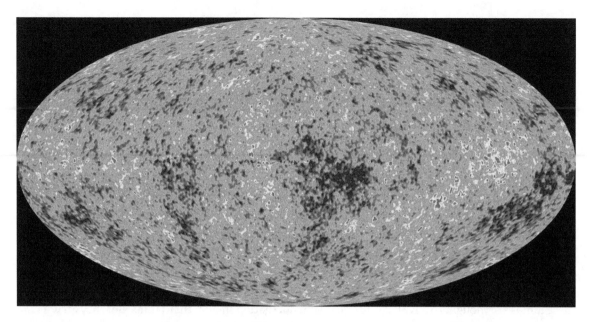

FIGURE 12.3   The cosmic microwave background, light coming from the origin of the universe, was first discovered by NASA's COBE satellite. This image (from the later WMAP mission) shows light emitted just after the Big Bang. The brighter areas had more matter, so they went on to become galaxies and clusters of galaxies.

SECTION 5. The Fate of the Universe

Another topic humans wondered about for centuries is the end of the universe. There's a wide range in philosophical traditions on this topic. Some predict catastrophe and apocalypse at the end, while others offer salvation, redemption, or bliss. Some offer both. The scientific study of what will eventually happen to the universe begins with the observed fact that the universe is expanding now. This expansion will either continue or it will stop. If it *does* stop, then the universe could reverse itself and start to shrink. What would cause this? Gravity. All the mass in all the clusters of galaxies (including huge quantities of dark matter) exerts gravity, which tugs on other galaxies. This could slow down the expansion, just like gravity slows down a ball that's thrown upward until the ball reverses direction and starts to head downward. Balancing the outward expansion of the universe with the force of gravity, astronomers envisioned three possible scenarios, which go by the following names:

open universe—expansion continues
closed universe—expansion stops and universe contracts
flat universe—something in between open and closed

In the first scenario, the universe could continue to expand if gravity is not strong enough to halt the expansion. This is what would happen if the universe didn't have enough mass to create the gravity needed to stop the expansion. In this case, the expansion would continue with galaxies getting farther and farther away. Eventually, galaxies that we see now would be so far away that we couldn't see them.

Individual galaxies, including the Milky Way, would probably remain together because their mass is so concentrated. But the distances between them would increase forever until the last one disappeared off the cosmic horizon. It would be a lonely end to the universe.

On the other hand, if the universe has enough mass, then gravity will pull the galaxies back together. In this case, we say the universe is **closed**. At some point, billions of years in the future, the present expansion will come to a halt and the expansion will turn into a contraction. Galaxies will come closer and closer together. Astronomers alive then would see light from such galaxies *blueshifted* instead of *redshifted*. Eventually, these galaxies would be pulled together into a high-density state similar to what happened during the Big Bang. This ending scenario is called the **Big Crunch**. What would happen next is anybody's guess. Since the conditions of the Big Bang (temperature and pressure) would likely be repeated, some have speculated that a new Big Bang would occur, starting a whole new universe, perhaps with new physical laws even. These notions are pure speculation currently, but I must admit the prospect of a cyclic universe that repeats expansions and contractions over vast periods of time has a certain appeal to me.

The third possibility that cosmologists considered, the so-called **flat universe**, can be thought of as a compromise between the two scenarios above. The universe would expand but gradually slow down. As the galaxies got farther and farther away, they would eventually coast to a stop, but only after they had slowly drifted extremely far from each other—so far that gravity would not be able to pull them back together. In this scenario, the galaxies don't fly apart at top speed, but the ending is just as lonely as in the open universe.

At this point, let's take a pause and reflect on these scenarios. Which would you prefer? Would you rather live in a universe that will eventually close in on itself? Perhaps not, if you are claustrophobic. Are you okay with the idea of galaxies drifting infinitely far away into space? Or does that seem too cold, dark, and lonely? If you got to choose what kind of universe we live in, which would you choose? And what about the in-between case, the **flat** universe? Do you prefer that?

The names of these scenarios, by the way, are chosen because each scenario has an impact on the **geometry of the universe**. By this, we mean the way space is curved. Remember how a black hole can curve space around it because of its mass? The theory of relativity also predicts that the mass in the universe should curve the space of the entire universe. Exactly how it is curved depends on how much mass there is, which we don't yet know precisely. If there is enough mass in the universe, it will bend space and time back on itself, forming a kind of sphere. In this closed universe scenario, you could, in principle, fly a spaceship off in one direction, very, very fast, and many, many years later appear from the other direction. You would have traveled around the entire universe to return, just the way ships can sail around the Earth. Unlike the Earth, which is three-dimensional, this sphere would be four-dimensional! In other words, it represents a curvature of our three-dimensional universe into a *fourth* spatial dimension! (Most people, including me, find this hard to visualize.) Space in the open universe would also be curved but in a different way than a sphere. The shape of the universe is this case would be like a sheet that is bent into the shape of a saddle that you might put on a horse. This space is curved but not curved back on itself. So, if you flew off in one direction, you'd never come back to the same place.

The third scenario is called the **flat** universe because the geometry of the universe would be flat—not curved in any way. Strange as it may seem, this scenario is now considered the most likely. That is because new evidence and new theories have arisen that give us a broader perspective on the origin and the fate of the universe than just these three scenarios. Figure 12.4 shows some of these possible shapes for the universe.

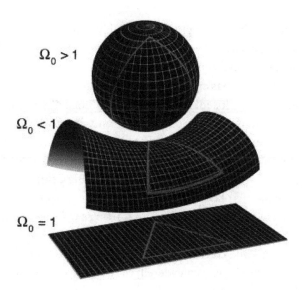

$\Omega_0 > 1$

$\Omega_0 < 1$

$\Omega_0 = 1$

FIGURE 12.4   The shape of the universe describes the way three-dimensional space is bent. According to Einstein's theory of gravity, if there is enough mass, the universe could be curved into a sphere-like shape. You could fly off in space to the left, then reemerge from the right, centuries later, having circled the universe! On the other hand, if there is not enough mass to counteract the expansion of the universe, then it will either be flat or curved into a saddle-like shape. Modern measurements and theory suggest the flat shape is most likely.

SECTION 6. Modern Cosmology

I learned those three scenarios for the fate of the universe when I was in college. But in the years since then, cosmology, like all fields of science, has changed. **Theoretical** cosmologists are constantly coming up with new hypotheses and new ideas. **Observational** researchers design new experiments that support some theories and reject others. Some of these new ideas have been incorporated into the current best theory, the Big Bang theory, *if* they are supported by evidence. Other ideas have not been tested yet and remain tentative. A huge amount of new evidence *has* been gathered in recent years, which has allowed astronomers to construct an entirely new picture for how the universe began and what might happen to it at the end. I will just describe two aspects of the modern Big Bang theory here, but you should be aware that cosmology is an active field of research, both theoretical and observational. You can read news stories about new discoveries and insights every month.

The first aspect of modern cosmology I will discuss is called **inflation**. This idea, which is now part of the Big Bang theory, proposes that the early universe inflated. That is, it suddenly got much, much, much, much, much, MUCH larger. To be specific, the universe increased in size by more than a billion times in less than a microsecond! This would have happened *very* early in the history of the universe, before any elements were created and long before atoms existed. This inflation is dramatically different from the simple *expansion* that the universe presently experiences; it happened much faster, then was quickly over. Of all the theories that astronomers have proposed (some of them quite bizarre), why has this one been accepted by scientists into the Big Bang theory? Because evidence shows that this idea solves a problem: the **horizon problem**.

We mentioned before that the universe does not have an edge. But it does have a horizon, at least from our point of view. On Earth, the horizon is the farthest-away place you can see. If something is beyond the horizon, such as a faraway ship on the ocean, it is out of view. The **cosmic horizon** consists of the farthest-away parts of the universe that we can currently see.[7] Photographs from the Hubble Space Telescope show us some of the most distant galaxies. But the universe doesn't stop there. Presumably, there are many galaxies beyond the horizon whose light has not yet reached us. Light from these galaxies might reach us later. They are like ships beyond the horizon that might sail into our view in the future.

The farthest light we can see is the cosmic microwave background (CMB). This light has a problem. The CMB's light that comes from one side of the universe looks so similar to light from another side of the universe. The similarity of the CMB implies that these two parts of the universe were once together, with the same temperature. This is odd because these two parts of the universe are now so far away from each other that they should never have been in contact. Imagine you are on a ship in the middle of the ocean, and you see one ship approach you from the east and another from the west. Then, they both flash out exactly the same message to you with their lights. How could they both know what message to send? Surely they must have been in contact with each other before. Similarly, it seems as though different regions of the universe that are *extremely* far from each other must have been in contact at some earlier point because the light we get from them is so similar. But the Big Bang model initially said they were *not* in contact because they were so far away from each other.

Here's where the **inflation theory** comes in. If the very early universe underwent an *extremely* rapid expansion, as inflation suggests, it would mean that parts of the universe that were once in contact with each other would now be very far away from each other—so far that we would otherwise think they couldn't have been in contact. This explains what we see in the cosmic microwave background, those two parts of the universe look similar because they *were* close together but separated when the universe stretched out during the inflation era, just a fraction of a second after the Big Bang. Cosmologists have included this idea, inflation, into the model for the early universe because it can explain the evidence. Indeed, it is the only plausible explanation that agrees with the evidence.

A second result of the universe suddenly getting much bigger is that the geometry of the universe would have become much *flatter*. You can see this by imagining any shape, such as a sphere, suddenly increasing in size immensely. If a basketball suddenly became as big as the Earth, you would hardly be able to notice that it was a sphere any more. Its curved surface would appear flat. The inflation idea thus predicts that the geometry of the universe would be flat (and not open or closed). In fact, when we try to measure the geometry of the universe, for example by checking how much mass there is in all nearby galaxies, we find that the universe *is* very close to being flat. The question of why the universe appears flat in its overall geometry was called the **flatness problem**. But it isn't a problem anymore because it was solved by the inflation idea.

---

7   Exactly how far away *is* the cosmic horizon? Since the universe is 13.8 billion years old, it makes sense to say that if something is more than 13.8 billion *light-years* away, there has not been time for light to travel from it to us. If some galaxy were just on the cosmic horizon, we would just barely be able to see its light now. During the time that this light traveled to us, the universe would have kept on expanding. So, currently such an object could be farther than 13.8 billion light-years. According to some estimates, such a galaxy would now be about 46 billion light-years away. These estimates are complicated by the possibility that the rate of expansion may have changed over time.

While inflation gave us insight on how the universe began, recent observations have illuminated how the universe might end. As we saw, there are three options: the current expansion could continue forever, or it could halt, then slow down. Or something in between. Astronomers realized that if the universe really is slowing down, then they should be able to see this by observing galaxies that are very far away. These galaxies would reveal that today's rate of expansion is slower than the earlier rate of expansion. To test this idea, astronomers would need to measure the velocity and distance of many galaxies. Measuring velocity is easy: just look at a galaxy's spectral lines. By measuring their redshift, you can determine how fast the galaxy is moving. Measuring distance to a galaxy is much harder. However, we saw that there are a few tricks astronomers can use, such as **standard candles**, things that always have the same luminosity. The dimmer they *look*, the farther away they are. One such standard candle is a Type Ia supernova explosion.

These explosions (see Chapter 8) occur when the mass of a white dwarf in a binary system increases to exactly $1.4\,M_{sun}$. The resulting explosion always produces the same amount of light and so can be used to judge distance. The problem is that you normally have to wait over 100 years before a supernova Type Ia goes off in a typical galaxy. Astronomers then cleverly figured out that if they observe *thousands* of galaxies, some are bound to have supernovae that are exploding this year! By carefully studying hundreds of these exploding stars, astronomers were able to make a stunning discovery about the expansion of the universe. It isn't actually slowing down, as they had expected—**it is speeding up**! This discovery implies that there is some force that is pushing galaxies apart at large distances. But we don't know of any such force that could do this. Since every force has an energy associated with it, astronomers invented the term **dark energy** to describe whatever it is that must be pushing the galaxies apart. The discovery that the universe is accelerating was entirely unexpected. When the discovery was first announced, there were two large teams working on the problem. The fact that both came to the same conclusion gave astronomers more confidence that their results were correct. Several years later, leaders of both teams were awarded the Nobel Prize in Physics.

However, we still don't know what dark energy is. One possibility is that Einstein's theory of gravity, which controls the universe at the largest sizes, could be a little more complicated than was previously thought. By adding an extra term into his equations, called the **cosmological constant**, astronomers have been able to match the recent supernova data. The notion that instead of slowing down, the universe could be **accelerating** has some curious and even disturbing implications for the end of the universe. If this acceleration continues, then everything now held together by gravity—even our solar system and the Sun—will be ripped apart! But this frightening scenario, called by some the Big Rip, is not a sure thing. Since we don't know what dark energy is, we can't say how it will behave as the universe ages.

At this point, we should compare and contrast dark energy with dark matter. While we don't really know what either is, I would say that the evidence for dark matter is stronger. Dark matter is an unknown type of matter, which, nonetheless, behaves in the same way as all other matter: it creates gravity. Dark energy, on the other hand, must be a new phenomenon, either a different kind of gravity or a new force of nature entirely.

SECTION 7. Pondering the Universe

We can briefly summarize the cosmology we covered in this chapter as follows. Evidence from astronomical observations shows that the universe we live in began very hot and gradually cooled off in stages, first forming elements, then atoms, and eventually stars and galaxies. The initial explosion of matter (the Big Bang) left behind light that we can see today (the cosmic microwave background). Study of these galaxies and the CMB has revealed that the universe is expanding, and it probably will continue to expand indefinitely, depending on how space is curved by matter and energy. The earliest moments of the universe witnessed an extraordinarily rapid expansion called inflation. Some aspects of this picture may seem bizarre to you. They seem bizarre to me too … and I'm an astronomer. Perhaps it is because I study extrasolar planets and not cosmology, but some notions in the Big Bang theory go against my notion of common sense. For example, the idea that everything in the observable universe was once contained in a small volume that inflated and expanded to its present size boggles my mind and challenges my common sense. On the other hand, perhaps we should *expect* theories that explain the origin of the universe to disagree with common sense. After all, what we call common sense is just a collection of memories and experiences and ideas we have that have helped us to survive in the world we find ourselves in. We shouldn't *expect* it to provide much insight into the origin of the universe.

Cosmology addresses questions that humans have pondered for thousands of years: how did the universe begin? How will it end? Such questions are also addressed by fields such as philosophy, religion, and mythology. Every culture on Earth has a creation myth of some sort. These describe how the universe came to be and where humans came from. Perhaps you are familiar with some of these already, depending on your cultural or religious traditions or background. There is a huge variety in these stories, reflecting the diversity of humans from around the world. Some people have even said that the Big Bang theory is a modern creation myth.

The purpose of scientific theories like the Big Bang is not to challenge or displace traditional philosophies or religions. It is to satisfy the human desire to understand where we came from. There are two differences, however. The first is that the scientific story for the origin of the universe is based on evidence, like all scientific theories. This means that if new evidence comes to light, a scientific theory will be changed or abandoned entirely, not something that happens often in fields like religion and politics. The second difference is that a scientific approach will be understood and accepted by all people, regardless of their cultural, national, or religious backgrounds. People from every part of the Earth are capable of doing science and testing theories with their own experiments. No scientific theory would be widely accepted unless it was widely tested, and this includes tests by people from all over the Earth.

WRAP-UP

In several previous chapters, we noticed that humans keep finding, much to their surprise, that we aren't at the center of everything. In this chapter, we found that not only is our galaxy not at the center of the universe, but that there *is no center* to the universe. Nor can we say that there is an edge to the universe beyond which there is no universe. What we can say is that the universe is expanding. Edwin Hubble measured its rate of expansion using the Doppler effect. The redshifted galaxies he observed implied that the universe is about 14 billion years old, and it began in a hot, dense Big Bang. Later measurements of the cosmic microwave background helped us to develop a consistent theory of the origin of the universe, the Big Bang theory. But this theory is incomplete; it still cannot address the earliest moments. We can, however, use that theory and observations of exploding supernovae in distant galaxies to predict the future fate of the universe. Current data suggest that the expansion will continue and even increase in scope. The universe is *accelerating*. Cosmologists have thus addressed some of the age-old questions about the origin and fate of the universe, but not all. There are still many mysteries to be explored.

REFLECTION QUESTIONS

1. The entire universe, even the surface of the Earth, is bathed in the faint afterglow of the Big Bang. This cosmic microwave background light is faint but has been clearly detected many times, here on Earth and by spacecraft launched above Earth's atmosphere. Explain where the CMB came from. What crucial transition in the history of our universe produced it?

2. If someone pointed to a periodic table of the elements and asked, "Where did all those elements come from?" how would you answer? Which of them could you say came from the Big Bang, and which were produced by stars? How do exploding stars play a role? (Hint: Look at Section 3 of this chapter and also back to Chapter 8.)

13

PLANETS

We, this people, on a small and lonely planet

Traveling through casual space

Past aloof stars, across the way of indifferent suns

To a destination where all signs tell us

It is possible and imperative that we learn

A brave and startling truth

—Maya Angelou, "A Brave and Startling Truth"

I t's time to head home. After stretching out to the farthest reaches of space and going back to the earliest moments of time, we are now going to return to Earth and see it in a new light. Earth is the only place in the universe where we know life exists. Could life exist elsewhere? We'll devote the final chapter of this book to that question. But first, we need to explore the most likely places for life to exist: planets. Before we talk about the familiar planets that orbit our Sun, we need to think about planets in general. That is, the planets that orbit *other* suns—other stars. Planets outside our solar system are called **extrasolar planets**[1] or **exoplanets**. In this chapter, we'll see how they can form and how astronomers (including me!) have now discovered many of them. We'll see about how remarkably common exoplanets are and if possibly some of them have the right conditions for life. We'll then turn to our own solar system and the planets we understand the best. Since our ultimate goal is to understand the chances of life in the universe (Chapter 14), we'll focus mainly on two planets, Venus and Earth. Each of these can teach us something about life.

---

1 *Extrasolar* means outside of our solar system, just like *extraterrestrial* means outside the Earth (*terra* = Earth).

SECTION 1. Planet Formation

How could a planetary system like our solar system form? Well, our first clue is the way the planets in our solar system are arranged—they are all found in a single flat plane called the **ecliptic plane** (see Chapter 2). This suggests that they may have all formed in a flat disk. As we saw in Chapter 7, when a star forms, a large gas cloud condenses and starts spinning. The material that is spinning fast enough to avoid being pulled into the center tends to form a disk. (This process is similar to the formation of galaxies too; see Chapter 11.) So theoretically, we should expect to find such disks around newly formed stars. And we do! These disks are not as hot as stars, so they produce light that has a longer wavelength than visible light, including infrared, microwaves, and light with wavelength of a few millimeters or less. Using specialized detectors, astronomers have captured images of disks surrounding numerous young stars. But such light is absorbed by molecules like CO_2 and water in our atmosphere. The ALMA Telescope was built in the Atacama Desert of Chile to make these types of measurements. The location is ideal for this because the area is extremely dry; some parts of it can go for years without any rain at all! Figure 13.1 shows one of the discoveries ALMA made: disk of matter orbiting a young star. What is remarkable is the fact that the disk has gaps in it where some matter seems to have disappeared. A likely possibility is that this matter has clumped together to form planets.

But even these remarkable images do not show actual planets. For years, astronomers hoped to capture an image of a planet orbiting another star besides the Sun. But it is not easy because stars are so bright and planets are so dim. However, in recent years, specialized techniques have been able to capture a few **direct** images of large planets orbiting nearby stars (see Figure 13.2).

FIGURE 13.1   Images of a protoplanetary disk surrounding a nearby young star, made by the ALMA Telescope array in Chile. The gaps in this disk may be caused by the formation of planets.

SECTION 2. Other Stars Have Planets

In terms of sheer numbers, the most successful techniques for discovering exoplanets involve **indirect detection**, in which we find evidence of a planet orbiting a star without being able to see the planet directly. How can we detect a planet if we can't see it? The same way we detect the wind: we observe its influence on something else, like a tree, whose branches sway back and forth. A planet orbiting a star will influence that star; it will exert gravity and tug the star gently back and forth as it orbits. The situation is similar to a double-star system, in which two stars orbit each other. As we saw in Chapter 6, the more massive star won't move as much as the lower-mass star. Stars are much more massive than planets, so when a planet orbits a star, the star hardly moves compared to how much the planet moves in its orbit. Still, if we are very careful, it is possible to detect this tiny wobble and thus discover a planet that we can't even see.

The most effective strategy for detecting wobbling stars involves the **Doppler effect**. As we saw in Chapter 4, when a star moves toward us, its light will appear bluer because the waves of light are scrunched together to a shorter wavelength, and blue light has a shorter wavelength. When a star is moving away from us, its light is stretched out, and we see a red shift. What if both happen? If a star wobbles because a planet orbits it, then it will move in a small circle[2] coming toward us, then away from us, alternatively. If we observe its light using a spectrograph, we'll be able to see the absorption lines shift, first becoming bluer, then redder. This is how a planet can be discovered, even if we can't see it.[3]

When I started graduate school at San Francisco State University, I joined a team of researchers who were searching for planets using this method. At that time, no planets were known outside our solar system orbiting other stars. This team worked for years to perfect a technique that could detect tiny Doppler shifts to discover planets. I've been searching for planets ever since then. To give you some feel for this work, I'll go over our technique and then discuss some discoveries.

Based in San Francisco, we used the nearest large research telescope, which is at Lick Observatory on Mount Hamilton. We would go there about every other

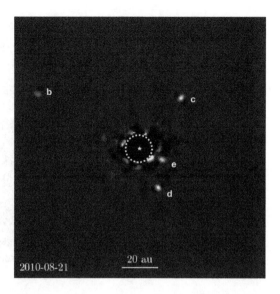

FIGURE 13.2   Images of planets orbiting nearby stars give visual proof that our Sun is not the only star with planets. This photo of the star HD 8799 was taken on August 21, 2010, at Keck Observatory using infrared light. You can't actually see the star; its light has been intentionally blocked by a dark spot placed in the camera (dotted circle). This allowed astronomers to capture light from three large orbiting planets (b, c, d, and e). But these planets are nothing like the planets in our solar system. They are all larger and more massive than Jupiter (our largest planet), and two of them (c and b) orbit at distances larger than Pluto's distance from our Sun. To discover solar systems more like our own, astronomers use indirect techniques.

month and stay up all night for three nights observing stars. (Astronomers sleep during the daytime, a bit like vampires!) When we pointed the telescope to a star, its light went into a spectrograph that spread the light out into different colors that were photographed digitally. Dark absorption lines in this spectrum would reveal the star's velocity at that time, after careful analysis. To discover a planet, we would observe the same star month after month for several years and look for changes in its velocity, indicating that it was wobbling because of a star orbiting it.

I worked on this project for two and a half years as a student at San Francisco State. In addition to my trips to the observatory, I calculated how the Earth's movements interfered with our measurement of stars' speeds and wrote computer programs to account for these movements. Just after I left San Francisco State and began to study for a PhD degree at UCLA, a big announcement hit the news: the first exoplanet had been discovered around a normal star. The discovery was made not by our group but by two astronomers from

---

2   Actually, an ellipse. Both the planet and the star move in an ellipse.

3   NASA has an animation of this process: https://www.youtube.com/watch?v=WK0WAmiP_Dk

(a)   (b)

FIGURE 13.3   Leading exoplanet researcher Debra Fischer (a) and the Lowell Discovery Telescope (b), where she leads a project to discover Earthlike planets. (The dome of this telescope is also shown on the front cover of this book. Lowell Observatory where the planet Pluto was discovered in 1930.)

Switzerland, whom we regarded as our friendly competitors. Whenever a scientist claims to have discovered something important, other scientists challenge this claim. This healthy skepticism is a normal part of science. The discovery of the first extrasolar planet was so groundbreaking that many wondered whether it was correct. So, to be sure, our group observed the star in question, called **51 Pegasi**, for four straight nights. Indeed, we found that it was wobbling, just as the Swiss astronomers claimed. When our group announced the confirmation of this exoplanet, the worldwide community widely accepted the find as valid. In 2019, these two astronomers, Michel Mayor and Didier Queloz, won the Nobel Prize in Physics for their discovery.

But what kind of planet had they discovered? Their measurements and ours showed the planet was at least as massive as Saturn, but orbiting the star 51 Pegasi in only 4.2 days. That means that if you lived on this planet, you'd have a birthday every 4.2 days!! But you wouldn't want to live there. The planet is so close to the star that its temperature would be thousands of degrees—you'd be scorched! No such planet exists in our solar system. Our closest planet, Mercury, orbits every 88 days and is much farther away from our Sun. In the months and years that followed, several more massive planets orbiting close to a star were discovered. They became known as **Hot Jupiters** and were not expected to exist by astronomers … until they were discovered. One of the things I like most about science is that when we go searching for something we expect to find, we often find something different! The universe is full of surprises.

Since the discovery of 51 Pegasi's planet in 1995, several hundred exoplanets have been discovered using this Doppler shift method. While my group didn't find the first such planet, we did discover most of the first 100 exoplanets, launching a new field of research, exoplanets. Soon, other methods were used to make more discoveries. One such method relies on pure chance. If we are lucky, then an exoplanet's orbit might be oriented so that the planet passes *directly* in front of a star. While we still would not see the planet, we could detect the dimming in the light of the star that happens because the planet blocks some of its light. This is called the **transit method** and is very similar to what happens when we see a solar eclipse: our Sun is blocked by the Moon. In the case of transits, not all the light of the star is blocked by the extrasolar planet. We just notice that the star becomes dimmer by about 1 percent or usually much less.

After successfully discovering several planets this way, astronomers realized that they could find even smaller planets if they could more precisely measure the light from stars to see if it was dimming. The problem is that any light passing through Earth's atmosphere gets a little distorted, which puts a limit on how precisely we can measure it. The solution is to launch a telescope in space. In 2009, NASA launched the Kepler Space Telescope to find transiting planets as small as Earth. Since the odds of a planetary system having just the right orientation to transit are low, the Kepler mission had to observe *many* stars—over 100,000 in fact! It did this by observing a part of the sky near the galactic plane, where stars are packed together on the sky.

The results were stunning. After nine years of observations, Kepler has discovered over a thousand planets outside our solar system. While most of these were giant planets, hundreds were smaller, harder-to-detect rocky planets. Discovery of such planets, which resemble Earth, lets us learn whether or not there could be other planets orbiting other stars in our galaxy that might be similar enough to Earth to host life. If a planet has the right conditions for life, it is called a **habitable planet**. But what are those conditions? Take a moment yourself to write down a list of all the things you think are essential for life. What does life need?

There's no right answer to this question because life can take on many forms, perhaps even forms quite different from the life we find on Earth. One factor required for all life on Earth is liquid water. If temperatures stay below the freezing point (0°Celsius) or above the boiling point (100°C), then life (as we know it) won't exist. Using this temperature range, we can define a region called the **habitable zone**, the region around any star in which water can exist as a liquid. Any planet in that region is considered a habitable planet. Earth is in our Sun's habitable zone and is the only place in our solar system with liquid water.[4] We astronomers get very excited when we discover a planet orbiting another star that is at the right distance for water to exist. There are now a few dozen habitable planets, many of them discovered by the Kepler mission.

While the stars surveyed by Kepler were about 1,000 light-years away, a habitable exoplanet may exist much, much closer. In fact, an exoplanet was discovered orbiting the closest star to the Sun, Proxima Centauri, in 2016. The discovery was made using the Doppler shift method by a team that included Paul Butler of the Carnegie Institution of Washington, DC. (An exoplanet pioneer, Paul developed a planet detection technique as a student at San Francisco State University. He was my mentor when I worked at the Carnegie Institution.) The Doppler shift data for Proxima revealed a planet orbiting this star every 11 or 12 days, with a mass similar to Earth's. This discovery is particularly interesting because it means that there could be a chance for life on the nearest star to the Sun. Just to be clear, if a planet is **habitable**, then it *could* have life; this doesn't mean that life has been found there. I should also clarify that by *close*, we mean that Proxima Centauri is *only* 25 trillion miles away. This is too far away to imagine humans traveling there in any of our lifetimes; however, some scientists have contemplated sending very small space probes on a 20-year journey to explore this planet.[5]

After the first exoplanets were found in the 1990s, a great era of discovery began. So many planets have been discovered that it is impossible for me to discuss them all.[6] I'll just mention a few that I find interesting. One question that intrigues me and other astronomers is, "How special is our solar system?" If our

---

4   Water might exist for brief periods of time on Mars and probably flowed there millions of years ago.

5   For more information, check out the Breakthrough Starshot Project at https://breakthroughinitiatives.org/initiative/3

6   If you want to explore some of them, check NASA's exoplanet archive at https://exoplanetarchive.ipac.caltech.edu

solar system just happens to have some very rare properties, then perhaps the existence of life on Earth is a freak coincidence. In this case, we might not find life elsewhere in the universe. On the other hand, if our solar system is more or less "normal," then the conditions by which life formed *here* would exist throughout the universe. Since many of the first exoplanets to be discovered were Hot Jupiters unlike anything in our solar system, we began to wonder if our solar system was the odd one out. However, research led by my colleagues Debra Fischer (Figure 13.3) and Paul Butler showed that the star Upsilon Andromedae[7] has multiple planets orbiting it, not just one. This early discovery helped us realize that multiplanet systems, like our solar system, are quite common. There are now hundreds of stars known with multiple planet systems.

The field of exoplanets is extremely active, and discoveries are constantly being made with a variety of new techniques. For example, in 2018, NASA launched the Transiting Exoplanet Survey Satellite (TESS) to discover planets using the same method as the pioneering Kepler Telescope. With improved precision, TESS can discover planets as small as Earth. I was very excited by one of its first discoveries, a planet twice the size of Earth orbiting a star in the southern skies called Pi Mensae. I recognized the name of the star because I had helped to discover another, much larger planet around it years before. The TESS mission has been very successful, discovering dozens of new planets and finding hints of many more.

We can summarize the discoveries this way:

- Planets form frequently around stars; at least 25 percent of stars have a planet orbiting them, possibly much more
- Exoplanets are found to have a wide range of masses and orbits
- Many stars have multiple planets orbiting them
- Some habitable planets have now been found; there are certainly many more
- So far, no other planets are known with life

SECTION 3. Our Solar System

In previous chapters, we discussed how humans learned how the planets in our solar system orbit. We discussed Galileo's observations of phases on Venus, which showed that the Sun must be at the center of the solar system, not the Earth, and Johannes Kepler's study of Mars that showed that planets orbit in ellipses, not circles. But now that we have studied other systems of planets orbiting other stars, we can see our own solar system in a new light. For example, we can be grateful that we don't have a large planet in a highly elliptical orbit in our solar system. Such a planet would throw the Earth out of its orbit with its strong gravity.

To understand our solar system better, I like to view it from the perspective extraterrestrial beings would have if they came here and studied our planets. The first thing they would notice is that there are four very large planets made of gas. Jupiter, Saturn, Uranus, and Neptune are called gas giant planets. Jupiter is the largest in size and mass, but even its mass is tiny compared to the Sun, about 0.1 percent. The next thing they would notice is that closer to the Sun there are four small, rocky planets, Mercury, Venus, Earth, and Mars. These planets' atmospheres are thin compared to the size of the planet. We refer

---

7   This star is found in the constellation Andromeda and appears close in the sky to the Andromeda Galaxy. But the star is part of our Milky Way Galaxy. We now know of at least four planets orbiting it.

to these planets as terrestrial because they are all similar to Earth—*Terra*. Everything else orbiting the Sun is much smaller. I imagine the extraterrestrials would probably lump them all into one category—the "small stuff." This includes comets, asteroids, and what we call **dwarf planets**. Dwarf planets can be found in the **Main Asteroid Belt** between Mars and Jupiter, and also another belt farther out called the **Kuiper Belt**. The first dwarf planet, called Ceres, was discovered in the Main Belt in 1800.[8] But it is only recently that we've been able to explore the Kuiper Belt and discover several asteroids there also.

These discoveries led a group of astronomers meeting in 2006 to vote to reclassify Pluto as a **dwarf planet**. Pluto had been called a planet since its discovery in 1930. So, this demotion was controversial with the general public and with many astronomers, and still is. On the one hand, it makes sense because Pluto is much smaller than any other planet and is similar in size to some other Kuiper Belt objects. On the other hand, the definition that astronomers used to demote Pluto is confusing for nonexperts, including some astronomers.[9] In the real universe, of course, Pluto didn't change when humans put it in a new category. What do you think about Pluto's designation? Should scientists redo the names they use to describe things as more data become available?[10] Should one vote by a group of astronomers be sufficient? Should the public be involved?

To me, what's most interesting about Pluto is that it has now been visited by a spacecraft made by humans. In July 2015, NASA's *New Horizons* spacecraft flew past Pluto at a speed of 84,000 km/h (52,000 mph) after a journey of 5 billion kilometers (3 billion miles). With a close flyby, we got photos of Pluto in amazing detail, unlike anything we could get from Earth. This led to a host of discoveries, including the discovery of glaciers on Pluto. On Earth, glaciers are made of ice—frozen water—but Pluto is so cold that its glaciers are made of frozen air! (See Figure 13.4.)

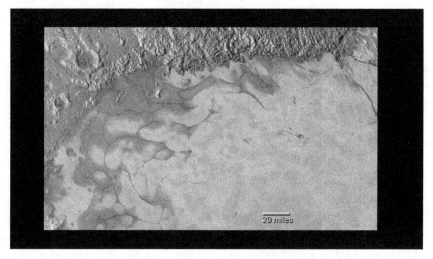

FIGURE 13.4 Image of the surface of Pluto from NASA's *New Horizons* mission. The smooth areas contain frozen nitrogen glaciers that can flow, just like the ice glaciers on Earth.

---

8 It was regarded as a planet when it was discovered but then demoted to dwarf planet.

9 The definition involves a planet's ability to clear its orbit of other objects in its "neighborhood" (e.g., through gravitational interactions).

10 Renaming happens in other fields, such as paleontology. When I was a kid, it was common to refer to one dinosaur species as *brontosaurus*. However, many years later, I realized that experts in the field used the name *apatosaurus* when classifying this dinosaur scientifically. I just recently learned that a new study, published in 2015, found evidence that the species should be reclassified again, leading to a revival of the name *brontosaurus*!

Pluto is just one planet that humans have explored. Over the years, dozens of spacecraft have been sent out from Earth to study the planets in detail. They have been launched by the United States, by the former Soviet Union and later Russia, by the European Space Agency, by Japan, and by international teams of scientists working together. The amount of information we have gathered from these missions is enormous—in fact, too large to include in this book. However, I will put links to some of these missions at the end of this chapter so you can explore them yourself. Since the final chapter of this book is on the prospects for life in the universe, I will focus in this chapter on just two terrestrial planets, Earth and Venus. While only one of these planets, Earth, is known to have life, they all have something to teach us about how life could form in space, how it can survive, and why it sometimes might not survive.

SECTION 4. Earth Interior: Geology

Earth is the only known home of life. To understand the Earth, we will study its **interior** and its **atmosphere**. While the ground you stand on is solid, *below* Earth's solid **crust** is a layer of rock that is actually liquid, or molten. When Earth formed about 4.5 billion years ago, many isotopes of radioactive elements were included in the new planet. The slow decay of these elements produces enough to melt the rock below the surface of the Earth. The solid crust of the Earth, therefore, is floating on liquid rock below, much like how sheets of ice float on liquid water. And like ice sheets, Earth's crust is broken up into large pieces, called **tectonic plates**. These plates are constantly moving, but quite slowly. The boundary between two plates is an area of intense geological activity. There are three ways plates can interact at these boundaries. They can come together (converge); they can spread apart (diverge); or they can slide past each other.

If two plates come together, one of the plates will be pushed down below the other, causing it to melt. This process is called **subduction**.[11] It is common for rock from the melted plate to work its way upward through cracks in the plate above, to the surface and create a volcanic eruption. This molten rock (also called **magma**) solidifies and can build up layer by layer into a volcanic mountain. This subduction process is responsible for the creation of the Cascades mountain range in the Pacific Northwest United States, which includes Mt. Rainier in Washington State, Mt. Hood in Oregon, and Mt. Shasta in California. Subduction zones can also create powerful earthquakes, such as the 2011 Tohoku quake in Japan, which also caused a tsunami and a catastrophic meltdown at a nuclear power plant.

It is also possible for tectonic plates to pull apart from each other. This usually happens at the bottom of the ocean[12] and is observed as a **seafloor spreading ridge**. If you look at a globe, you can see them as long lines down the middle of some oceans, such as the Atlantic. As the plates separate, hot molten rock moves up from below and then touches the ocean, cooling and solidifying. This is where the newest rock on Earth is created. The tectonic plates on either side of the Atlantic Ocean are pulling apart from each other. This means that in the past, the continents on either side of the Atlantic were closer together. In fact, about 150 million years ago, South America and Africa were joined. You can see how they fit together by comparing the outlines of their modern coastlines.

---

11   *Sub-*, as in *subway* or *submarine*, means "below."
12   Although it can happen on land; the East African Rift is an example.

Plates don't have to collide or separate. They can move alongside each other. This third type of boundary, called a **transform fault**, is of greatest interest to me. That's because the university where I work, San Francisco State, is just 1 kilometer away from one—the San Andreas Fault—which is said to be the most dangerous earthquake fault in the United States! This fault is the boundary between the North American Plate and the Pacific Plate, which is moving north at an average rate of 3 centimeters each year (just over 1 inch a year). But this motion isn't constant. Over time, tension builds up, and then there is a sudden slip—an earthquake—in which the plates may move many centimeters or more. Such a slippage happened in 1906, causing the Great San Francisco Earthquake, one of the largest urban natural disasters in history. Over 3,000 people were killed and much of the city was destroyed, both by the quake and the ensuing fire.

From our human point of view, earthquakes and volcanoes are natural disasters that can have a catastrophic impact on people, especially if we are unprepared. But from the point of view of nature, they are simply evidence that our planet is geologically active. In fact, this tectonic activity can have positive impacts on life. A great place to witness this is the Hawai'ian Islands, specifically Hawai'i Volcanoes National Park on the Big Island of Hawai'i. There, you can witness ongoing volcanic eruptions that continuously create new land and also see earlier lava flows that now provide a habitat for plants and animals. The entire island chain, which is home to incredible natural diversity, was created over a few million years by a constant upwelling of magma from the center of the ocean, making island after island as the large Pacific Plate slowly moved.

Another example is the **carbon cycle**. The movement of the plates causes volcanic eruptions which spew carbon dioxide (CO_2) into the atmosphere. Some of this gas becomes dissolved in the water of the oceans (just like salt can dissolve in water). In the ocean, CO_2 is used by microorganisms in the ocean, which absorb the CO_2 and use it to make a tiny shell. Just like seashells you might find on the beach, these shells are made of calcium carbonate ($CaCO_2$). When the microorganisms die, their shells fall to the bottom of the ocean and stay there. In this way, carbon is removed from our atmosphere and deposited on the sea floor, but not forever. Because tectonic plates move, this sea floor will eventually get pushed under another continent. This subduction process causes the sea floor to melt, and the carbon in the shells will then be erupted back into Earth's atmosphere as CO_2. Carbon has been "cycling" between the atmosphere, the oceans, and the sea floor of Earth for millions of years and has maintained suitable conditions for life.[13] This balance is now being disrupted by humans, who are putting CO_2 into Earth's atmosphere at a rate never before seen in geologic history.

SECTION 5. Earth's Atmosphere and Climate Change

Take a deep breath. Did you ever stop to think about what exactly you are breathing when you inhale? What is air? If your first thought was oxygen, then your priorities are in the right place; without oxygen in our air, we couldn't live. But air is *not* oxygen. Mostly it is nitrogen, nearly 80 percent. Oxygen makes up about 20 percent. Perhaps you knew that. But did you know that once there was *no oxygen* in our

---

13 In fact, it has been proposed that microorganisms on Earth regulate Earth's temperature and other conditions to make life favorable. This is called the Gaia Hypothesis.

atmosphere? Over 2.5 billion years ago, we didn't have oxygen on Earth. It was added to our atmosphere after certain microscopic algae became abundant on Earth. (They release oxygen as a waste product.) That event had a profound impact on our planet. It is called a catastrophe for some organisms because they went extinct, but it was required in order for oxygen-breathing organisms, like us, to exist.

Some of the most important molecules that make up our atmosphere are found in small concentrations—less than 1 percent. Take water vapor, for example. Water molecules are dissolved in air the same way salt can dissolve in water. The amount of water in our air varies from almost 0 percent in very dry places to 3 percent in humid areas. If you take a cold beverage container out of the refrigerator and leave it outside, you'll notice water forming on the container. This water comes from the air. The coldness of the beverage causes it to condense from air to liquid form, the same way dew forms before dawn. When air cools,[14] water dissolved in it condenses into liquid droplets, forming clouds. Rain from such clouds provides us with water to drink. The amount of water in our atmosphere varies from place to place but doesn't increase or decrease over time. If the humidity in one area gets too high, it rains. As we'll see, the same is *not* true of carbon dioxide.

TABLE 13.1   COMPOSITION OF EARTH'S AIR

Molecule or Atom	Fraction
Nitrogen (N_2)	78%
Oxygen (O_2)	21%
Water Vapor (H_2O)	1.5%
Argon (Ar)	0.9%
Carbon Dioxide (CO_2)	0.4%

Before we continue, let's try out a simple question:

Why does it get cold at night?

What would you say? Take a moment and come up with your best explanation of why this happens. Or perhaps ask a friend and see what they say. All our lives, we've noticed that it gets colder at night, but the reason is not obvious. One answer might be, "The sunlight stops shining on things," but that can't be the whole story because it doesn't immediately get cold when the Sun goes down. The reason it gets colder and colder through the night is that something *invisible* is happening. As we saw in Chapter 3, anything warm will emit light with a range of wavelengths. The most light is emitted at the peak wavelength, which depends on temperature. Earth itself emits **infrared** light, or IR. So, all night long, this light goes out into space, carrying away heat energy. The loss of this heat is what makes it colder and colder at night until sunrise, when the Sun's light heats up our part of the Earth again. But not all the infrared light that Earth emits makes it into space. As it turns out, this explains a global mystery.

---

14   For example, when wind pushes air up the side of a mountain, clouds often form.

We know how much energy the Sun produces (see Chapter 5) and we know how much of this energy reaches Earth. We also know how much energy is *radiated by Earth* in the form of infrared light. Putting this together, if we assume these are in balance, we come to a strange conclusion: Earth should be frozen over! Its average temperature should be –17°C (about 1°F), well below freezing. Since our conclusion is wrong, one of the assumptions we used to make that conclusion must be wrong. When we assumed that the energy leaving Earth balanced the energy it receives from the Sun, we neglected one thing, the atmosphere. Earth's atmosphere prevents some of the infrared light that cools the Earth from escaping. Instead, that light gets trapped by molecules in our atmosphere capable of absorbing IR. Molecules that can absorb IR are called **greenhouse gases**. They prevent the Earth from fully cooling down, a process called the **greenhouse effect**.

Have you heard of the greenhouse effect? It is named for greenhouses, places where plants are grown. Greenhouses are made of glass because glass has the property that it allows the Sun's visible light to pass through and warm up the plants inside, but the glass *traps* the IR light these plants give off, making the whole place much warmer than it would be. If you've ever gotten into a car that was left parked in a sunny spot for a few hours, then you know how the greenhouse effect can warm things up. Our planet, of course, isn't surrounded by glass walls. It is surrounded by an atmosphere made of gas. The greenhouse gases that warm up our atmosphere are water vapor (H_2O), carbon dioxide (CO_2), and methane (CH_4). As a scientific phenomenon, the greenhouse effect is neither good nor bad. Indeed, without it, Earth would be frozen. But one greenhouse gas—carbon dioxide—is having an increasingly harmful effect on life on Earth, which is what we'll explore next. Let's see what's up with **climate change**.

A good way to understand our Earth is to look into its past. Fortunately, there are many ways to do this. The geological discoveries we discussed in the last section came from the study of ancient rocks. To learn about Earth's *atmosphere* in the past, we use ancient *ice*. Places like Antarctica have thousands of feet of accumulated ice, some of which is almost half a million years old. It got there long ago, falling as snowflakes. Between the flakes, small amounts of air were trapped, which now form bubbles in the ice. These bubbles let us know the composition of Earth's atmosphere in the distant past, and they also reveal changes in Earth's temperature.[15] Figure 13.5 shows the concentration of CO_2 in Earth's atmosphere and the temperature of Earth for the last 800,000 years. You will immediately see an interesting pattern: **when there is more CO_2, it is hotter**. This is not surprising: greenhouse gases trap heat and prevent the Earth from cooling. The level of CO_2 in our atmosphere has changed over Earth's history for geological reasons, such as volcanoes. There have also been very small changes in Earth's orbit that have influenced the average temperature of Earth. Take a look at the labels on the graph. The upper figure measures CO_2 in parts per million (ppm). The highest level previously occurring was 300 ppm, meaning that for every 1 million molecules in Earth's atmosphere, 300 of them are CO_2. This is the same as saying that the CO_2 never got above 0.3 percent. But now, as I write this in 2021, the CO_2 is 416 ppm and will probably be higher as you read this.[16]

---

15   The temperature data is obtained in a fascinating way, by isotope analysis. Precipitation (rain or snow) will have a higher or lower concentration of heavier isotopes (such as deuterium, the heavy isotope of hydrogen, which we discussed in Chapter 5), depending on its temperature.

16   If you want to check the current level for yourself, go to https://www.co2.earth

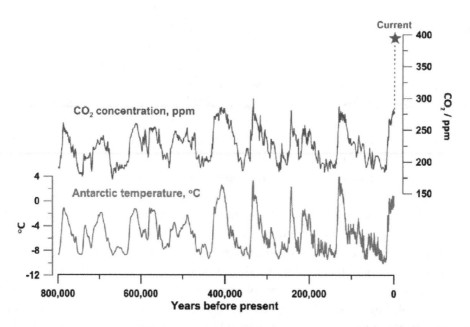

FIGURE 13.5   The amount of carbon dioxide in Earth's atmosphere, measured in parts per million (CO_2 concentration, ppm; upper graph), and the temperature of Earth's atmosphere in degrees Celsius (lower graph) over the last 800,000 years. When Earth had more CO_2, it was hotter—not surprising, since CO_2 is a greenhouse gas. But in this whole time, CO_2 levels never got above 300 ppm—not until humans began polluting Earth's atmosphere by burning fossil fuels.

While the CO_2 level never got above 300 ppm for the last million years, things changed dramatically when humans came along. More specifically, the most dramatic change in CO_2 in Earth's history began during the **Industrial Revolution** and continues until today. Starting in the late 1800s, humans first began to burn **fossil fuels** for the first time. Fossil fuels consist of plant or animal matter deposited in the Earth millions of years ago. Common examples are coal, natural gas, and petroleum, which is refined into the gasoline that powers most cars. This increase in CO_2 level is clear in the figure, which shows historical times. The cause of this increase in CO_2 levels is well known; humans are now burning so much coal and gas that we are putting over **30 billion tons** of CO_2 into the atmosphere.

Say, do you drink carbonic acid? If you enjoy carbonated soda drinks, then yes, you do. Carbonic acid is what gives those drinks their fizz. It is made by dissolving carbon dioxide in water, which also happens on Earth. When CO_2 levels increase in the atmosphere, some of that CO_2 gets dissolved into our oceans, making our oceans more acidic. This is called **ocean acidification,** and it is creating a major problem because the oceans are now beginning to dissolve coral reefs (important habitats for fish) and damaging marine organisms.[17]

But the most noticeable effect of excess CO_2 in our atmosphere is **global warming**. The average temperature of the Earth is steadily rising. This observed fact is not disputed because it is so easy to measure; you just need a thermometer, and we've had good thermometers for over 100 years. The results of these measurements are clear: *in the last 30 years, Earth has warmed dramatically*. In fact, the rise is

17   You can find a summary of the problem by the National Oceanic and Atmospheric Administration here: https://oceanservice.noaa.gov/facts/acidification.html

most dramatic in the last 10 years, with new record-breaking hot temperatures in 2016, 2017, 2018, 2019, and 2020. Based on these accurate temperature measurements, you live in the hottest period of Earth's recorded history. And just to be clear—this warming IS caused by human-made CO_2 in Earth's atmosphere. Measured levels of CO_2 have increased dramatically, and CO_2 does cause warming (it is a greenhouse gas). In spite of the claims of some science-deniers, *there is no plausible alternate explanation*. Furthermore, the *isotopes* of carbon in Earth's atmosphere match those found in fossil fuels that have been burned since the 1880s—a clear fingerprint of human activity.[18] We should probably note here that in spite of this evidence, several prominent politicians have falsely claimed that global temperatures are not increasing or that humans are not causing global warming (they refuse to say who is causing the warming, however). Scientific ignorance is indeed rampant!

However, people like you, who are educating themselves about science, are part of the solution to this problem. Awareness of this situation is growing. In fact, humans first realized that CO_2 would cause climate change in the 1800s (!), so this isn't a new problem. Let's take a look at a few of the severe consequences of climate change and then turn our attention to solutions.

The effects of global warming, long predicted by scientists, are now being observed around the world. As Earth gets hotter, ice melts. Glaciers that have been in cold mountain areas for centuries are disappearing. Ice-covered Greenland is melting at a very high rate, as is Antarctica. Recently, several large ice shelves in Antarctica have broken up and melted. One of them, the Larsen B Ice Shelf, existed for over 10,000 years and was larger than the state of Rhode Island. When ice on land melts, the water goes into the ocean and causes sea levels to rise. Many parts of the world, such as Florida, Bangladesh, and the Maldives will be even harder hit. Long before this century is over, hundreds of millions of people who live in these areas will be forced to leave their homes, creating enormous disruptions and humanitarian crises around the world.

The thought of these ongoing and future crises can be overwhelming at times. But the fact that we know the *cause* of global warming means that we know the *solution* to the problem. The solution is to reduce CO_2 emissions and remove CO_2 from the atmosphere. You may be surprised to learn that the people of the world all got together and resolved to solve this problem back in 1997. Meeting in Kyoto, Japan, 163 countries signed the Kyoto Accord to reduce emissions. So what happened? Well, at the time, the United States was the largest carbon dioxide polluter in the world. When the United States announced that it would not honor the principles of the Kyoto Accord,[19] other countries felt like they didn't have to do their part either. China, for example, built hundreds of coal-burning power plants and is now the number-one carbon dioxide polluter in the world. But much of the world took Kyoto to heart and found ways to reduce carbon emissions. Electric utilities can generate energy renewably using solar and wind power at a fraction of their cost decades ago. As individuals, there is much we can do to reduce our so called carbon footprint, the amount of carbon we each emit into the air every year.

---

18   See https://www.realclimate.org/index.php/archives/2004/12/how-do-we-know-that-recent-cosub2sub-increases-are-due-to-human-activities-updated/ and the references therein for details.

19   The Kyoto Accord was signed in 1999 by US Vice President Al Gore, who then ran for president in 2000. Although he won the popular vote, he didn't become president. The United States then pulled out of the Kyoto Accord, setting back the fight against climate change for decades.

Are you currently taking actions to reduce your carbon footprint? Do you get around on public transportation or by bike instead of using a gasoline-burning car? If you do drive a car, you can buy a hybrid or electric car. There are also steps you can take around the home to reduce energy consumption, such as limiting use of air conditioners and heaters, and insulating the walls of your house better. You can even ask your utility company to provide carbon-free electricity. But some of these steps can seem costly, especially for people who don't have a lot of money. Governments can provide incentives to encourage behavior that helps sustainability. However, governments are actually doing the opposite; around the world, governments subsidize the destructive fossil fuel industry with over \$5 trillion in benefits per year (Cusick 2015)! An obvious first step is to cut these destructive subsidies. A next step is **carbon tax rebates**, which require those who create the most CO_2 to pay for their impacts. In this system, *all* citizens would get rebates, which they can either spend on expensive polluting products or cheaper clean products. This makes it much easier to afford electric cars, for example. Such carbon tax rebates have already been in effect in Canada for years. Other steps involve generating much more electricity with solar panels and wind, and storing that energy, for example in powerful batteries. All these technologies already exist but are not widely used. Climate change **is** a solvable problem. Currently, however, political leaders are not implementing solutions, in spite of the broad popular support of these solutions. So far, they have chosen to do little to stop carbon-polluting humans from committing planetary suicide.

That's why the people of Earth who care about the future are taking matters into their own hands. Citizens in every country are organizing into groups that promote a sustainable future, contacting political leaders, and demonstrating in the streets. Young people, whose future is at stake, have been at the forefront of this change. Youth movements such as the Sunrise Movement and Fridays for Future have led the way. Different groups focus on different aspects of the problem, including carbon taxes, shutting down coal-burning plants, education about the greenhouse effect, and climate justice. As a scientist myself, I feel an obligation to do my part. That's why I've joined with my colleagues to help form Astronomers for Planet Earth, a worldwide organization promoting a whole-Earth perspective on climate awareness. More resources that you can use to get active can be found at the end of this chapter. As we will discuss in the next chapter, the long-term future of humanity on Earth will be decided in the next few years by people like you.

SECTION 6. Venus

If you couldn't live on Earth, where would you live? If you are looking for a planet that's about the same size as Earth, then the clear choice is Venus. Mars is only half the size of Earth and a tenth the mass; Mercury is even smaller. Jupiter and Saturn are hundreds of times larger, and they don't even have a solid surface to stand on; they are gas. The size and mass of Venus closely match the Earth, so you'd feel a normal force of gravity. (Indeed, Venus is sometimes called Earth's sister planet.) There's just one problem: you would instantly burn to death, and your body would be corroded by toxic acid. The temperature of Venus is hotter than an oven. Venus is even hotter than Mercury, which is closer to the Sun. Why? The reason is interesting and provides a lesson to us here on Earth.

Our understanding of Venus came slowly. A Russian-built space probe landed there in 1967, detecting sulfuric acid in a dense atmosphere made mostly of carbon dioxide. Shortly after landing and detecting very high temperatures, the probe fried and died. Decades later, NASA sent a spaceship into orbit around Venus to map out its surface. This wasn't easy; the planet is covered in clouds that obscure any visible photos of its surface. To bypass this problem, NASA's craft sent radio waves through the clouds and reflected them off Venus, revealing a surface of valleys, some mountains, and many craters caused by impacts from asteroids and comets. One thing was missing, however. There was no evidence of plate tectonics, the process that causes volcanoes and earthquakes on Earth. This process also recycles the carbon in Earth's atmosphere, as we mentioned before. Without plate tectonics, the CO_2 has never been removed from Venus's atmosphere but has built up to a level of 96 percent. For comparison, Earth's atmospheric concentration is around 0.04 percent (or 400 parts per million).

We saw how CO_2 heats up Earth's atmosphere. But the greenhouse effect on Venus is much worse. Heat, in the form of infrared light, emitted by the surface of Venus is trapped by the atmosphere to a much larger extent than on Earth. This is why the surface of Venus is hotter than an oven's broiler (880°F or 471°C), so hot that any life form we know of would be immediately cooked. Venus provides a warning to us on Earth. If we allow CO_2 levels to continue to rise, we will make our planet uninhabitable. This will happen long before the CO_2 level gets close to 96 percent. We know from geological records on Earth that if the CO_2 level gets up to even 0.1 percent (or 1,000 ppm), then huge regions of the Earth, including large portions of the United States, will flood as the ice caps melt. But we can avoid this catastrophic fate if we cut our CO_2 output dramatically and begin removing it from our atmosphere. Whether or not this happens will be up to you.

WRAP-UP

In this chapter, we considered planets. While planets themselves only make up a small portion of the universe, they are incredibly important because we live on a planet ... the only planet now known to harbor life: Earth. Whether or not *our* planet continues to remain habitable depends on the actions we humans take, and how we make use of the scientific knowledge we already have. Back in Chapter 2, we introduced the scientific method as the most reliable way to understand our world and predict the future.

We rely on the conclusions of science to safely fly on airplanes and drive cars through intersections, not to mention using computers and cell phones. If science didn't work, then these devices wouldn't work. Yet there are many people who assume they can simply deny any of the conclusions of science if they feel like it. Some reject lifesaving medical information during a pandemic; others deny the conclusion that humans are causing serious changes to Earth's climate. Denying science is like saying that you don't need to stop at red lights because you don't believe the theory of electricity that controls those lights. It is not only foolish, it endangers other people's lives.

In this chapter, we saw that habitable planets can exist, but they are rare. In our solar system, Venus started off similar to the Earth, but ended up hellishly hot. In the final chapter, we will consider the profound question of whether or not humans will make contact with extraterrestrials. We'll see that this can only happen if we ourselves *live long enough* to make contact. And we will only live long enough if we learn how to keep our own planet habitable.

REFLECTION QUESTIONS

1. Astronomers have now begun to find planets that may be suitable for Earthlike life forms (habitable planets). In this chapter, you reflected on what conditions are necessary for life *as we know it*. Can you now think of some other forms of life that are very different from what we find on Earth? Their body shapes and sizes might be different, as would their source of energy. What kind of planets would they live on? What planetary conditions would support this new kind of life?

2. As we saw, the habitability of Earth is threatened as humans dump more greenhouse gases into the atmosphere. What do you think *you* can do (or are already doing) to reduce such emissions? What policies or changes would *you* put in place to fight global warming if/when you become a leader?

BIBLIOGRAPHY

Cox, A., ed. *Allen's Astrophysical Quantities*. Berlin, Germany: Springer, 1999.

Cusick, D. "Fossil Fuel Subsidies Cost $5 Trillion Annually and Worsen Pollution." *Scientific American*. May 19, 2015.

New York Times Editorial Board. "The World Solved the Ozone Problem. It Can Solve Climate Change." *New York Times*. December 7, 2019. https://www.nytimes.com/2019/12/07/opinion/sunday/ozone-climate-change.html

Information on Exoplanets:
NASA has several sites with more information about exoplanets:

The Exoplanet Catalog lists nearly 5,000 discoveries as of 2022. https://exoplanets.nasa.gov/discovery/exoplanet-catalog/

The "Exoplanet Travel Bureau" helps you plan a (pretend) trip to another planet. https://exoplanets.nasa.gov/alien-worlds/exoplanet-travel-bureau/

This animation shows how an orbiting planet causes light from a star to get redder and bluer because of the Doppler effect. https://www.youtube.com/watch?v=WKoWAmiP_Dk

Planets in Our Solar System:
These NASA sites give you more information planets in our solar system:

Cool things we learned about Pluto. https://www.nasa.gov/feature/five-years-after-new-horizons-historic-flyby-here-are-10-cool-things-we-learned-about-plut-o

Ice flows on Pluto. https://www.nasa.gov/feature/new-horizons-discovers-flowing-ices-on-pluto

NASA's *Juno* mission to Jupiter and its moons. https://www.nasa.gov/mission_pages/juno/main/index.html

NASA's *Cassini* mission spent 20 years flying to Saturn and observing the planet and its moons (one of which was found to have ice volcanoes)!

https://solarsystem.nasa.gov/missions/cassini/overview/

Several NASA missions have visited Mars, most recently the *Perseverance* Rover. https://www.nasa.gov/perseverance

CO₂ Levels and Climate Change:

You can find scientific information about CO_2 levels, how they are measured, and what their effects are at these sites:

https://climate.nasa.gov/news/2616/core-questions-an-introduction-to-ice-cores/

Ice Core Data: https://www.co2.earth/co2-ice-core-data

This site lets you explore the Keeling Curve (amount of CO_2 in the air) over different time ranges. https://keelingcurve.ucsd.edu

Check to see if your neighborhood will be flooded by climate change at: https://www.floodmap.net; or: https://coast.noaa.gov/slr/

Organizations and Political Movements Addressing the Climate Crisis:

Astronomers for Planet Earth: Professional and amateur astronomers, teachers, and students have united to form this group promoting perspective on climate awareness. http://AstronomersForPlanet.Earth Citizens' Climate Lobby, putting a cost on carbon. https://citizensclimatelobby.org

Fridays for Future is a student-led movement founded by Greta Thunberg. https://fridaysforfuture.org

Project Drawdown, removing carbon from the atmosphere. https://www.drawdown.org

The Sunrise Movement is a youth-led effort to reverse climate change. https://www.sunrisemovement.org/

350.org is a global grassroots effort to keep CO_2 levels below 350 ppm. https://350.org

CREDITS

Fig. 13.1: Copyright © by ALMA (ESO/NAOJ/NRAO) (CC BY 4.0) at https://commons.wikimedia.org/wiki/File:HL_Tau_protoplanetary_disk.jpg.

Fig. 13.2a: Copyright © by Jason Wang, et al. (CC BY 3.0) at https://commons.wikimedia.org/wiki/File:HR_8799_Orbiting_Exoplanets.gif.

Fig. 13.3a: Source: https://commons.wikimedia.org/wiki/File:Debra_Fischer.jpg.

Fig. 13.3b: Copyright © by SSR2000 (CC BY-SA 3.0) at https://commons.wikimedia.org/wiki/File:Discovery_Channel_Telescope.JPG.

Fig. 13.4: Source: https://www.nasa.gov/sites/default/files/thumbnails/image/nh_04_mckinnon_02b.jpg.

Fig. 13.5: Source: David King, et al., *Climate Change: A Risk Assessment*, p. 14. Copyright © by Center for Science and Policy, University of Cambridge.

14

LIFE IN THE UNIVERSE

Extraordinary claims require extraordinary evidence.

—Carl Sagan

Have you ever seen a UFO? Actually, many people have. Even I have. Several times, I've seen an object (O) that was flying (F) through the sky which I could not identify, making it unidentified (U). There are many phenomena (both natural and human-made) that happen in the sky from time to time that people may not be able to identify and so might be reported as UFOs. Some examples are shown in Figure 14.1. But when most people hear the term UFO, they think of spaceships from another planet. So, let's take a scientific look at the evidence for the claim that extraterrestrial (ET) spacecraft[1] have visited the Earth.

SECTION 1. Are We Alone?

Many people have claimed to have seen something that they interpret as an extraterrestrial spacecraft. Some people even claim to have been abducted by aliens and experimented on, while others claim that ETs have given them profound knowledge. How should we interpret such claims? If there are a large number of claims, should we believe them? No, not if we are approaching the topic scientifically. What matters is not the quantity of claims but the quality of the evidence. The topic of extraterrestrial life is

---

1   By the way, *extraterrestrial* means "beyond the Earth" since *terra* means Earth.

(a)   (b)

(c)   (d)

FIGURE 14.1   Images that some people claim are evidence of extraterrestrial spaceships. In 1950, a photograph (a) was captured in McMinnville, Oregon, which some claim shows a "flying saucer." (Careful analysis of the photo showed a string suspending the object from wires.) Another object was photographed over Passaic, New Jersey (b). A triangular shape appeared on images made by the crew of the **USS** *Russell* while the US Navy ship was off the coast from San Diego, California. The last image (d) is a deliberate hoax made by the author. While on vacation in Lakewood, Colorado, my nephew threw a frisbee in the air, and I took this picture. It wasn't very hard.

so bogged down with false claims that many scientists were reluctant to even discuss it. One of the first to do so was Enrico Fermi, the Italian American physicist who built the first nuclear reactor with his colleagues at the University of Chicago in 1942.[2] Realizing that any advanced ET civilization would have access to nuclear power, he calculated that the extraterrestrials should be able to travel the vast distances

---

2   Fermi was an immigrant to the United States who fled persecution in Europe. The nuclear reactor (called Chicago Pile 1) was built under the seats of the football stadium at the University of Chicago (Rhodes 1986)!

between the stars in only a few million years. Since Earth is 4.5 *billion* years old, they would have had plenty of time to travel here if they only had a small head start, compared to us. Given the large number of stars in our galaxy, Fermi speculated and concluded that if space-faring ETs existed, they should be here now. He then asked the simple question:

"Where are they?"

The apparent lack of evidence for visitors from other planets in spite of their ability to get here is called the **Fermi Paradox.**

Years later, the astronomer Carl Sagan was fascinated by the topic and considered it one of the most important questions humans have ever pondered. To study the topic scientifically, we need to pose a testable question, such as: "Is our species (humans) the only intelligent life in the universe; and if not, have other life forms visited us?" Sagan came up with a simple, scientifically valid way to analyze all the claims of extraterrestrial contact. He said:

"Extraordinary claims require extraordinary evidence."

The claim that *any* life exists anywhere besides the Earth is extraordinary. If proven, it would radically change our understanding of biology, chemistry, and astronomy and even impact fields such as psychology and religion. Therefore, we should not accept such a claim unless it is accompanied by very strong evidence. A verbal description by one person of a spacecraft or an ET abduction is not strong evidence. The story could be made up, or be a false memory or misunderstanding. But people who make such claims should not be labeled as liars or crazy.[3] Our goal is not to disparage people (who may be reporting in good faith to the best of their memory) but to examine the evidence critically. If multiple people claim to have witnessed the same event, then that constitutes stronger evidence, especially if the people do not know each other. But eyewitness reports are still weak evidence in comparison to photographic evidence, or even better, videos. Better still would be physical evidence that anyone can examine, such as a whole spaceship, or even part of one. Having investigated dozens of examples of evidence over more than 20 years, I can say that I have never seen strong evidence that extraterrestrial spaceships have visited Earth.[4]

But that doesn't mean that there haven't been some fascinating sightings. Figure 14.2 shows some photographs of unusual, even bizarre, things that have happened in the sky. Each example I've chosen was photographed by several different people, confirming that they really happened. But in each case, the phenomenon can be explained by human or natural activity. But what about the small number of confirmed photos of blurry or unclear objects that can't be explained? Does our lack of explanation prove that these shapes are spaceships? Well, just because you don't have a good explanation for something doesn't mean that extraterrestrials are involved. Personally, I would love to see quality evidence for ET visitors. So let's put our critical thinking skills to work and talk about what *would* constitute good evidence.

---

3 There are also scientists who attempt to understand claims of extraterrestrial contact/abduction/abuse from the perspective of psychology.

4 But my mind is still open. If you have any evidence of ET visitors, please share it with me! I would love to be one of the first people to discover extraterrestrial life.

(a)

(b)

(c)

(d)

FIGURE 14.2   Natural phenomena are responsible for many UFO sightings. Lenticular clouds (a) are seen near large mountains, like Mt. Hood. A bolide (b) is a large meteor that glows as it enters the atmosphere. An even larger meteor can leave a smoke trail and a meteorite when it crashes, as happened in 2013 in Chelyabinsk, Russia (c). The Sun can also cause halos and glowing parts of the sky when its light interacts with water crystals high in the atmosphere (d). People reporting UFOs may be giving an honest account of what they thought they saw.

COMMON MISCONCEPTION

Misconception: "If something is unexplained, it must be *paranormal*."

Fact: For example, if you and three friends are all planning to meet at a restaurant at 7 p.m. and one friend is missing, what would you do? Would you call your friend or send them a text message? Perhaps ask your other friends if they know anything about the missing person? Suppose none of this worked and nobody could explain why your friend didn't show up. Would you then conclude that extraterrestrials must be involved, perhaps abducting your friend? Obviously not. However, many people use this same logic when they see a UFO image for which there is not a clear scientific explanation and conclude that the photo proves that ETs have visited Earth.

DO TRY THIS AT HOME: PHOTOGRAPH FLYING OBJECTS

To get a feel for standards of evidence regarding UFOs, try this. Search online for claims of photos that some people say show extraterrestrial spacecraft. Download one such photo of your choice onto your computer. Then go on an outing to your local airport. You don't need to go into the airport; in fact, it might be better if you were a couple of kilometers away. Wait for an airplane to fly overhead or nearby and try to get a photo of it. Take enough time to photograph several planes and choose the best photo. Then put your photographs side by side with the photo that claims to be an ET spaceship. Perhaps post them both on social media. Ask your friends questions like, "What is shown in each photograph?" "How sure are you that this photo shows a flying vehicle?" Using their answers, develop your own criteria for what constitutes good evidence that extraterrestrials have visited Earth. In Figure 14.3 you can see two of my photos.

(a)

(b)

FIGURE 14.3   Identified Flying Objects. I once saw a spaceship fly right in front of me, and I got photos! In 2012, NASA retired the space shuttle *Endeavour* and sent it to a museum in Los Angeles, riding on top of a special 747 jet plane. The plane flew past the Golden Gate Bridge, allowing me to take these clear photos, along with thousands of other people. This is what a spaceship looks like, flying through Earth's atmosphere. Compare with Figure 14.1.

The first thing to consider is the *source* of the evidence. If it is a photograph, then who took the photo? Where were they when they took the photo? Think about it: if *you* saw a spaceship in the sky above you, what's the first thing you would do? Probably take a photo and send it to your friends, and publish it online, and perhaps report it to local news sources (and hopefully to your local astronomer). It would then be easy for people to find you and ask about what you saw ... and judge your reliability. Ideally, we would like to know the photographer's name, their location, and what equipment they used for the photo. Better than a photo is a video, which, in fact, is just many photos. This can give us a better sense of motion and the context in which the object appears. But the video should also be attributed to a known person and preferably should include enough of the ground to determine clearly where it was filmed. Multiple photos and videos taken by different, unrelated people would constitute much stronger evidence. In fact, given how many people have the ability to shoot a video using a cell phone these days, I would now say that anything observed by only one person should be viewed with suspicion. We also have to ask, "What does the video actually, clearly show?" Is it just a vague or blurry shape, such as a circle or triangle? Or can we clearly see the structure of an object that we can identify as a spaceship? Imagine taking a photograph of an airplane with your cell phone. If extraterrestrial spacecraft were visiting the Earth, we should expect to have dozens, if not hundreds, of clear photos of them.

SECTION 2. Life on Earth

Since there is currently no reliable strong evidence that extraterrestrials have visited Earth, our scientific approach to this topic leads us to next ask Fermi's question, "Why not?" There are several possible answers. Perhaps ETs don't *want* to contact us. This idea, called the Zoo Hypothesis, supposes that humans on Earth are a bit like an animal in a zoo, being studied by more intelligent life forms but not disturbed much. Perhaps ETs are waiting for us to achieve a level of intelligence or development before contacting us. This idea has been explored extensively in science fiction.[5] Another idea is that extraterrestrials are among us now but are hiding themselves, using advanced abilities. Unfortunately, neither of these ideas can be studied scientifically because they do not lead to testable predictions. All good scientific theories must make predictions that can be used to check if the theory is correct or not. So, for example, if the idea that ETs are here and cloaking themselves to look like humans is correct, then we would expect to see a lot of normal humans. Unfortunately, that's exactly what we would see if the theory were wrong.

So, let's move on to another possible answer to the Fermi Paradox. Perhaps we haven't seen ET spaceships because extraterrestrial life is extremely rare in the universe or even doesn't exist in our galaxy at all, besides the Earth. We must consider the profound possibility that the answer to the question "Are we alone?" might be "Yes." In other words, the only intelligent life there is in our galaxy is us. In this case, if we fail—that is, if we humans can't find a way to sustainably live into the future and end up destroying ourselves—then the only chance for the flowering of intelligent life among 100 billion stars will be lost.

So *perhaps* intelligent life is rare in our galaxy. But if so, why? This is a question we *can* attempt to answer using **biology**, the science of life. To begin, try to imagine the **origin of life on Earth**. When Earth formed about 4.5 billion years ago, it was such a hostile place that life could not have existed; asteroids and comets were constantly colliding with Earth,[6] and the surface of our planet was covered in molten lava. But later, the Earth cooled, and life formed surprisingly quickly. We know this because we have discovered tiny, fossilized life forms in rocks that are 3.8 billion years old. So how *did* life form on Earth? You may be surprised to learn that there are hundreds of scientists trying to solve this fascinating

---

5   For example, in the book and movie *2001: A Space Odyssey*, extraterrestrials placed a device on the Moon long ago. When humans advanced to the point of exploring the Moon, the device sent signals to the ETs that humans are ready to make contact. Also, viewers of the *Star Trek* series will be familiar with the Prime Directive, which prevents contact with civilizations until they reach a certain level of development.

6   We know this because that swarm of asteroids left craters that still exist on the Moon (Earth's early craters have been erased by erosion).

problem, the **origin of life**. If they discover that life can only form as a result of an extremely rare cosmic coincidence, then perhaps we *are* alone as the only life forms in our galaxy. If the odds of life forming are, say, 100-billion-to-one against, then we would only expect *one* planet in our galaxy to develop life—us. But if life can form easily, then we might expect thousands or even millions of planets in our galaxy to have life. Let's see what these origin-of-life scientists have found.

The earliest experiment in this field happened a long time ago in 1952. Stanley Miller and Harold Urey tried to simulate the early Earth, to see if life could form then. They filled a glass sphere with gases thought to exist on Earth at that time, such as methane (CH_4) and ammonia (NH_3) and added two sources of energy: heat, in the form of boiling water, and electricity in the form of wires that would make sparks. Such energy sources could be found in the early Earth, for example, in the form of lava flows and lightning. While they didn't create life, what they found was remarkable. After running the experiment for several days, they found several **amino acids**, which are important building blocks from which protein is made. This **Miller-Urey experiment** thus proved that the basic building blocks of life could have formed on the early Earth. Later experiments made improvements to the original idea, and managed to create some of the base molecules that make up DNA. This implies that the early Earth probably had many of the *ingredients* for life. But just having all the ingredients present isn't enough (as anyone knows who has made cookies or a cake). These ingredients must have somehow arranged themselves into living organisms that can reproduce.

The first big step would be to arrange the original building blocks into a large molecule similar to DNA.[7] Inside the nucleus of each of our cells, DNA provides the instructions for all the features that your body has (e.g., the shape of your lungs) and all the things your body does (e.g., how to digest food). But what's most important about DNA is that it is the only molecule that can **make copies of itself**. It can do this because it has two strands, each of which has all the information needed to make another copy. This information is stored in four molecules labeled A, T, C, and G.[8] It is amazing to me that just these four letters are needed to spell out the instructions for how our bodies are made and how they work. But the instructions are long—the entire human genome has 4 billion of these letters arranged into 23 chromosomes. If self-replicating molecules formed in the early Earth, they could make millions of copies of themselves, which could then evolve into more complex molecules. Presumably, this process then led to the evolution of **cells**, small bags that hold in some of the vital molecules, including DNA, which is often contained in the center of the cell or **nucleus**.

These cells could be considered the first true living organisms on Earth. In time, they evolved into more complex multicellular life forms. As described by **evolution theory**, new organisms that are better adapted to their environments will reproduce more effectively, passing along their DNA code to their descendants. After billions of years of evolution, **intelligence** eventually arose. Organisms evolved brains and could think. Only in the last 1/100th of 1 percent of Earth's history did humans arise. In the last hundred years or so, humans have developed technology that enables us to send messages across the stars

---

7   DNA, short for deoxyribonucleic acid, was discovered in 1952 after British chemist Rosalind Franklin took an image of matter inside the nucleus of a cell using X-rays. The image was then obtained, without her permission, by two other researchers who were awarded the Nobel Prize for the discovery of DNA.

8   Which stands for adenine, thiamine, cytosine, and guanine. These four are called nucleic bases. Another base, uracil (U), is found in RNA, a molecule similar to DNA but made up of a single strand, whereas DNA has a double strand.

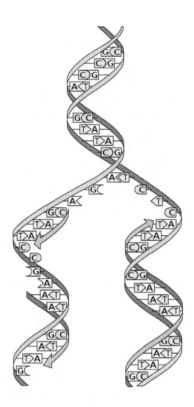

FIGURE 14.4   Diagram of a DNA molecule reproducing inside a cell. Unlike most molecules, DNA has the amazing ability to make copies of itself. It does this using two paired strands made up of four possible nucleic bases: A, T, C, and G. Base A pairs with T and base C pairs with G. This way, when DNA splits, each half will collect the missing bases (which are floating around the cell) and make a new full copy of the original DNA. This is how cells divide and reproduce.

and even launch spaceships on interstellar voyages. We know *that* life arose here on Earth, but we don't yet know *how* it formed, nor how likely this is to happen anywhere else. If we want to know whether or not life exists somewhere else in the universe, we'll have to try to find it ourselves.

CHALLENGE STATEMENT

Before reading Section 3, write down your response to this challenge statement. The goal here is not to come up with a "right" answer but to reflect on what ideas you *already have* and how you process them.

Part 1: Do you agree or disagree with this statement?

"There are no other advanced intelligent life forms in our Milky Way Galaxy. Humans are alone."

Part 2: Whether you agree or disagree, describe *why* you have this opinion. What informed your opinion, and what ideas and facts support your conclusion?

For fun, try challenging a friend with this same statement and see what their opinion is and what evidence they use to support their opinion.

SECTION 3. The Search for Extraterrestrial Life

It would be fascinating to make contact with an intelligent extraterrestrial species. But how? There are three main ways: we could try to send spaceships out from Earth to contact them; we could try to send them a message; or we could listen in to messages *they* are sending to *us*. The first idea, sending spaceships, is probably the worst (in spite of what you may have seen in sci-fi movies). It is very difficult to send a spaceship out of our solar system and across interstellar space to another star. At the speed of our current spaceships, this would take tens of thousands of years. Nevertheless, five of our spaceships exploring the planets have flown out of our solar system. Just in case they are picked up by extraterrestrials someday, we have sent messages onboard. In the 1970s, the planets aligned in such a way that it became possible to send spacecraft to several outer planets at once. In 1973, NASA sent two spacecraft, *Pioneer* 10 and 11, to visit and photograph the planets Jupiter and Saturn. And in 1978, NASA launched two more spacecraft, the *Voyager* 1 and 2 probes, with better equipment to fly by Jupiter and Saturn and also Neptune and Uranus. These missions returned our first close-up images of these planets and also made many discoveries, including dozens of moons, and even a volcano on Jupiter's moon Io. The spacecraft picked up speed as they flew past each planet, allowing them to go fast enough to escape the Sun's gravity and leave the solar system. So, they will probably wander through interstellar space forever. Since there is nothing to erode them, these probes will likely outlive our own Sun and *might* end up being the

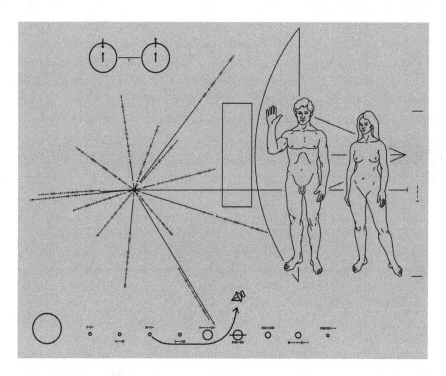

FIGURE 14.5 The *Pioneer* Plaque is one attempt by humans to communicate with extraterrestrials. It was placed on the *Pioneer* spacecraft, which left the solar system for interstellar space. It shows a human man and woman, the spacecraft, and a map of our solar system. The long lines indicate the Sun's position relative to nearby pulsars, whose pulse periods are given in terms of the frequency of light from a hydrogen atom (top left).

last traces that human life existed. Realizing this, a team of NASA scientists designed messages to put on the probes that could be read by extraterrestrials, just in case the probes get picked up. The *Pioneer Plaque*[9] shows a male and female human to the same scale as the spacecraft, so ETs will know our size. It also shows a map of our solar system, along with some strange-looking symbols. The lines indicate the distances to the nearest **pulsars**, which, along with the pulse periods, could be used to locate our Sun within the Milky Way Galaxy. The *Voyager* spacecraft also have these markings but also contain sounds of Earth, stored on an old-style phonograph record made of gold. A fifth space probe, NASA's *New Horizons* passed by Pluto in 2015, capturing the first detailed images of this distant dwarf planet. It is also leaving our solar system now. But none of these spacecraft are unlikely to contact extraterrestrials since they will not pass by any stars for millions of years.

Instead of sending space probes, which are slow and expensive to make, we could instead send out something that is cheap and very fast—**light**. Radio waves have low energy, so it is easy to generate them. Since they are a form of light, they travel at the speed of light, 300,000,000 km/s. Extraterrestrials, if they exist, could pick up a message if we chose to send one. Actually, we're already sending out such messages without knowing it! Our television and radio transmissions are sent out from large towers. The purpose of these antennas is to send radio waves to listeners on the ground, but some of those waves fly off into space, where they could be picked up. Earth's first radio and TV transmissions began in the 1940s, so they are now over 80 light-years away. The first transmissions ETs might pick up would be those showing a planet engulfed in World War II. What would they think about what they saw? As time went on, they would get to see some of the more recent examples of human civilization. My guess is they would be very confused. These types of signals are called "leakage radiation" because humans are only transmitting them to space accidentally. Instead, we could intentionally compose a message that an extraterrestrial would find easy to understand (or at least easier). But what would we say? What are the essential things an ET should know about humans, our planet, and the other life forms we share the planet with? Since extraterrestrials would not speak any human language, how should we communicate?

DO TRY THIS AT HOME: WRITE A MESSAGE TO EXTRATERRESTRIALS

First, think about what you would like to know about extraterrestrials if they were discovered. They might very well want to know the same things about us. As you start to compose your message to an ET, remember that it will take many years to get to them, so any current people or events you refer to will be in the distant past (and possibly forgotten) when the message arrives. Next, think about how you can get across this message without using your native language, which ETs probably won't speak or read (unless you teach it to them). The language of mathematics is universal and can be used. You might also use pictures, but be careful. They can easily be misinterpreted.

There are several ways to send a message, like radio waves or optical light pulses, so that's not the hard part. The final question is a moral one: *should* you send your message? Extraterrestrials are likely much more powerful than we are. If your message tips them off to our existence, then what do you think is most likely to happen? Do you think extraterrestrials will be hostile to us, as depicted in many Hollywood movies? In the next section, we will see that if ETs exist, they likely will have overcome many of the hostilities that still threaten our planet.

---

9   https://en.wikipedia.org/wiki/Pioneer_plaque

In 1974, radio astronomer Frank Drake and colleagues used the Arecibo Telescope in Puerto Rico to deliberately send out a message in the direction of a globular cluster. Their goal was to demonstrate that interstellar communication was possible, and to think about what to say and how to say it. Figure 14.6 shows their message. Given time, could you decode it? Strong, beamed messages, like this **Arecibo message**, would be easier for ETs to detect. But to send a beamed message, we need to point the telescope toward a specific location. But where? We don't know where they might be. There have been a few other attempts to beam messages out into space, but such efforts are considered to be mostly symbolic.

The most effective way to search for extraterrestrials is probably to try to detect messages *they* might be sending to *us*. There are many ways to send a message across the stars, but the least expensive, in terms of energy, is to transmit radio waves. Back in 1960, astronomers Frank Drake and Carl Sagan pointed a radio telescope to two stars to see if any radio waves were coming from them. As expected, they didn't detect any signals from ETs, but did show that a new field of research was possible—**SETI**, the Search for Extra Terrestrial Intelligence. In the first *comprehensive* search for ET radio signals, Benjamin Zuckerman and Patrick Palmer surveyed 670 stars using a large radio telescope. Many subsequent searches by different observers using different radio wavelengths followed. One SETI researcher is Jill Tarter, who, after earning a PhD from UC–Berkeley,[10] dedicated her career to the search for extraterrestrial life, organizing several ET searches and helping to found the SETI Institute in Mountain View, California. In spite of the scorn she received in her early career (for not doing "serious science"), her scientific leadership is now widely recognized. She served as the inspiration for the lead character in the excellent movie *Contact* (1997) about the search for extraterrestrial life.[11]

Part of the challenge in searching for ET radio signals is deciding which wavelength (or frequency) of light to tune into. Detecting radio waves from space is similar to choosing a radio station from a dial on a portable radio, like one in a car. Each radio station transmits at a different frequency (e.g., 103.7 MHz). But what frequency would an ET transmit at? Scientists have

FIGURE 14.6 The Arecibo message was transmitted by astronomers into space in 1974 using the Arecibo Telescope in Puerto Rico. It consists of a series of radio wave pulses that can be arranged to form this pattern. The message encodes human beings' home planet of Earth, our number system, our size and population, and important molecules for life. It was beamed in the direction of globular cluster M13 and will reach there in about 22,000 years.

10   Tarter also coined the commonly used term brown dwarf to refer to objects smaller than stars but larger than planets.

11   This movie was based on the book *Contact* by Carl Sagan.

tried searching all possible frequencies for thousands of stars, but this requires an enormous amount of computer time to process all the data. One project (SETI@home) enlisted the public to help process the data using home computers. Other projects have searched using other types of light, such as optical or infrared. Over the years, hundreds of SETI searches have been conducted, and thousands and thousands of stars have been surveyed. The fact that no other life has been detected, in spite of all this effort, might be telling us that advanced life is rare in our galaxy. But most SETI researchers say that an ET signal might still have escaped detection. For example, some frequencies of radio waves are blocked by Earth's atmosphere, and thus haven't been checked yet. What if an extraterrestrial is using those frequencies to transmit their messages? They might not use radio waves at all. If they had a lot of energy at their disposal, ETs could transmit messages using high-power lasers. Searches for this type of signal have been conducted but not as many stars have been searched.

Could there be numerous undetected ET civilizations throughout our galaxy? We can't really answer this question unless we come up with a way to estimate how many civilizations exist in our galaxy and how many of them have already transmitted messages that we could detect. After Frank Drake's first search for extraterrestrial life was unsuccessful, he tried to make a very, very rough calculation of how many extraterrestrial civilizations there might be in our galaxy. The reason he focused on our galaxy, and not the billions of others, has to do with the speed of light. It takes light millions of years to travel between galaxies, so we'll never be able to have two-way communication with beings in another galaxy. But just in our galaxy, there are hundreds of billions of stars, and there may be millions—or even billions—of habitable planets. Do any have life? Do any of these have intelligent life that we might communicate with?

SECTION 4. Will We Make Contact?

Frank Drake wanted to very roughly estimate the number of intelligent extraterrestrial civilizations in our galaxy, which he called N. To do this, he thought of all the factors that would influence whether or not such civilizations exist. He could then just multiply those factors together to get N. At first, he didn't care whether or not he knew the values of these factors; the goal was to frame the question of extra-terrestrial life in a scientific way. This is now known as the **Drake Equation.** It can be written like this:

$$N = N_* \times f_p \times n_e \times f_l \times f_i \times f_c \times f_L.$$

To begin, Drake figured there needed to be a star that is stable and provides energy for a long time. We'll have to exclude high-mass stars, because they only live a few million years. Let's imagine we know exactly how many suitable stars are in our galaxy, and we call that number: N_*

Life as we know it can't live inside a star: they are too hot. The next question is: how many of these stars have planets? All of them? Let's say that some fraction of these stars do have planets—call this fraction f_p. Of these planets, how many would be habitable, like Earth? Habitable planets must be the right distance from their star and have an atmosphere that supports life. Drake called the number of 'Earth-like' planets per star: n_e. But even if the right conditions exist, only a fraction of habitable planets will actually form life. We saw that researchers are still trying to figure out how life formed on the Earth.

Let's call the fraction of habitable planets on which life actually forms f_l. But not all life forms become intelligent and communicate across the stars. Some, like the dinosaurs on Earth, can succeed for millions of years without developing much intelligence. Will 10 percent develop intelligence, or would it be more like 80 percent? This unknown fraction is called: f_i.

Even if we imagine an intelligent alien civilization on some other planet, it might not develop the technology needed to communicate. Let's say a fraction, f_c, of these stars have successfully developed a high-tech civilization that can communicate with us. If we knew all these numbers and fractions, could we then say how many stars in our galaxy had intelligent life that we can communicate with? The answer is NO. We have overlooked one factor that might be the most important of all.

Think about our civilization on Earth. We have been able to communicate with extraterrestrials for only around 70 years, since the development of radio technology. But during this same time period, we humans have engaged in several activities that threaten our own existence, for example: pollution, climate change, overpopulation, and nuclear war. It is entirely possible that our whole civilization could destroy itself just 30 years into the future. If so, then we would only have been "communicative" for about 100 years. If this is typical of other civilizations, then we'll have a huge problem in making contact. That's because the messages they send to us will only be transmitted during a brief century-long period between the advance of high technology and that civilization's destruction. If we are to communicate with ETs, then they *must* be long-lived. If they can exist for thousands or even millions of years, then there's a good chance they will be able to transmit a message that we can receive. And we have to live long enough to receive the message also. We can summarize all this by trying to estimate the lifetime (in years) of an advanced civilization such as our own. Frank Drake called this number **L**. He multiplied all these factors together into what is called the Drake Equation. Unlike some other equations, this one isn't intended to make precise calculations. Indeed, most of the inputs to the **Drake Equation** are unknown or only known roughly. Your guess is as good as anyone's. The following box shows the Drake Equation and allows you to put in your own values and come up with your own estimate of the number of ET civilizations.

DRAKE EQUATION

I'll share with you my best estimate, and then you can try your own. Again, the point of this activity is to guess how many ET civilizations live in our galaxy and thus determine whether or not we will ever contact one.

$$N = N_* \times f_p \times n_e \times f_l \times f_i \times f_c \times f_L$$

$$N = \underline{} \times \underline{} \times \underline{} \times \underline{} \times \underline{} \times \underline{} \times \underline{}$$

Each of the values labeled **f** will be a fraction, like 0.5 (50 percent) or 0.10 (10 percent) and so will range from 0.0 to 1.0. Here are my best estimates. Feel free to fill in your guesses in the blanks above.

N$_*$ is the number of stars in the Milky Way Galaxy. There's no way to count the stars, of course, and it is actually hard to even estimate their number. I typically just use the round figure of 100 billion stars. But estimates range from 100 billion to 400 billion. So, I'll use 250 billion here.

(continued)

f_p is the fraction of stars with planets. In the last few decades, exoplanet astronomers (including me!) have discovered so many planets, that I would say that **nearly all stars have at least one planet** (several have more than one). I'll guess that $f_p = 1.0$ (in other words, 100 percent).

n_e is the number of Earthlike planets in each planetary system. One study analyzed 42,000 stars and estimated about 20 percent of stars in our galaxy have an Earth-sized planet. We can now multiply the first three factors to estimate that there are **50 billion habitable planets in the Milky Way!**

f_l is the fraction of these planets on which life actually arises. My guess is that it is difficult for life to arise on a planet. The combination of chemical elements might not be ideal, and the star itself may zap the planet with intense X-rays (many stars do this, luckily not the Sun). I guess that only 1 percent of already habitable stars have life. This would still give us 500 million planets with life.

f_i is the fraction of these planets where **intelligent** life evolves. This factor is the hardest for me to estimate, since I'm not an expert on life on Earth. Evolution can select for more intelligent species, but does not always do so.[1] I'll say that life in the universe normally does *not* evolve intelligence: $f_i = 0.01$ (1 percent).

f_c is the fraction of planets where intelligent life develops into an advanced civilization that can communicate with us. At first thought, it seems likely to me that life-forms with "intelligence" (however we define it) would, eventually, develop high levels of technology. Only a small fraction of that planet's inhabitants would need to become high-tech for that technology to spread around the planet. But there are many forms of intelligence, and not all of them are inclined toward technology. To communicate, we need the extraterrestrial civilization to send us a message using radio waves or some other system. I'll say only half go high-tech: $f_c = 0.50$ (50 percent). Multiplying our previous figure of 500 million inhabited planets, the last two fractions (0.01 and 0.5) give us 2.5 million advanced civilizations that could be communicating with us.

f_L is the fraction of these high-tech civilizations that actually survive long enough to communicate with us. To estimate this, we need to divide two factors: how long a high-tech civilization survives, and how long the host planet survives before its star changes into a red giant and makes life impossible. The second factor is easy to estimate: sunlike stars can survive a few billion years—let's say 5 billion. Then $f_L = L/(5 \text{ billion years})$, where **L is the lifetime of an advanced civilization**. This final factor is the hardest of all to estimate and perhaps the most important. Once a civilization has developed advanced technology, with all its advantages and risks, how long will it survive? Let's say that earthlings developed advanced technology around the 1940s when we began to develop radio communication technology (and also developed nuclear weapons and reactors). In the text, I consider two possibilities. In the first, civilizations only last about 100 years. In this pessimistic scenario, the Drake Equation implies that there would only be a handful of other civilizations in our galaxy, maybe only one—us. If N = 1, then we are alone. On the other hand, if civilizations can endure longer, say, thousands or even millions of years, then the final factor, **f_L**, will be close to 1, and we would expect thousands or even millions of other civilizations in our galaxy. In that case, we will surely make contact.

---

1   The dinosaurs lived for over 100 million years and did fine with tiny brains ... until an asteroid hit the Earth 65 million years ago.

SECTION 5. Conclusion

We have now come to the end of this chapter on astrobiology, and the end of the book. We began by thinking about how to judge the numerous claims extraterrestrials are visiting the Earth. As much as I would love to make contact with extraterrestrials, there is no evidence that they have ever visited our planet. This made us wonder if they are even out there, or if we are alone. To help answer that question, we noted that life arose relatively quickly after Earth formed and cooled down. The Miller-Urey experiment (Section 2) and others like it show that self-replicating molecules could have formed on the early Earth. This makes it at least *plausible* that forms of life are found all throughout our galaxy and others. But no experiment has "created" life, and we still can't say if the formation of life from nonliving matter is likely or unlikely to happen on other planets.

Another approach is to answer the question by looking for signs of intelligent life using radio telescopes. Dozens of searches spanning several decades have scanned thousands of nearby stars for signals at a range of wavelengths. Nothing has turned up except a few blips and glitches. The lack of any signal so far seems to indicate that the ETs, if they exist near to us, are not intentionally sending us messages. They could be more distant, they might just not be very talkative, or they might in fact be nearby but transmitting messages in ways we have yet to detect. Or they might not exist. A comprehensive search for extraterrestrial life will produce a profoundly interesting result whatever its outcome. If we find other species to talk to, imagine the conversations we will have; what knowledge we will learn, and perhaps even share. But if we find that we are alone, *that* result might be more profound. It would mean that the only chance for the astronomical phenomenon of intelligent life to flourish and grow is right here on our home planet. The unique and precious status of Earth as a life-supporting planet would come into sharp focus for everyone.

Perhaps our SETI searches will discover extraterrestrial life next week. Or perhaps they never will. We saw that the question of whether or not we will ever make contact with another world depends to a large extent on how long other advanced civilizations can survive. This is the factor **L** in the Drake Equation. If **L** is a small number, like only 100 years, then it means that most advanced civilizations destroy themselves quickly. Perhaps their greed for energy and power leads them to consume their planet's resources and pollute its atmosphere, leading to global apocalypse. Or perhaps they succumb to hatred and start a world war with nuclear weapons, or *worse*. Looking at our own civilization, we realize that tragically foolish scenarios like these are not out of the question. The current leaders of our nations and businesses have put the Earth on a collision course with catastrophe.

But this doesn't have to be our destiny. The true value of **L** may be millions of years, perhaps a billion. If we are ever to make contact with extraterrestrials, it means that *it is possible* to survive technological adolescence and become a stable, mature, long-lasting civilization. We humans clearly have the capacity to overcome hatred and greed. We already know what needs to be done. To survive, humans must stop polluting the environment with greenhouse gases and other toxins. We need to see people from other parts of the world, and those in our own country, as fellow humans, not enemies to fight or oppress. We *can* create a world where resources are used sustainably and the peoples of Earth do not waste them fighting each other. In this scenario, humans could continue to live on Earth for thousands or even millions of years. Perhaps we would evolve into a space-faring species and explore the stars, or perhaps we would be content with the bounty and beauty of our own Earth and solar system. In any case, humanity is fast approaching a decision point between

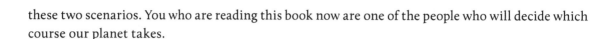

these two scenarios. You who are reading this book now are one of the people who will decide which course our planet takes.

REFLECTION QUESTIONS

1. Attempt your own calculation of the Drake Equation, using your own best guesses. Based on your estimate for the number of extraterrestrial civilizations in our galaxy, do you think humans will make contact with one of them? Ask at least one friend whether or not we will make contact, and compare that person's thoughts with yours. Were they more or less optimistic about the prospects for contact?

2. Scientists from many fields study the origins of life on Earth. If we can understand how life began here, it will give us insight into the prospects for life in the universe. Do an online search for news stories about research on the origins of life. Pick one research project and write a one-page summary of what you learned. You can then tell a friend, "Did you know that people are trying to figure out how life began?"

3. As a final reflection, perhaps write down some of your thoughts on these topics: Has your perspective of the universe (of which you are part) changed after reading this book? What new ideas were interesting enough for you to possibly pursue later? Did the book make you question some ideas you held before? Did it make you confident in your previous notions, or both? In any case, thanks for reading this book. I hope you enjoyed it.

BIBLIOGRAPHY

Rhodes, Richard. *The Making of the Atomic Bomb*. New York: Simon & Schuster, 1986.

Sagan, Carl. *Contact*. New York: Simon & Schuster, 1985.

Zemeckis, Robert, dir. *Contact*. 1997; Burbank, CA: Warner Bros. Pictures.

Drake Equation:
Cassan, A., Kubas, D., Beaulieu, J. P., Dominik, M., Horne, K., Greenhill, J., Wambsganss, J., Menzies, J., Williams, A., Jørgensen, U. G., Udalski, A., Bennett, D. P., Albrow, M. D., Batista, V., Brillant, S., Caldwell, J. A. R., Cole, A., Coutures, Ch., Cook, K. H., Dieters, S., Dominis Prester, D., Donatowicz, J., Fouqué, P., Hill, K., Kains, N., Kane, S., Marquette, J-B, Martin, R., Pollard, K. R., Sahu, K. C., Vinter, C., Warren, D., Watson, B., Zub, M., Sumi, T., Szymański, M. K., Kubiak, M., Poleski, R., Soszynski, I., K., Ulaczyk, J., Pietrzyński, G., Wyrzykowski, L. "One or More Bound Planets per Milky Way Star from Microlensing Observations." *Nature* (2012), 481 (7380): 167–169. arXiv:1202.0903. Bibcode:2012Natur.481..167C. https://doi.org/10.1038/nature10684. PMID 22237108

Europe's GAIA mission has mapped 1 billion stars:

http://www.esa.int/Science_Exploration/Space_Science/Gaia/Gaia_s_billion-star_map_hints_at_treasures_to_come

http://astrobiology.com/2013/11/1-in-5-sun-like-stars-has-earth-size-planet-in-habitable-zone.html

Petigura, E. A., Howard, A. W., and Marcy, G. W. (2013). "Prevalence of Earth-size Planets Orbiting

Sun-like Stars." *Proceedings of the National Academy of Sciences* (2013), **110** (48): 19273. arXiv:1311.6806. Bibcode:2013PNAS..11019273P. https//doi.org/10.1073/pnas.1319909110

Shostak, Seth. "A Bucketful of Worlds." *Huffington Post* (February 3, 2011). Retrieved April 24, 2021. The *Kepler* planet-finding space mission has allowed us to deduce that there are 30,000 habitable planets within 1,000 light-years of Earth.

Fermi Paradox:

The Fermi Paradox in a Nutshell. https://www.youtube.com/watch?v=sNhhvQGsMEc

https://waitbutwhy.com/2014/05/fermi-paradox.html

One possibility (advanced by Robin Hansen) is that extraterrestrials do not exist (or are rare) in our galaxy because there is a "Great Filter" that prevents life from developing to an advanced stage. There are a number of possible filters, and we don't even know if we ourselves have overcome that filter. https://web.archive.org/web/20100507074729/http://hanson.gmu.edu/greatfilter.htm

Search for Extraterrestrial Intelligence (SETI):

Mann, Adam. 2020. "Extraterrestrial Evidence: 10 Incredible Findings About Aliens from 2020." *Live Science* (December 24, 2020). https://www.livescience.com/alien-discoveries-2020.html

The SETI Institute (http://www.seti.org) has a page on the first SETI search. https://www.seti.org/seti-institute/project/details/early-seti-project-ozma-arecibo-message

Zuckerman, B., and Tarter, J. "Microwave Searches in the U.S.A. and Canada." *Strategies for the Search for Life in the Universe (Proceedings)* (1980). Astrophysics and Space Science Library, **83**: 81–92. Bibcode:1980ASSL...83...81Z. https://doi.org/10.1007/978-94-009-9115-6_10. ISBN 978-90-277-1226-4

CREDITS

Fig. 14.1a: Source: https://commons.wikimedia.org/wiki/File:Trent1_600dpi.jpg.

Fig. 14.1b: Source: https://commons.wikimedia.org/wiki/File:PurportedUFO2.jpg.

Fig. 14.1c: Source: https://commons.wikimedia.org/wiki/File:USS_Russell_UFO_-_July_2019.png.

Fig. 14.2a: Copyright © by Yaping Wu (CC BY-SA 3.0) at https://commons.wikimedia.org/wiki/File:Lenticular_cloud_over_Mount_Hood.jpg.

Fig. 14.2b: Source: https://commons.wikimedia.org/wiki/File:Bolide.jpg.

Fig. 14.2c: Copyright © by Alex Alishevskikh (CC BY-SA 2.0) at https://commons.wikimedia.org/wiki/File:2013_Chelyabinsk_meteor_trace.jpg.

Fig. 14.2d: Source: https://commons.wikimedia.org/wiki/File:Sun_halo_optical_phenomenon_edit.jpg.

Fig. 14.4: Source: https://commons.wikimedia.org/wiki/File:DNA_replication_split.svg.

Fig. 14.5: Source: https://commons.wikimedia.org/wiki/File:Pioneer_plaque.svg.

Fig. 14.6: Copyright © by Arne Nordmann (CC BY-SA 3.0) at https://en.wikipedia.org/wiki/File:Arecibo_message.svg.

Index

About the Author

Chris McCarthy is an astronomer working at San Francisco State University. He has taught college astronomy for over 15 years. His field of research is extra-solar planets (exoplanets), which he began to study in the 1990s, before the first ones were found. Together with colleagues, he has discovered over 25 planets, three brown dwarfs, and three planet-forming disks around other stars. He is coauthor of over 30 research papers published in scientific journals. He earned a bachelor's degree at the University of California, Berkeley, a master's degree from San Francisco State University, and a doctorate from University of California, Los Angeles.

Dr. McCarthy has also worked with elementary and high school teachers to improve science education programs and has given dozens of public talks on astronomical discoveries. He is on the board of Mission Science Workshop (http://missionscienceworkshop.org), which provides hands-on science experiences to underserved youth in San Francisco public schools. Recently, he helped to organize Astronomers for Planet Earth, (http://AstronomersForPlanet.Earth) which is tackling the global climate crisis from an astronomical perspective through education and institutional reform.

His hobbies include tinkering and ultimate Frisbee, and he is a lifelong backpacker. After graduating from college, he hiked the entire Pacific Crest Trail from Mexico to Canada. He lives in San Francisco with his wife and son.

CPSIA information can be obtained
at www.ICGtesting.com
Printed in the USA
LVHW051215131222
735083LV00001B/16